the Grapevine Great British
where to eat vegetarian
restaurant guide

www.grapevineguides.co.uk

Published by Grapevine Guides Ltd
PO Box 5555
Maidenhead
SL6 3ZG

© Grapevine Guides Ltd 2004
All rights reserved

Designed by Lawrence & Beavan
London

Maps by David Yelland

Printed by Fuller Davies, Suffolk

ISBN 0-9547243-0-5

The publisher and writers have made great efforts to ensure the
accuracy of information in this book. However, they can accept
no responsibility for any loss, injury or inconvenience sustained
as a result of information or advice given.

Please note that restaurants can close or change hands, opening
times can vary, cuisines do alter and chefs move on. We would
always advise you to call the venue to check first, particularly if
there are details which are important to your visit.

the Grapevine Great British
where to eat vegetarian
restaurant guide

Compiled and edited by
Daryl Burton

Additional writing by
Julia Chamberlain

Grapevine Guides Ltd

with thanks

This guide wouldn't have been possible without the help and goodwill of vegetarians the length and breadth of the UK.

The editor is immensely grateful for information and feedback from:

☐ Paul Appleby ☐ Manjit Biant ☐ Sally Blower ☐ Pat Buckingham
☐ Alicia Burne ☐ Linda Burton ☐ Phil Cross ☐ Clair Cullinane
☐ Sue Daniels ☐ Heena Davé ☐ Chris Deacon ☐ Anita de la Riviere
☐ Amy Eagles ☐ Diana Elvin ☐ Margaret Glover ☐ Jill Greenway
☐ Marilyn Harrison ☐ Barbara Jackson ☐ Barbara Kay ☐ Louise Lawrence
☐ Philippa Lennox ☐ Nina Lubman ☐ Holly Machin ☐ Harry Mather
☐ Paul Mehr ☐ Val Moffat ☐ Penny Noakes ☐ Marion Pace
☐ Roseann Pannier-Taylor ☐ Dawn Platten ☐ Jan Potter ☐ George Rodger
☐ Rob Sier ☐ Peter Simpson ☐ Gillian Smart ☐ Susan Smith
☐ Jane Strehlow ☐ Natalie Tharraléos ☐ Christine Thorpe ☐ Dave Whalley

☐ And especial thanks to Hilly Beavan and Anthony Lawrence

If there's a restaurant you think we should be featuring, drop us a line or fill out the online form at www.grapevineguides.co.uk and we'll get the Grapevine spies onto it!

www.grapevineguides.co.uk

Introduction

Welcome to the **Grapevine where to eat vegetarian restaurant guide.**

Covering England, Scotland and Wales, we'll show you where to find everything from fast food to fine dining – via veggie pubs, meat-free cafés and all-you-can-eat vegetarian buffets.

An instant solution to that all-too-familiar problem of peering through restaurant windows to see if they've anything more exciting than veggie lasagne or broccoli bake on offer, The Guide will help you to discover over 500 great places to eat – from a vegetarian café in the Scottish Highlands to a meat-free Reggie Perrin-themed Indian restaurant in Devon.

Pop a copy in the car glovebox and take the guide with you on holiday, days out and visits to friends. You can rely on the user-friendly county maps to locate the nearest best-bet for a great choice of delicious vegetarian food.

The Grapevine Guide is completely independent – we don't take paid-for listings or advertising from anyone – so if we (or the local vegetarians) don't reckon you'll be delighted with the range of meat-free options on offer at a restaurant, it doesn't get listed.

And you won't find The Guide padded out with dozens of identikit chain restaurants – we all know where these are – but we will show you independent cafés, bistros, restaurants and bars that you'll be thrilled to discover.

So, don't put up with microwaved veggie lasagne any more. Get out there and enjoy a fantastic range of veggie food at these places instead!

Daryl Burton ☐ Editor

Serving times

Many venues have opening hours extending beyond those shown. These times give an indication of when earliest and last food orders are.

Credit Cards

Information relates to Mastercard and Visa. If you're planning to pay with another sort of plastic (and want to avoid the washing up), check with them first.

Cromford

Derbyshire

- The Promenade
  Scarthin
  Cromford DE4 3QF
- 01629 823272
- Serving times:
  Mon–Sat
  10am–5.30pm
  Sun 12–5.30pm
- No credit cards
- Non-smoking
- Not licensed
- Children welcome
- 20 seats

Vegetarian Café

Scarthin Books Café

Tucked away from the marketplace, seek out this café in a superb bookshop by the village pond. Inhabiting a one-time domestic kitchen, there are only 20 seats, but you do get to look out onto the comings and goings in the shop itself.

There's normally some vegan goodies available, and gluten-free cake, and they try to use locally grown (occasionally from their own garden) organic produce where possible. Choose from dishes such as soup, homity pie, pizza, nut loaf, and mushroom pâté, all with salad or bread. They support an Apple Day celebration each October, with fruit crushing outside on the prom – worth a trip in itself.

In an attractive village, they're open every day except Christmas and Boxing Day.

Omnivorous Café

Longlands Eating House

Open for lunch and snacks, Longlands is a proper café with some good vegetarian options: quornburgers and salad, chickpea casserole with naan, filled jacket potatoes and a good selection of very reasonably priced cakes. There's also a children's menu featuring veggie sausages and chips, which reverses the trend and offers adult portions, a neat idea.

Alcohol can be served as part of meal, so you can have beans on toast and a glass of chardonnay if you feel so inclined. Breakfasts are available on Saturday and Sunday mornings, and they'll do you a fruit smoothie in the summer.

It's right next door to the petrol station, so your car can refuel at the same time.

Hathersage

Derbyshire

- Main Rd
  Hathersage S32 1BB
  Above outdoor
  equipment shop
- 01433 651978
- Serving times:
  Mon 11am–4.45pm
  Tues–Fri 10am–4.45pm
  Sat–Sun 9am–5.30pm
- Major credit cards
- Non-smoking room
- Licensed
- Children welcome
- 55 seats
- Light meals from £2.50,
  mains from £6

Glossop

Derbyshire

- High St West
  Glossop SK13 8HU
- 01457 852417
- Serving times:
  Mon & Wed bar
  hotpot available
  Thurs–Sat 5.30–9pm
  Sun 1–9pm
  Closed Tues
- Booking advisable
- No credit cards
- Non-smoking
- Licensed
- Children welcome
- 20 seats

Vegan Restaurant

The Globe

Right on the edge of Derbyshire's spectacular Peak District is The Globe – an unusual but welcome combination of real ale free house, live music venue and 100% vegan restaurant.

The cosy 20-seat restaurant is open evenings Thursday-Sunday, as well as for Sunday lunch, with bar snacks and hot pot available on Monday and Wednesday evenings. All mains (choose from the ever-changing menu on the blackboard) come with a salad selection, veg and potatoes, and a complete three course meal will set you back less than £10. Naturally, you'll find a great choice of vegan wines and beers. But it's not only vegans who'll enjoy eating here – Paula's cooking earned them a finalist place in 'The Publican' food awards.

Vegetarian Café

Good For You World Food

This friendly co-op run café has a wholefood shop and also functions as a community centre. It goes without saying they air child friendly, with a play area. You can also book your private party here.

The soup and at least two daily specials are vegan, and there are plenty of gluten-free options from a mainly organic menu with specials that change every few days. There are light soups in summer, chunky ones for winter, gluten-free pasta salads, potato and vegetable bakes, different curries and red onion tarts. Look out for the mixed vegan fry-up, and the half price children's specials. Also on offer: takeaway sandwiches, no-bacon butties, cakes, crumbles and flapjacks – some vegan – and fair trade tea and coffee.

Matlock

Derbyshire

- 23 Firs Parade
  Matlock DE4 3AS
- 01629 584304
- Serving times:
  Mon–Sat 10am–4.30pm
  Cakes & drinks only
  after 3.30pm
- Major credit cards
- Non-smoking
- BYO with no corkage
- Children welcome
- 35 seats
- Snacks from £2.50

156

157

Booking Info

Please note that restaurants can get busy at unexpected times. If you're making a special journey, always book!

Licensed

Many venues have just a table licence, so you'll need to order a meal if you fancy an alcoholic drink.

Smoking

Many restaurants featured are completely non-smoking. Some have designated non-smoking sections, but these areas often aren't in separate rooms.

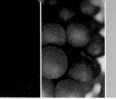

Contents

See over for full county index.

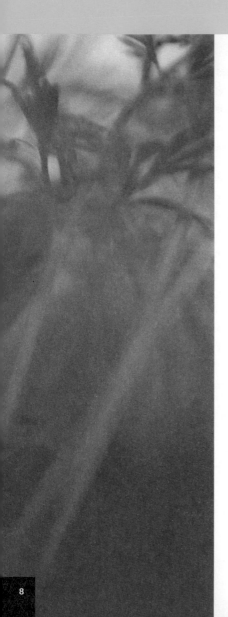

County index

A note on English counties

The English counties have been subject to many boundary amendments and renaming exercises in a series of changes over the last 30 years. We've generally used the latest English county boundaries and names, with a couple of exceptions (for example, Middlesex, which theoretically no longer exists – but try telling that to someone who lives there). Additionally, many of the recently introduced unitary authorities have been reassembled into more traditional county regions which we hope gives a better sense of place.

cornwall

devon

cornwall • devon

Cornwall

Devon

Bude □

Boscastle **1**
Tintagel **9**

CORNWALL

Bodmin □

4 □
Liskeard

Newquay □

St Austell □   **2** Fowey

10 **11** Truro

St Ives   □ Redruth

8 **3** Hayle

□ Falmouth

5 **6** Penzance

□
Helston

□ Ilfracombe

□ Barnstaple
□ Bideford

 DEVON   □ Tiverton

□ Okehampton
                    15 Exeter
          13 Chagford

Newton Abbot **16**   □ Teignmouth
21 Yelverton
     Dartington **14**   **19** Torquay
7 □ Saltash   Totnes **20** □ Paignton
17 **18** Plymouth   **12** Brixham

cornwall • devon

- The Old Mill
  Old Rd
  Boscastle PL35 0AQ
- In large mill complex by harbour
- 01840 250223
- Serving times:
  Mon-Sun
  11.30am-4.30pm
  Closed Wednesdays
- Major credit cards
- Non-smoking except courtyard
- Not licensed
- Children welcome
- 45 seats including courtyard
- Pasties and soups from £1.95

The Miller's Pantry

The café is situated in an old mill near the National Trust harbour, and has an outside courtyard seating 30.

Cornish cream teas are vegetarian, so fill your face with two scones, jam and clotted cream and a pot of tea or, more modestly, have a toasted teacake or cheese scone.

Toasted cheese sandwiches are the same price as the cream tea (surely, no contest) and you can select your own unique toastie extras (pineapple and marmite anyone?), or be more sensible and have the posh version with stilton and pear. Soup of the day is usually vegan, and comes with a roll and butter. Vegan Cornish pasties are also on offer.

There's freshly ground coffee and they have decaf.

- 10 Lostwithiel St
  Fowey PL23 1BD
- 01726 833023
- Serving times:
  Wed-Sun 7-10pm
  Nov-March open
  Fri-Sat only
- Booking essential in summer
- Major credit cards
- Non-smoking
- Licensed
- Children welcome
- 30 seats
- Mains from £9

Terra Firma

In the historic part of Fowey, this stylish modern restaurant offers a predominately vegetarian menu, so you can expect a decent choice of both starters and mains. Kick off with mushrooms fried in butter and nutmeg on egg-fried bread, or potato skins with guacamole, and choose from main courses such as roasted vegetables with tikka sauce or vegetable-filled pancakes with lentil sauce. Vegans are looked after with selections such as fajitas, or roasted veg with green chilli and coconut. Mains are also available in half price children's portions.

Fancy a dessert? What about chocolate cheesecake with a warm chocolate sauce, or banoffee pie?

Needless to say, booking is essential in the summer.

Cornwall

Hayle

Pizza Patio

Al fresco dining that's as good as you're going to get outside of the Med, Pizza Patio is a long way from your average pizzeria for both its food and location.

Proper pizzas made with fresh dough and loaded with appealing toppings would be reason enough to visit, but grab a bottle of chianti and one of the outside tables to watch the sun go down as the tide fills Hayle Pool to make the most of it.

There's also a selection of starters like jalapeño peppers, potato skins with dips, garlic mushrooms and breads together with a range of pastas.

There's a takeaway service, but with surroundings like this, plan ahead and book to eat in.

- 35 Commercial Rd
  Hayle TR27 4DE
- 01736 753745
- Serving times:
  Mon-Sun
  6.30-10.30pm
- Major credit cards
- Non-smoking inside
- Licensed
- Children welcome
- 110 seats total
- Mains from £4.95

Cornwall

Liskeard

Halfway House

This popular pub with a garden and patio on the edge of Bodmin Moor aims to provide good fresh local food.

Start with battered mushrooms, garlic breads, creamed garlic mushrooms or the fresh soup of the day. Main courses include pasta bakes – either Provençal and mushrooms, or broccoli and cheese – a vegetable lasagne, ploughman's lunch and baked potatoes with sweet and sour mushrooms, cheese, beans or coleslaw. Gluten-free meals are also available.

Children are welcome (assuming they're not the race-around-and-scream-a-lot variety) and most of the menu is available in children's portions.

They serve cocktails, and often have soya milk. Do book if you're in a party of six or more.

- Twowatersfoot
  Liskeard PL14 6HR
- 1 mile from Trago Mills
- 01208 821242
- Serving times:
  7 days 12-2pm
  & 6-9pm
- Major credit cards
- Non-smoking area
- Licensed
- Children welcome
- 120 seats
- Starters from £2.50

Cornwall

- Bread St
  Penzance TR18 2EG
- Above health shop
- 01736 362828
- Serving times:
  Mon-Sat
  9.30am-4.15pm
  Open Fri evenings
  7-8.45pm
  Closed Sundays
- Booking essential
  for Fri evenings
- Major credit cards
- Non-smoking
- Licensed
- Children welcome
- 50 seats
- Mains from £4.50

Archie Browns

Tellingly busy with holidaymakers and residents alike, Archie Browns uses local organic produce where possible. The main room is above the health food shop, and there's also a small courtyard. Select your lunch from soups (for example, vegan lentil, orange and tomato), hummus and pitta, mushroom burgers or a chickpea tagine amongst many other choices from the daily-changing specials menu. Children can enjoy small portions from the adult menu.

To follow, choose from divine cakes like apple and almond, treacle tart, or gluten-free crumble with vegan custard. A glass of wine or beer with lunch is a welcome bonus, and the choice is all organic and vegan.

Do book if you're planning to visit for the special Friday evening buffets.

- 36 Causeway Head
  Penzance TR18 2ST
- 01736 366740
- Serving times:
  Mon-Wed 10am-4pm
  Thurs-Sat 10am-10pm
  Sun 10am-6.30pm
  June-Sept open later
  Mon-Wed
- Major credit cards
- Smoking throughout
  except lunchtimes
- Not licensed, BYO
  evenings £1 corkage
- Children welcome
- 32 seats

Yam Parlour

Yam Parlour is a bustling, vibrant place with recycled wooden furniture and a very cool bar made from old copper immersion tanks. There are pavement tables, and their planned courtyard should now be open.

The menu, which changes weekly, is always at least half vegan. Daytime meals include falafel, soups, beanburgers, hummus and the like; evenings are a little more sophisticated with dishes such as butter beans cooked in cider with pot barley, and wild mushroom risotto. On Saturday, breakfasts are served until 4 pm (which definitely gets our vote) and come from all round the world. There are freshly pressed juices, soya smoothies, soyaccinos and fair trade tea and coffee.

Yam Parlour is also a film and photography gallery and they show short films in the loos. Go see.

The Crooked Inn

A traditional country pub with a garden and front courtyard, the Crooked Inn is popular for its relaxed atmosphere. They also have animals wandering about outside as an added attraction.

The chef is vegetarian, so you can eat here with confidence. There are some tasty bakes on offer: cauliflower, broccoli and pasta with mustard sauce, stilton and almonds, or garlic mushroom and potato with mozzarella, together with a couple of curries.

Prize for the most-rarely-seen-dish goes to the mushrooms Caribbean, where they come sautéed in Malibu with pineapple, cream, baby corn and ginger, and finished with coconut.

Less substantial choices include potato wedges and dips, or a deep fried vegetable combo for two.

- Trematon
  Saltash PL12 4RZ
- 01752 848177
- Serving times:
  Mon-Thurs
  11am-2.30pm
  & 6-9.30pm
  Fri-Sat 11am-2.30pm
  & 6-10pm
  Sun 11am-3pm
  & 6-9.30pm
- Major credit cards
- Non-smoking area
- Licensed
- Children welcome
- 80 seats
- Mains from £6

Bean Inn Vegetarian Café

The only completely vegetarian place to eat out in St Ives, (and home to the Wild Planet Art Gallery), they work hard here with fresh homemade food – organic where possible.

Café by day, restaurant in the evening, with a garden and decking – you'd be happy to park here for a basic vegetable and tofu stir fry with a zesty sauce or the sublime roast tempeh, red onion marmalade, herb mash potato and vegetables among other scrummy fare. The menu changes regularly and Friday nights are a world cuisine buffet night; they also do Sunday roasts. You can even book a room with a view in the Coast B&B and have a veggie breakfast. Now, where's the map...

- Coast B&B
  St Ives Rd
  Carbis Bay
  St Ives TR26 2RT
- 01736 795918
- Serving times:
  Easter-October
  Tues-Sun 10am-10pm
  Ring for openings
  out of season
- No credit cards
- Non-smoking
- Applying for licence,
  currently BYO with
  no corkage
- Children welcome
- 52 seats including
  24 outside
- Evening starters £2.95,
  mains £6.45

17

Wyldes Café

- Bossiney Rd
  Tintagel PL34 0AH
- 01840 770007
- Serving times:
  Apr-Oct 7 days
  10am-5pm
  Nov-Mar Fri-Mon
  10am-3pm
  Closed Jan-early Feb
- No credit cards
- Non-smoking
- Not licensed
- Children welcome
- 22 seats
- Snacks from £2

So much more than a café, serving a selection of fine Indian tea and named origin coffees, Wyldes is responsive to special dietary requirements and takes real pride in using lots of local produce and only free range eggs. The full veggie breakfast is a real plateful which includes good vegetarian sausages, or just opt for the breakfast bap of fried egg and quorn. More than half the menu is vegetarian – all clearly marked and cooked separately.

The 'for something different' selection can include fried halloumi with sunblush tomatoes, or Provençal vegetables with melted goat's cheese.

Even the bread rolls, filled to order, are worth a meditative chew rather than a fast gulp.

The Feast

- 15 Kenwyn St
  Truro TR1 3BU
- 01872 272546
- Serving times:
  Mon-Sat
  10am-4.30pm
  Fri & Sat evenings
  6.30-9pm on last
  weekend of month
- Booking recommended
  evenings
- No credit cards
- Non-smoking
- Licensed
- Children welcome
- 45 seats and some
  outside tables
- Starters from £2

The Feast is open for coffee, lunch and tea, and for dinner on the last weekend of the month. There's also a menu of Belgian beers, if you want to write off the afternoon.

The main course of the day is displayed on a board, but there's also quiche and salad, main course vegan salads, baked spuds, sandwiches and pitta pockets filled with minty cottage cheese, tomato and olive or carrot and sweetcorn. Best of all there are savoury and sweet pancakes (spinach and cheese is a favourite). Most of the food is organic. All cakes are made on the premises, some are vegan or suitable for diabetics. If you are unrestricted, sink your fangs into some real Cornish clotted cream ice cream with hot chocolate sauce.

Fodders Restaurant

Fodders' comprehensive and predominately vegetarian menu also clearly marks which dishes are vegan, or can readily be prepared without dairy produce.

Based above Truro's Pannier Market, there is always a large range of salads – carrot and peanut, red cabbage with raspberry dressing, and couscous with lemon and herbs can feature among the many selections. Hot lunch choices on the daily specials board can include spicy rice and cashew-stuffed squash, tagliatelle with mushrooms, nuts and seeds in a white wine sauce, or mushroom and aubergine stuffed peppers with a goat's cheese topping.

There's also an impressive vegetarian and vegan cake menu and, if you fancy a change from tea, try a Fodders' hot white chocolate with marshmallows.

- Pannier Market
  Back Quay
  Truro TR1 2LL
- 01872 271384
- Serving times:
  Mon-Sat 10am-5pm
  Full menu served
  11.45am-3pm
  Closed bank holidays
- No credit cards
- Non-smoking
- Licensed
- Children welcome
- 64 seats
- Mains from £6.95

Cornwall

The Garret Café

This small, family-run café is on the inner harbour of Brixham's conservation area. Open from 8.15am for an early morning cup of coffee, they have special menus on Friday evenings and Sunday lunch.

There's a good vegan choice, and diabetic and gluten-free diets are catered for. Everything's very reasonably priced, and starters or snacks include guacamole, garlic bread, tomato and feta salad or soup. More substantial options are vegetable stir fries, halloumi or hummus with pitta, and beanburgers as well as the day's specials. Good children's choices of veggie sausages, burgers, nuggets or pizza with chips are additive-free and come with a drink for around £2. Desserts are made daily, juices and smoothies to order.

- Beach Approach
  Brixham TQ5 8JL
- 01803 882610
- Serving times:
  Mon-Thurs
  8.15am-5pm
  (summer to 8.30pm)
  Fri-Sun 8.15am-8pm
  (summer to 9.30pm)
- Booking advisable
  Fri eve & Sun lunch
- Major credit cards
- Non-smoking
- Not licensed, BYO with
  no corkage
- Children welcome
- 20 seats
- Starters from £2

Devon

- 76 The Square
  Chagford TQ13 8AE
- 01647 432571
- Serving times:
  Mon-Sat 12-4.30pm
  Full menu served
  until 3pm
- No credit cards
- Non-smoking except
  courtyard
- Not licensed
- Children welcome
- 20 seats & courtyard
- Soup from £3

The Courtyard Café

There's always a great selection of home-cooked food at this organic café in a wholefood shop on the edge of Dartmoor. Homity pie, vegetable and polenta bake or spicy potato pie for vegans, pizza and salad, shepherd's pie, and often a dozen more choices for vegetarians.

Savouries and cakes are often wheat-free, and there are also delicious chocolate brownies or a banana and almond trifle. Freshly pressed fruit juice and a huge range of herbal tea and coffee – with or without caffeine – are available.

This is a not-for-profit community co-operative, using locally grown organic ingredients, where sustainability is the watchword and children are especially welcome.

- Cider Press Centre
  Dartington
  Totnes TQ9 6JB
- 01803 862388
- Serving times:
  7 days 9.30am-5pm
  Closed Sun
  Xmas-Easter
- Major credit cards
- Non-smoking
- Licensed
- Children welcome
- 80 seats

Cranks

Set within a craft centre where you can wander around shops selling pottery, farm foods, stationery, books and (of course) Dartington glass, Cranks is one of the most famous names in vegetarian restaurants. As you would expect, there is a wide choice: they offer a daily menu, with vegan options such as curries, polenta with roast vegetables, and mushroom pie. Wheat- and sugar-free alternatives available.

Children are catered for with a separate menu offering, for example, burgers and pizza. Drinks range from wine and beer to homemade lemonade and banana smoothies, with the option of soya milk in tea or coffee. In the summer, you can sit outside under a shady tree. The perfect retreat.

Herbies

An unpretentious and friendly place for lunch and dinner where the chefs take wheat-free and vegan diets in their stride.

Starters also make an excellent quick snack, with soup and a choice of different garlic breads, bruschetta, or stuffed vine leaves. Light meals include salad bowls, falafel in pitta, nut- or beanburgers and wraps, or you can opt for a jacket potato with a good range of tasty fillings. The mains include a Caribbean black pea and coconut rundown, cashew loaf, and a tagine of vegetables and dried fruit, each served with three salads. Choose a pudding from the various cakes, desserts, ices and sorbets shown on the blackboards.

There's plenty of choice and some good wines, beers and speciality teas to be enjoyed.

- 15 North St
  Exeter EX4 3QS
- 01392 258473
- Serving times:
  Mon 11am-2.30pm
  Tues-Fri 11am-2.30pm
  & 6-9.30pm
  Sat 10.30am-4pm
  & 6-9.30pm
- Booking advisable
  Fri & Sat evenings
- Major credit cards
- Non-smoking area
- Licensed
- Children welcome
- 55 seats
- Starters from £2.25,
  mains from £5.75

Country Table Café

Karen and Alan Brady's Country Table Café in the heart of Newton Abbot has recently been extended to include a separate, more contemporary Mediterranean style area alongside the popular, more homely traditional café. There's a full range of paninis, jackets and vegetarian homemade bakes, together with lunchtime specials and a wide range of mixed salads.

Breakfasty goodies such as vegetarian sausage or bacon baps are served all day, and vegans are well looked after with choices like ratatouille, hummus and nut rissoles, together with the option of soya milk, margarine and egg-free mayonnaise.

High quality Costa coffee, quite possibly Devon's largest teacake (don't say we didn't warn you), and Swedish Glace vegan ice cream complete the mix.

- 12 Bank St
  Newton Abbot
  TQ12 2JW
- 01626 202120
- Serving times:
  Mon-Sat 9am-4pm
  Occasional Saturday
  evenings
  Closed bank holidays
- No credit cards
- Non-smoking
- Not licensed, but BYO
  with 50p corkage
- Children welcome
- 74 seats
- Lunch special from
  £4.75

- 38 Looe St
  Plymouth PL4 0EB
- 01752 202616
- Serving times:
  Mon 10am-5pm
  Tues-Sat
  10am-8.30pm
  Lunch served 12-2pm,
  evening meals served
  5-8.30pm, light
  refreshments outside
  these times
- Book for the monthly
  world cooking nights
- Major credit cards
- Non-smoking area
- Licensed & BYO wine
  with £1.60 corkage
- Children welcome
- 55 seats
- Snacks and light
  meals from £1.90

Plymouth Arts Centre

This vegetarian restaurant has been a favourite in Plymouth for more than 25 years. The arts centre that houses it is in a pair of Grade II listed 18th century buildings, with gallery space and a good independent cinema. You can arrange a combined cinema and restaurant deal, and there are monthly themed cooking nights as well as a special three course menu on Thursdays.

Each day there's a choice of at least six dishes, all well under a fiver. You could be choosing mushroom biriani with a dhal and yoghurt sauce, spinach lasagne, Cajun puff pastry pie or a spicy fruit and nut risotto. There are always several salads, plus jacket potatoes and soup, and you would be hard pushed to find a better vegan selection at any restaurant this side of Bristol.

Desserts are £1.75 and include old fashioned delights like sherry trifle and bread and butter pudding, as well as fruit crumbles, fruit salad and cakes.

The Friday evening monthly themed nights – for example Middle-eastern, Caribbean or African – are excellent value and genuine forays into a national style of cooking, where much more than lip service is paid to the traditions and flavourings of each region. Booking is advisable for these – call for details of the next event.

Outside of the main lunchtime (12-2pm) and evening (5-8.30pm) ordering times there's a range of light refreshments. If you've enjoyed your meal (and we can almost guarantee you will), why not pick up a copy of owner Annie Mason's recipe book, featuring some of the restaurant's most popular dishes?

Veggie Perrins

"I didn't get where I am today by eating meat..." you know you're in for an unusual dining experience at Veggie Perrin's – the walls are adorned with photos from the TV series – but the inspiration behind the cuisine has a serious basis in non-violence. And they must be doing something right – this long-established family-run Gujarati restaurant celebrates its 10th anniversary in 2005.

Lunchtime eat-as-much-as-you-like buffets (Mon-Sat) are just £4.50 – while a takeaway curry and rice can be had for under £2. In the evenings, an extensive à la carte menu demands time to browse properly – start with kachori (lightly spiced vegetables and lentils in pastry, served with chutney and salad) or potato-based bateta wada, then move on to curries, dhals and VP specials which include lots of homemade paneer dishes, baked aubergine fried with ginger, garlic and rich spices, or paun bhajee – a special mixture of fresh vegetables with toasted paun buns: very spicy. Most starters are around the £2 mark, while mains are generally under a fiver, plus rice or breads. Everything is available to take away, at discounted prices.

To follow: 'Sunshine Desserts' – naturally! Mango delight, or coconut ice cream in a half coconut shell, or kulfi – not exactly what C.J. built his empire on, but this is 21st century Plymouth, not 1980s Coleridge Close.

Veggie Perrins also organises Speciality Theme Nights – alternate Gujarati/South Indian cuisine on Tuesdays, or an evening buffet on Mondays (all you can eat for £6.50). The restaurant is licensed with a full range of Indian beer, wines and spirits, as well as juices and sweet or salted lassi.

- 97 Mayflower St
  Plymouth PL1 1SD
- 01752 252888
- Serving times:
  Mon-Sat 12-2pm
  & 6-10pm
- Booking recommended
- Major credit cards
- Non-smoking
- Licensed
- Children welcome
- 40 seats
- Starters from £2

Devon

Devon

- 327 Babbacombe Rd Torquay TQ1 3TB
- 01803 200900
- Serving times:
  7 days 6-8.30pm
  Closed 4 weeks mid Oct-mid Nov
- Booking essential
- Major credit cards
- Non-smoking
- Licensed
- 20 seats
- Three courses from £15

Anstey's Cove Hotel

This wholly non-smoking hotel and restaurant is a previous winner of a 'Best Hotel in South Devon' award. Well placed for the holidaymaker, it's near the beach and handy for some lovely scenic coastal walks.

The owner is vegetarian, and there's a great range of meat-free options with a comprehensive vegan selection including dishes such as celery and bean casserole or baked aubergine.

The menu is a happy blend of both traditional West Country and some Indian-influenced dishes, where an asparagus starry gazy pie sits alongside a vegetable thali. Desserts include a vegan chocolate gateau, fresh fruit tart and rum truffles. They use locally-produced fruit and vegetables, and there's also a choice of wine from nearby vineyards. Booking essential.

Devon

- 87 High St Totnes TQ9 5PB
- 01803 862605
- Serving times:
  Mon-Sat 10am-5.30pm
  Wed, Fri & Sat evenings 7-9.30pm
  Fri opens 9am
- Booking recommended for evenings
- No credit cards
- Smoking in garden only
- Licensed
- Children welcome
- 48 seats & garden
- Snacks from £1.50, evening mains from £6.25

The Willow Restaurant

At the top of the town, this restaurant works hard to provide a different lunch and evening menu every day, with special Indian nights also putting in an appearance.

Traditional pine furniture and bright tablecloths, with oil lamps coming out at night, make for a cosy atmosphere, and there's always at least one vegan main dish, plus several starters and desserts.

Main courses from the lunch menu can include interesting quiche – such as celery, red onion and camembert – aubergine and spinach layer, big salads, rolls and baked potatoes. The evening's Sunny Island casserole is an inviting combination of peppers, courgettes, mangetout and sweet potatoes in a coconut sauce, with lime and ginger marinated tofu chunks.

More than worth a visit, do book in the evening.

The Skylark Inn

Sit in the garden and enjoy the moorland around this pub which serves lunch and dinner seven days a week.

Pub favourites like fried camembert and cranberry dip and cheesy garlic mushrooms open the batting, and are followed with a choice of a dozen or so mains such as stews, stroganoffs, curries, and bakes, including the vegan Thai vegetables with noodles, and celery, bean and coriander chilli.

Jacket potatoes and pasta will stoke you for a moorland walk, and your vegetarian offspring can refuel from a couple of choices such as mini pizza or bean and veg grills – although, we're sad to say, they're restricted to the garden area: this traditional inn doesn't have a children's licence.

- Clearbrook
  Yelverton PL20 6JD
- 01822 853258
- Serving times:
  Mon-Sat
  11.30am-2.15pm
  & 6.30-9.15pm
  Sun 12-2.15pm
  & 6.30-9pm
- Major credit cards
- Smoking throughout
- Licensed
- 50 seats
- Mains from £7

Devon

bristol • somerset

Bristol

Somerset

bristol • somerset

Minehead □

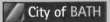 City of BATH

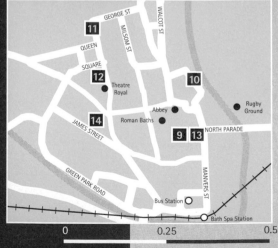

BRISTOL

■ Bristol

□ Clevedon

■ Bath

□ Weston-Super-Mare

Wells 20

Frome 15

16 17 18 Glastonbury

□ Bridgwater

19 Taunton

SOMERSET

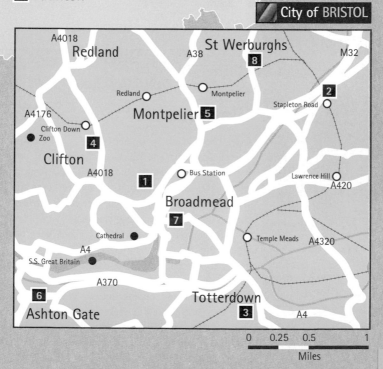

City of BRISTOL

A4018

Redland

St Werburghs

A38

M32

8

Redland ○

Montpelier ○

2

Stapleton Road ○

A4176

Montpelier 5

Clifton Down ○

● Clifton Down Zoo

4

Clifton

A4018

1

Bus Station ○

Lawrence Hill ○

A420

Broadmead

7

Cathedral ●

Temple Meads ○

A4320

A4

S.S. Great Britain ●

A370

6

Totterdown

Ashton Gate

3

A4

| 0 | 0.25 | 0.5 | | 1 |

Miles

29

- 27 St Michael's Hill
  Bristol BS2 8DZ
- 0117 929 2834
- Serving times:
  Tues-Thurs 6-10pm
  Fri 6-10.30pm
  Sat 6-11pm
- Booking essential
  weekends
- Major credit cards
- Non-smoking area
- Licensed
- Children welcome
- 60 seats
- Starters from £4.50

Anthem

This candlelit restaurant, a warren of rooms in a 17th century building, has a casual atmosphere, and you'll find yourself eating to a very definitely non-muzak African and south American soundtrack.

Starters are predominately vegetarian: Vietnamese-style spring rolls with a lime and chilli dip, mozzarella and ratatouille calzone, or interesting meze and salads lead into mains which can find you choosing between a vegan tofu, okra and red pepper-stuffed aubergine or a roast vegetable-filled gougère.

Open evenings Tuesday to Saturday, you'll need to book at weekends. If you're in this part of Bristol in December, they're also open for lunch in the run-up to Christmas.

- 1 William St
  Totterdown
  Bristol BS3 4TU
- 0117 972 0938
- Serving times:
  Tues-Thurs 7-9.30pm
  Fri-Sat 6.30-9.45pm
  Closed Sun & Mon
  Open for lunch during
  December
- Booking essential
  Fri & Sat
- Major credit cards
- Non-smoking
- Licensed
- Children welcome
- 70 seats
- Two courses
  from £15.50

Glasnost

From the sublime - roasted papaya stuffed with spinach, asparagus and applewood cheese with sesame dressing, to the ridiculous - Baileys and Malteser cheesecake, Glasnost has something for everyone. There's a separate vegan menu, they aren't fazed by coeliacs and are always willing to adapt.

With two courses for £15.50 or three for £18.50, they are aiming for some interesting sauced and salsa'd dishes at reasonable cost. The courgette, parsnip and wild rice burger sounds like a friend to the people as does the watercress and leek soup with crème fraiche.

It's essential to book at weekends, and advisable the rest of the time. The restaurant is non-smoking throughout, and children are welcome, although there's no separate menu.

Café Maitreya

Although they'd only been open a year, in 2003 Café Maitreya was voted 'best restaurant in Bristol for a vegan meal' by the highly respected local vegan guidebook. Indeed, 60% of the menu is vegan, and vegetarians will find themselves as close to restaurant paradise as it comes.

Described as modern contemporary with Mediterranean influences, the lunch menu of more than 10 choices can include dishes such as slow-roasted tomatoes with olive oil, basil and wholemeal toast, grilled field mushrooms in ciabatta with Dijon mustard and salad, and the Maitreya meze of oven roasted vegetables, spiced puy lentil salad, hummus, marinated olives and sourdough bread. And for those who just can't resist the classic British breakfast try the wicked 'mega Maitreya' of jumbo sausage, eggs, tomatoes, mushrooms, beans and toast. There's also a wide range of ciabatta and rolls available.

The evening menu offers such delights as goat's cheese-stuffed vine leaves, sweetcorn patties, honey roasted butternut squash tart, marinated fennel and tofu kebabs, and Japanese-style stir fried noodles with wild mushrooms and pak choi. And, if you're a dessert fan, round the evening off with puddings like chocolate coconut roulade, caramelised pear flan, or the divine rhubarb, strawberry and star anise compôte.

All the alcohol served is organic and vegetarian, and there is a range of fresh vegetable juices and smoothies including Sweet Surrender (pear juice, banana, live yoghurt) and the cleansing and recuperating Stinger (carrots, celery and ginger). Go there. Now.

- 89 St Marks Rd
  Easton
  Bristol BS5 6HY
- 0117 951 0100
- Serving times:
  Tues 7-9.45pm
  Wed-Fri 12-3pm
  & 7-9.45pm
  Sat 11am-4pm
  & 7-9.45pm
  Sun 11am-4pm
- Booking recommended evenings
- Major credit cards
- Non-smoking
- Licensed
- Children welcome
- 35 seats
- Two-course evening menu from £11.95

- 46 Whiteladies Rd
  Bristol BS8 2NH
- Next to old
  ABC cinema
- 0117 923 9212
- Serving times:
  Mon-Sat 12-2.15pm
  & 6-10.15pm
  Sun 12-2.15pm
- Booking essential Fri
  & Sat evenings
- Major credit cards
- Non-smoking area
  except Sat
- Licensed & BYO
  wine/champagne
- Children welcome
- 160 seats
- Starters from £4.75,
  mains from £10

Hullabaloos

This Anglo-French-Mediterranean restaurant is in a Regency building with dining over three floors. Booking is essential on Friday and Saturday evenings, but you could chance it for Sunday lunch. A strict vegan meal can be prepared with notice.

There's a good value early evening set menu, but looking à la carte, start the meal with asparagus spears with lemon and hollandaise sauce – a simple dish that only a really good kitchen will produce with confidence. Main courses include wild mushroom and sweet basil and cashew nut roast with fresh tomato sauce.

Satisfy any sweet pangs with an apricot and raspberry crème brulée. They are licensed but generously don't charge corkage if you bring your own wine or champagne.

- 12 York Rd
  Montpelier
  Bristol BS6 5QE
- 0117 942 6687
- Serving times:
  Tues-Sun 6-12pm
- Booking
  recommended
- No credit cards
- Non-smoking
- Licensed
- Children welcome
- 34 seats

One Stop Thali Café

Straightforward, inexpensive, freshly prepared Indian food. Served thali-style, the day's dishes combine to produce a well-balanced and healthy meal. Simple, really – but it's popular enough that booking's recommended most of the time. Dishes such as paneer with a fenugreek and mustard seed sauce, and the Keralan red pepper and sweet potato subzi often feature, but every night's combination is different.

You can also take away – join the Tiffen club and you'll get your very own Tiffen Tower (a stack of stainless pans) to take away the night's specials in. Once you've joined, it's a very reasonable fiver a fill-up. What a very good idea. You'll also find One Stop catering at festivals like Glastonbury, The Big Chill and Shambala.

Riverside Garden Centre

Open daily for brunch and lunch, this offers more than yer average garden centre adjunct. The brunch options include pancakes and syrup, fruit poached in Earl Grey tea, or eggy bread with rosti and grilled tomatoes.

There's a choice of light bites – cannellini beans with artichoke hearts on mixed salad, homemade soup or a substantial plate of vegetarian sausages with thyme and onion gravy on colcannon mash. Platters of tapas or meze in various sizes are priced from £5-£14 – the last must be enormous!

Local produce is used throughout and there's a monthly evening five-course dinner which, judging from the day menu, would be well worth booking for. Children are also well looked after; as well as high chairs there's an outside play area.

- Clift House Rd
  Southville
  Bristol BS3 1RX
- Behind Spaces
  Storage Centre
- 0117 966 7535
- Serving times:
  Mon-Sat 10am-3pm
  Sun 11am-3pm
- Major credit cards
- Non-smoking inside
- Not licensed
- Children welcome
- 70 seats
- Light bites from £2.95,
  lunch from £4.95

Royce Rolls

The well-known and loved café in the 18th century Corn Exchange is famed for its relaxed and friendly atmosphere and The Royce Roll, an own-recipe masterpiece specially designed to be filled.

There are two non-veg items, if you're going to have a hissy fit about it – a smoked salmon bagel and a tuna mayo roll – but everything else is OK, with some vegan and gluten-free choices.

The range of flapjacks, pasties, pastries and samosas is simply vast and they have own-blend coffee and tea as well as loads of herbal choices. Sit in, or out in the summer, or grab yourself a great picnic lunch. Christmas shoppers can make it a lunch stop as they also open Sundays in December.

Great standard of food prepared on a budget.

- St Nicholas Market
  The Corn Exchange
  Bristol BS1 1JQ
- 0117 982 4228
- Serving times:
  Mon-Fri 7.30am-4pm
  Sat 9.30am-5pm
  Open Sundays in
  December
- No credit cards
- Non-smoking
- Not licensed but BYO
  with no corkage
- Children welcome
- 25 seats

- Watercress Rd
  St Werburghs
  Bristol BS2 9YJ
- 0117 924 5592
- Serving times:
  Wed-Sun 10am-4pm
  Booking recommended
  for Sun lunch
- No credit cards
- Non-smoking
- Not licensed, BYO
  with no corkage
- Children welcome
- 38 seats

St Werburghs City Farm

As well as the farm attached to this café, there's a children's playground and outdoor café seating for fine weather. Food is Moroccan, Mexican, Spanish and French influenced – but with very British jacket spuds, toasted sandwiches and full vegetarian breakfasts also making an appearance.

Soups, hummus, selected olives and guacamole make the introductions. You can follow up with quesadillas, main course falafel or lasagne. Organic ice cream, bread and butter pudding and gluten-free brownies round off the event.

There's also a children's menu, plenty of vegan choice, and organic and gluten-free specials.

You can hire the café for evening functions, but otherwise it's a daytime-only venue.

- 2 North Parade
  Passage
  Bath BA1 1NX
- 01225 446059
- Serving times:
  Mon-Fri 10am-10pm
  Sat 9am-11pm
  Sun 10am-10pm
- Major credit cards
- Non-smoking
- Licensed
- Children welcome
- 40 seats
- Daytime mains
  from £6.50

Demuths

This famous vegetarian restaurant provides mouthwatering fare from morning to evening. Breakfast on filled bagels, toast and marmalade or the full cooked platter, or visit at lunch for wraps crammed with salad, falafel, and roasted veg or a tomato and dolcelatte tart amongst more than a dozen or more choices.

Evening meals can include smoked tofu pâté or local soft cheese with ciabatta for starters, and main courses of Cajun-spiced bean strudel or oyster mushroom and asparagus tagliatelle. Desserts feature organic ice creams, Balinese black rice pudding and vegan chocolate fudge cake. There's a children's menu of sandwiches and toasties, and a good organic wine list.

Demuths also run a vegetarian cookery school and holidays, visit www.demuths.co.uk for full details.

Riverside Café

Very central, in the beautiful tourist heart of Bath by Pulteney Bridge, and popular with locals and visitors alike, this daytime café (with early evening opening promised for the summer) offers plenty of vegetarian choices. Have one of their freshly squeezed orange juices while you deliberate over the menu. The grilled goat's cheese salad or the vegetable pâté with chutney? Enchiladas, refried beans and guacamole or red onion and gruyère tart? Other specials can include posh cheesy tarts, vegetarian sausage and mash, roast veg pastas and homity pie.

The owner previously ran a vegetarian restaurant in Cornwall, so we reckon you can eat here with confidence.

- 17 Argyle St
  Bath BA2 4BQ
- 01225 480532
- Serving times:
  7 days 9.30am–5pm
  Open later during summer months
- Major credit cards
- Non-smoking
- Licensed
- Children welcome
- 40 seats
- Mains from £6

Somerset

The Porter

Love this place – a traditional pub with higgledy-piggledy levels and a brick cellar with great hideaway coves. The food is all vegetarian, some of it fair trade, and well informed staff know what's what if you have any food allergies. There's also always a good vegan selection. You can get pie and chips, sandwiches, baked spuds, a vegetarian cooked breakfast and a nut roast Sunday lunch.

Nothing super inventive, just good value pub food that happens to be vegetarian. It's a great local, with music several nights a week and a truly excellent comedy club on Sunday nights with top circuit acts. Plan a weekend in Bath and make sure you come here to relax.

- 15 George St
  Bath BA1 2EN
- 01225 424104
- Serving times:
  Mon-Sat 11am-9pm
  Sun 12-9pm
- Major credit cards
- Smoking throughout
- Licensed
- Children welcome until 9pm except in bar area
- 150 seats
- From £2.75

Somerset

- 28 Barton St
  Bath BA1 1HH
- 01225 314864
- Serving times:
- Mon-Sat 12-2.30pm
  & 6-11pm
- Sun 12-11pm
- Booking advisable
  weekends
- Major credit cards
- Smoking throughout
- Licensed
- Children welcome
- 38 seats
- Mains from £7.50

The Walrus & Carpenter

In the manner of Victor Kyam, Andrew Robinson enjoyed his local restaurant so much that he bought it. Now celebrating its 30th year – a remarkable achievement in an industry which has a notoriously high casualty rate – The Walrus & Carpenter treats its vegetarian customers to a varied and interesting menu in candlelit surroundings.

Most of the starters are vegetarian: choices include potato skins, hummus, garlic mushrooms and nachos, then select from around half a dozen separately listed vegetarian mains such as mushroom moussaka, or nut loaf with a mushroom and watercress sauce. There are also vegan options in the ratatouille, chilli, and penne in a tomato and basil sauce.

- 3 North Parade
  Passage
  Bath BA1 1NX
- Next door to
  Sally Lunn's
- 01225 484200
- Serving times:
- Mon-Sat 12-2.25pm
  & 6.30-10.50pm
- Booking essential
- Major credit cards
- Non-smoking floor
- Licensed
- Children welcome
- 65 seats
- Starters from £4.50,
  mains from £7.50

Tilleys Bistro

At the heart of the heritage trail in Bath, near the Abbey and the oldest house in town, Tilleys is an Anglo-French delight for vegetarians.

There's a set lunch menu with some vegetarian options which changes fortnightly, but if you visit in the evening you'll be rewarded with a much more comprehensive à la carte choice. Order what you will from a selection of cold salads and hors d'oeuvre, a handful of warm tarts and terrines, and several interesting hot dishes like wild mushroom pancake or a satay of tofu, pineapple and vegetable with a spicy peanut sauce. Add some decent dauphinoise potatoes or red cabbage braised in cider as sides, and settle down for a serious nosh.

Bath

Yum Yum Thai

The name may invite a little snigger, but this relaxed Thai restaurant delivers. Situated in a lovely Georgian square, there's a lot of repeat business here and it's popular with locals. There's plenty of vegetarian choice – usually dishes that are adapted by substituting tofu – and Thai fragrant rice is included in the cost of a main course (unless it's noodle based).

Choose from kai pat takrai – stir fried tofu in chilli oil with mushrooms, pepper and lemon grass, or battered vegetables in sweet chilli and plum sauce, as well as more than a dozen other options.

There are lunchtime specials from 12 to 2.30pm, and they have an outdoor seating area. Evening booking advised, especially if you want the non-smoking section.

- 17 Kingsmead Sq Bath BA1 2AE
- 01225 445253
- Serving times:
  Mon-Sat 12-2.30pm & 6-11pm
  Sun 6-11pm
  Usually closed bank holidays
- Booking recommended for non-smoking area
- Major credit cards
- Non-smoking area
- Licensed
- Children welcome
- 65 seats
- Mains from £7.95

Frome

The Garden Café

This attractive modern café in the centre of Frome also has a lovely walled garden which seats 35 people. Food is mainly organic and there's a range of light meals as well as a good selection of more substantial main courses. Enjoy soup, salad bowls, focaccia and salad, or toasted sandwiches with organic brie, cranberry and celery or hummus with roasted vegetables. Yummy mains include cashew nut and bean patties, savoury pancakes with salad or Thai green curry with tofu and lemon rice.

The desserts are enough to have you kick the door down: chocolate brownies with hot chocolate sauce, cream and cherries, or organic ice cream as well as daily specials and pastries. The Garden Café can also cater for your vegetarian garden party.

- 16 Stony St Frome BA11 1BU
- 01373 454178
- Serving times:
  Mon-Thurs 9am-5pm
  Fri-Sat 9am-9pm
  Sun 11am-4pm
- No credit cards
- Non-smoking inside
- Licensed
- Children welcome
- 25 seats & 35 in courtyard
- Starters from £2.95, mains from £5.20

37

Somerset

- 5a High St
  Glastonbury BA6 9DP
- 01458 834284
- Serving times:
  Wed-Thurs 11am-9pm
  Fri-Sat
  10.30-am 10pm
  Sun 11am-9pm
- Booking advisable
  weekend evenings
- Major credit cards
- Non-smoking
- Licensed
- Children welcome
- 40 seats
- Mains from £7

Café Galatea

It's best to book for weekend evenings at this well established restaurant and gallery. There's a lot of repeat business from international travellers, and it's easy to see why Café Galatea is so popular.

All the food is cooked to order – so special diets are taken note of and ingredients can be substituted – and Jeanette Williamson, a partner in the business, cooks every shift herself in order to maintain her exacting standards.

There are vegan options for many of the vegetarian dishes, a really savoury sesame stir fry, mushroom pancakes, homemade soup or nachos. You can enjoy a drink with your meal, including local organic cider or premium brand spirits. And if you're sticking to tea or coffee, soya milk is available.

Somerset

- 17a High St
  Glastonbury BA6 9DP
- 01458 833896
- Serving times:
  7 days 11.30am-4pm
- No credit cards
- Smoking in separate
  conservatory
- Not licensed, BYO
  with £1 corkage
- Children welcome
- 50 seats
- Starters from £3,
  mains from £5

Rainbow's End

A courtyard, a fountain, a Grade II listed building and Glastonbury: in café terms this is a crock of gold. The menu isn't vast, but with everything vegetarian and some exceptional vegan choices, you won't be complaining.

Soup with organic bread, flans, quiches and daily specials like Moroccan vegetables with tofu sit alongside sugar- and gluten-free cakes; the homemade hot fruity drinks (spicy apple, hot lemon, ginger and honey) or ginger beer and lemonade mean you'll be well refreshed, winter or summer. If you want to bring your own wine, corkage is only £1.

A relaxed family atmosphere pervades and people really do turn up from all round the globe to eat here.

White Spring Café

A mile or so out of the centre of town on the way to the Tor itself, and next to the Chalice Well Gardens, the White Spring is a cave-like building which sprouts from the side of a hill. It's actually a Victorian reservoir, built at the confluence of a number of springs, and water still flows along a channel in the floor.

Often rich with the smell of incense, the café is dimly lit and has a strong spiritual feel in keeping with the whole Glastonbury experience.

There's very limited parking, but do drop in on your walk before the hike up the Tor and refuel on a selection of toasties, soups, salads, burgers and cakes – or the more bistro-style selection of food that's available in the summer.

- Wellhouse Lane
  Glastonbury BA6 8BL
- 01458 830406
- Serving times:
  Summer 7 days
  10am-8pm
  Closes earlier in winter
- No credit cards
- Smoking throughout
- Not licensed, BYO with minimal corkage
- Children welcome
- 100+ seats

Lotus Flower

There's a separate vegetarian menu at this local Thai and you'll find some vegan options too. They use organic produce where possible and non-GM ingredients, and they're happy to cater for special diets.

Drink Thai beer with the set vegetarian menu – a feast at £17.50 each. You can enjoy mushrooms in rice and coconut batter, satay vegetables and spring rolls with a second course of hot and sour soup, followed by asparagus, bean sprouts, baby corn and green beans in spicy coconut sauce with lime leaves, and mangetout with aubergine in pringking sauce with Thai rice. You'll leave beautifully sated with aromatic, tingling flavours. Popular, especially at weekends when booking is strongly advised.

- 89 Station Rd
  Taunton TA1 1PB
- Opposite Royal
  Ashton Hotel
- 01823 324411
- Serving times:
  Tues-Sat 6-11pm
- Booking essential
  weekends
- Major credit cards
- Separate smoking room
- Licensed
- Children welcome
- 30 seats
- Set menu from £17.50

Somerset

- 4 Priory Rd
  Wells BA5 1SY
- 01749 678600
- Serving times:
  Mon-Sat 9am-5pm
  Full menu from
  11.30am
  Closed bank holidays
- Major credit cards
- Non-smoking
- Licensed
- Children welcome
- 86 seats

The Good Earth

Open daily for coffee and cake from 9am, and serving the full lunch menu from late morning, The Good Earth is a popular Wells landmark.

Check the blackboard for the day's menu – choices change regularly, though there are always vegan and gluten-free options and the kitchen makes good use of organic produce.

There's homemade bread with the soup; salads, filled jackets, and main courses such as shepherds pie, a tian of Provençal vegetables with smoked mozzarella, quiche, red onion tarte tatin and pizza. Ten different cakes vie with the daily dessert for your attention, so be ready for some serious decision making.

The restaurant is also blessed with a conservatory, and an additional courtyard area in the summer.

dorset
hampshire
isle of wight
wiltshire

dorset • hampshire • isle of wight • wiltshire

Dorset

Hampshire

Isle of Wight

Wiltshire

DORSET

Ansty

6 Marshwood   **7**

8   **5** Bridport   ▫

Lyme   Dorchester
Regis

Weymouth▫

20 Swindon

Chippenham

Avebury 15   19 Marlborough

17 18 Devizes

Trowbridge

□ Basingstoke

Warminster

16

□ Andover

HAMPSHIRE

□ Salisbury   □ Winchester

Petersfield □

Romsey 10

11 Southampton

□ Ringwood   9 Havant

Portsmouth □

12 Southsea

□ Cowes

1 2

Poole □   Bournemouth

3 4   14 Newport

Freshwater Bay 13

□ Shanklin

ISLE OF WIGHT

dorset • hampshire • isle of wight • wiltshire

- 73 Seamoor Rd
  Westbourne
  Bournemouth BH4 9AE
- Opposite Waitrose
- 01202 769959
- Serving times:
  Mon-Sat 10am-5pm
  Lunch served from
  11.30am
  Closed bank holidays
- No credit cards
- Non-smoking
- Licensed
- Children welcome
- 45 seats

Flossies

You shouldn't have any trouble spotting this traditional vegetarian restaurant – it's got bright yellow awnings and a big pink heart in the middle of its logo.

Inside you'll find a range of home cooked meals such as cauliflower cheese, aubergine bake, Spanish omelette and mushroom and spinach lasagne, together with vegan choices like nut rissoles and ratatouille. Children can choose small portions from the main menu. Flossies also serve excellent cakes, and their puddings can include fruit salads, pavlovas, apple crumble and treacle tart.

With a relaxed café feel, Flossies is a place you can visit for a decent spot of lunch, or just chill out with a cup of freshly ground coffee and the day's paper.

- 218 Holdenhurst Rd
  Bournemouth
  BH8 8AX
- 01202 552277
- Serving times:
  Mon-Thurs 11am-2pm
  & 6-11.30pm
  Fri 11am-2pm
  Sun 11am-2pm
  & 6-11.30pm
- Booking
  recommended
- Major credit cards
- Non-smoking
- Licensed
- Children welcome
- 30 seats

The Falafel Restaurant

This covers all the bases: dairy-free, kosher, children's portions, Israeli liqueurs, fresh fruit smoothies and a rare fresh almond drink. It's closed on Friday evening and all day Saturday, but open late on Sunday night, which could come in handy if you're in Bournemouth for a long weekend.

There some gutsy cooked salads and side dishes – including a whole head of baked garlic – as well as borek (stuffed pancakes or pastries), hot broth and couscous, aubergine dips, and hummus. There's a children's section of veggie sausage and chips or falafel, and some good desserts including dairy-free ice cream, baked bananas and a semolina, almond and honey cake. The many vegan options are clearly marked.

The restaurant is quite small, so it's best to book.

The Salad Centre

This vegetarian wholefood restaurant prepares dishes freshly each day with no artificial colourings, preservatives or other added chemicals, and their menu even gives you a recipe for ratatouille. The soup choice changes each day, and main salads have plenty of carbohydrate bases like pasta or rice, so you can fill a bowl and make a decent meal.

If you want something hot there's quiche, pizza, risotto, pasties, filled baked potatoes and daily specials such as broccoli and mushroom lasagne or lentil moussaka. Children can have half size portions if that's practical, or the café is happy to give you an extra plate if they're going to share some of yours.

- 667 Christchurch Rd Boscombe Bournemouth BH7 6AA
- 01202 393673
- Serving times: Mon-Sat 10am-5pm
- Major credit cards
- Non-smoking
- Not licensed, BYO with no corkage
- Children welcome
- 60 seats
- Mains from £3.50

Wessex Tales

How come you guys in Dorset get to be so lucky? Completely vegetarian, vegan-friendly and with a high proportion of organic ingredients, we want one of these restaurants next door too!

Starters include soup with onion and herb bread, hummus with pitta or an avocado salad, and a lunchtime choice of mains featuring sausage and chips, braised tofu, nut roast and masala dosas, as well as a range of baked potatoes with some very interesting toppings.

The evening selection is similar (sans the baked potato options), but with the addition of a couple of extra dishes such as chickpea curry. Wessex Tales is licensed, and you can also get a good soya cappuccino, cardamom coffee, herb and regular teas.

- Tudor Corner House 20 Ashley Rd Boscombe Bournemouth BH1 4LH
- 01202 309869
- Serving times:
  Tues-Thurs
  12-2.30pm
  Fri-Sat
  12-2.30pm & 7-10pm
  Closed Tuesdays after bank holidays
- Booking recommended
- No credit cards
- Non-smoking
- Licensed
- Children welcome
- 30 seats
- Starters from £2

Dorset

- 4-6 Barrack St
  Bridport DT6 3LY
- Opposite East St
  car park
- 01308 459466
- Serving times:
  Mon-Sat 9am-3pm
  Closed bank holidays
  Closed January
- No credit cards
- Non-smoking
- Not licensed
- Children welcome
- 50 seats

Green Yard Café

With a strong bias towards vegetarian food, The Green Yard Café has twice won the West Country Cooking Food & Tourism's 'Best Café in Dorset' award.

The menu changes daily, and can feature a range of soups – butternut squash and sweet potato or organic courgette – with other choices including roast onion tart, organic spinach and tomato lasagne or a stilton, leek, apple and walnut crumble.

Fresh fruit is pressed into service for a great range of smoothies, or try the homemade lemonade. Soya milk is available for tea and coffee. With just 20 seats in the courtyard and 30 in the café itself, please note that the Green Yard can get extremely busy in the summer.

Dorset

- Marshwood
  Bridport DT6 5QJ
- 01297 678254
- Serving times:
  Tues-Sun 12-2pm
  & 7-9pm
  Open Mondays
  during summer
- Booking essential
  during high summer
- Major credit cards
- Non-smoking area
- Licensed
- Children welcome
- 32 seats

The Bottle Inn

Booking is essential in the height of summer at this popular 15th century country pub. The comprehensive vegetarian menu features homemade food with a strong organic bias, and there's a vegan Sunday lunch option. Specials change regularly, but can include baked avocado with stilton and paprika, or brie wedges with cranberry sauce. You can also enjoy main courses such as a homely Hereford pie – filo pastry with leeks, apple, red Leicester cheese and cider, or a Thai green curry, basmati rice, mango chutney and poppadom. If it's bar snacks you're after, then a range of filled baguettes, ploughman's lunches or hummus and pitta may well do the job.

The Bottle Inn also hosts the world nettle-eating championships. Any takers?

The Fox Inn

This traditional English country pub in the centre of Ansty village – about 10 miles from Dorchester – has two separate restaurants as well as serving food in the bar. It offers a dedicated vegetarian menu with daily changing vegetarian specials and is open for dining seven days a week.

The menu includes pasta, risotto, a Ceylon style vegetable curry – baby corn, peppers, banana and pineapple in a lime, coconut and mango sauce – and a vegetable and nut stroganoff in lemon and brandy cream. Vegan options include the vegetable chilli and a cajun hotpot.

Children can share adult portions or choose from their own menu which includes macaroni cheese and a vegetarian pizza.

- Ansty
  Dorchester DT2 7PN
- 01258 880328
- Serving times:
  Mon-Sat 12-2.30pm
  & 6.30-9pm
  Sun 12-3pm
  & 6.30-9pm
- Booking recommended
- Major credit cards
- Non-smoking restaurant
- Licensed
- Children welcome
- 54 seats
- Mains from £5.95

Dorset

Café Clemence

Situated in the restored Town Mill site with its working waterwheel, you'll find Café Clemence in among potters, picture framers and an art gallery.

They've embraced the French notion of a choice of set menus as well as plats du jour, and there's some fine vegetarian choices and generally a vegan option too. Food is cooked to order, and may take a while at busy times.

They'll do you a veggie breakfast, lunchtime baguettes, vegetarian soups and warm salads as well as three set menus priced from £9.95 to £19.95. Sunday lunch has a vegetarian option (well it's French, Jacques, but not as we know it...), and they've received mentions in The Times and Country Living.

- Town Mill Mill Lane
  Lyme Regis DT7 3PU
- 01297 445757
- Serving times:
  Mon from 6pm
  Tues-Sun
  12-2.30pm & from 6pm
  Evening last orders
  vary with the season
- Major credit cards
- Non-smoking
- Licensed
- Children welcome
- 22 seats
  & 20 in courtyard
- Menu rapide from
  £9.95, 4 courses
  from £19.95

Dorset

Omnivorous Café Bar

Hampshire

- Havant Arts Centre
  East St
  Havant PO9 1BS
- 023 9248 0113
- Serving times:
- Mon-Sat
  9.30am-3.30pm
- Lunch menu
  served 12-2pm
- Evening opening on
  performance nights
- Book for evenings
- Major credit cards
- Non-smoking
  during day
- Licensed
- Children welcome
- 50 seats

Red Mango

An omnivorous arts centre café open for morning coffee, lunch and early afternoon tea, they'll also feed you on performance nights – often with a themed menu. So, if you fancy an evening of live band salsa having dined on brazil nut roast with a mango mojo sauce, you know where to come.

There are also comedy nights (we're assured this relates to the stage performance, not the menu) and regular monthly jazz evenings.

At lunchtimes, there are always soups, bakes, quiches and a large salad selection as well as sandwiches and jackets – and they aim for at least one vegan option in addition to gluten-free choices.

Omnivorous Chinese Restaurant

Hampshire

- 9 Bell St
  Romsey SO51 8GY
- 01794 514428
- Serving times:
- Mon-Wed 6-11pm
- Thurs-Fri 12.15-2pm
  & 6-11pm
- Sat 5.30-11.15pm
- Sun 12.30-10.30pm
- Major credit cards
- Non-smoking area
- Licensed
- Children welcome
- 70 seats
- Mains from £5

South Garden

There's a separate vegetarian section on the menu at this well-established Cantonese and Szechaun influenced restaurant, with some vegan choices as well. Stir fried cashew nuts with diced vegetables is popular, but there are also tasty delights such as stir fried mushrooms (straw, white and Chinese), or asparagus and celery with bean shoots.

The vegetarian set dinner begins with a number of starters – crispy cabbage, spring rolls and asparagus on toast – followed by soup and four main dishes including beancurd with Chinese veg, green pepper in blackbean sauce and sweet and sour deep-fried mushrooms.

They're open all day on Sundays and bank holidays, and takeaways are available at a huge discount if you decide to slum it at home.

Allsorts Psychic Café

Just the place if you're in need of a spiritual, as well as a caffeine or carbohydrate boost, Kelvin Woodage's bright and friendly Psychic Café also hosts tarot practitioners, reiki healers and psychic readers in the downstairs rooms.

Renowned locally for their cakes, there are also snacks and light lunches – pasties, burgers, chillis, salads, together with a daily special. And – if you're in luck on the day you visit – they offer a very fine vegetarian breakfast.

Remarkably good value, and the perfect place to chill out. Take in the art, photography and esoteric literature covering the walls, choose the window seat to watch the world go by, or (our personal choice) collapse on the sofa until you're ready for more cake.

- 22 Carlton Place
  Southampton
  SO15 2DY
- 023 8023 7561
- Serving times:
  Tues-Thurs
  10.30am-6pm
  Fri-Sat 10.30am-9pm
- No credit cards
- Non-smoking
- Not licensed
- Children welcome
- 20 seats
- Light lunch from £2

Hampshire

Country Kitchen

A counter service restaurant with a bright, modern look at the end of the Marmion Road parade.

At lunchtimes you'll be filling your plate from a range of dishes which can include brazil nut and tofu sausages, shepherds pie, crumble with horseradish and watercress, or a marinated tofu, tomato and onion balti – plus there's always a vegan choice.

Lighter options include soups and quiches, and you can also just pop in and enjoy a coffee with one of their very reasonably priced cakes or puddings. Open from 9am, six days a week (and Sundays during the run-up to Christmas), they also offer meat-free buffets through 'Wild Leaf' special event catering.

- 59 Marmion Rd
  Southsea PO5 2AX
- 023 9281 1425
- Serving times:
  Mon-Sat
  9am-4.45pm
  Closed bank holidays
  Open on the four
  Sundays before Xmas
- No credit cards
- Non-smoking
- Licensed
- Children welcome
- 80 seats
- Mains from £4

Hampshire

Freshwater Bay

- Julia Margaret
  Cameron Trust
  Terrace Lane
  Freshwater Bay
  PO40 9QE
- 01983 756814
- Serving times:
  Tues-Sun
  10am-4.45pm
  Open Mon on
  bank hols and
  school holidays
- Major credit cards
- Non-smoking
- Not licensed, but BYO
  with no corkage
- Children welcome
- 32 seats
- Mains from £4.95

Dimbola Lodge

Housed in the previous home of Julia Margaret Cameron – the pioneering 19th century portrait photographer – Dimbola Lodge is a Victorian-styled vegetarian restaurant, serving morning coffee, lunch and afternoon teas. Enjoy the commanding views over Freshwater Bay and the relaxed atmosphere, while choosing from a selection of quiches, salads and soups or one of the daily specials such as macaroni cheese, mushroom stroganoff or vegetable curry. Not licensed, they welcome customers bringing their own wine.

Much of the produce is locally sourced from organic Isle of Wight farms – get closer to the field your lunch was grown in by sitting outside in the garden area.

The museum and regular photographic exhibitions are also well worth a visit.

Newport

- Quay Arts Centre
  Sea St
  Newport PO30 5BD
- 01983 530055
- Serving times:
  Mon-Sat 10am-4pm
  Full menu served
  from 11.30am
  Closed some
  bank holidays
- Major credit cards
- Non-smoking
- Licensed
- Children welcome
- 80 seats
- Starters from £3

Quay Arts Café

Take advantage of the island location and sit out on the waterside terrace at this light and airy bistro in the thriving Quay Arts Centre. There's a commitment to healthy eating and gluten-free dishes, and always something tasty for vegans.

Savoury choices include stuffed peppers, nut roast, winter vegetable or lentil and spinach soup, or a sweet potato and goat's cheese filo torte, whilst those with a sweeter tooth aren't going to be disappointed with the good choice of homemade cakes which can include some interesting and unusual selections amongst the more usual fruit and nut efforts.

Children are taken care of with a half jacket spud with cheese and pineapple, or a packed-lunch style character box with sandwich, yoghurt, fruit and cake.

Circle Restaurant

The circle in question is the amazing Avebury Ring – a World Heritage site that truly deserves the title – and the restaurant itself is in a listed building.

Open from 10am daily, the full lunch menu is served between 12.00 and 2.00pm with a range of freshly prepared dishes which can include chilli wraps, ratatouille, quiches, salads, and a vegan and gluten-free cottage pie.

If you visit outside lunchtime and fancy a smackerel, rest assured that you're not going to be fobbed off with a limp, mass-produced apology of a snack; there are sandwiches with proper English cheese and homemade chutneys, or mushroom pâté with sprouted beans, as well as a good range of cakes, organic wines and local fruit pressés.

- High St
  Avebury SN8 1RF
- 01672 539514
- Serving times:
  Summer 7 days
  10am-6pm
  Winter 7 days
  10am-4pm
  Lunch served 12-2pm
- Major credit cards
- Non-smoking
- Licensed
- Children welcome
- 70 seats including
  outside area
- Sandwiches from
  £2.50, lunch
  from £3.95

Hillside Café

If you're travelling on the A303 to the West Country, and despairing of finding a roadside eaterie that isn't part of some chain with only a (very) token vegetarian choice, do yourself a favour and nip up the A36 for a couple of miles to Codford.

This roadside café uses separate fryers for its vegetarian food, and as well as the usual café fare does a complete vegetarian grill or can offer curry, lasagne or even a roast lunch with that essential accompaniment, vegetarian gravy.

Vegan isn't a foreign language to them, and smaller children's meals are available. They do however close early on Saturdays and aren't open, sadly, on bank holiday weekends.

- A36 Codford
  Warminster BA12 0JZ
- 01985 850712
- Serving times:
  Mon-Thurs 6am-7pm
  Fri 6am-5pm
  Sat 6am-11.45am
- No credit cards
- Smoking throughout
- Not licensed
- Children welcome
- 54 seats
- Full lunch from £4.50

- 7 Little Brittox
  Devizes SN10 1AR
- 01380 720043
- Serving times:
  Tues-Sat 7pm-late
  Takeaway
  8.30am-4pm
- Booking advisable
- Major credit cards
- Non-smoking
- Licensed
- Children welcome
- 40 seats
- Two courses from
  £14.95

The Bistro

Well, what a find. Owned and run by TV chef Peter Vaughan – who has a commitment to nutritionally balanced, healthy, good food – The Bistro is across the road from his café (see below), and the menu is based on recipes from his 'Naturally Balanced' cookbooks.

Enjoy an aromatic laksa soup with coriander and coconut, or a salad of baby artichokes and tomato with warm goat's cheese. Follow this with herb-crusted mushrooms and orange butter sauce on a parsnip and potato mash and, if it's on, don't miss The Bistro's roasted almond and red raisin biscuit torte with rose-petal syrup.

A short, sensibly priced wine list means this can be a really special evening out without breaking the bank.

- 4 Little Brittox
  Devizes SN10 1AR
- Serving times:
  Mon-Sat 10am-4pm
- Booking advised
  Saturday lunch
- Major credit cards
- Non-smoking
- Licensed
- Children welcome
- 24 seats
- Light lunch
  from £2.95

The Healthy Life

A daytime companion to The Bistro, visit Peter Vaughan's Healthy Life for a naturally balanced style of cooking where more than half the produce is locally grown.

The cosy, open plan kitchen may be familiar from television, and you can hire the café privately in the evenings. The lunch menu is very reasonably priced; enjoy a quinoa, sunflower seed and nut loaf – the sort of thing you wished you bothered to make yourself – Thai coconut curry, soup or a platter of organic local cheese (or cheddar-style Cheezly) with a salad on the side. Dishes are clearly marked for their vegan, gluten- or wheat-free credentials. Freshly squeezed organic juices also available.

Marlborough

Applebys

Open for breakfast, lunch and coffee, this pleasantly situated café really is a cut above.

Choose the day's hot lunch from the board, quiche and salad, a bowl of the (usually) vegan soup with a roll and butter, or sandwiches (of the sort you'd want, rather than just settle for). Good bread – including olive focaccia and wheat-free – filled with cheddar and chutney, brie and redcurrant, olive tapenade and roast vegetables, or feta, tomato and cucumber with a herb and carrot mayonnaise.

Appleby's also serves a range of Illy coffees (and offer half price hot drink refills), iced hazelnut or vanilla flavoured lattes, plus some very fine homemade cakes and cookies.

- 5 Old Hughenden Yard Marlborough SN8 1LT
- 01672 515200
- Serving times:
  Mon-Sat
  8.30am-5.30pm
  Lunch served
  12-2.30pm
  Closed Sundays
- Major credit cards
- Non-smoking
- Not licensed
- Children welcome
- 40 seats
- Soup from £2.70, lunch special from £6.20

Swindon

Parasol

Just around the corner from the Brunel shopping centre is Parasol – a modern, stylish upmarket Oriental restaurant with a separate vegetarian section on the menu. Start with crispy fried wanton 'puffs' or vegetarian hot and sour soup – and then choose from 10 main courses, mostly tofu-based (Kung Po beancurd, beancurd with cashew nuts in yellow bean sauce or stir fried assorted mushrooms). Most of the dishes are Chinese, but some are Thai – for example fried beancurd with chilli paste – and accompaniments include vegetarian Singapore spicy vermicelli.

Although Parasol is a large restaurant on two floors (non-smoking upstairs), it can get busy especially at weekends when it's advisable to book.

- 97 Commercial Rd Swindon SN1 5PL
- 01793 533188
- Serving times:
  Mon-Sat 12-2.30pm
  & 5.30-11.30pm
  Sun 12-10pm
- Booking recommended weekends
- Major credit cards
- Non-smoking area
- Licensed
- 160 seats

surrey
west sussex

Surrey

West Sussex

6 7 Richmond

8 9

10 Thornton Heath

Chertsey □

5

1 Croydon

Kingston

2

□ Leatherhead

4 Guildford □ □ Reigate

3 Farnham Dorking

SURREY

East Grinstead □

Crawley □

Horsham □

14 Petworth

WEST SUSSEX

11 12 13 Chichester □ Worthing

□ Bognor Regis

surrey • west sussex

Croydon

Surrey

- 265 High St
  Croydon CR0 1QH
- 020 8688 7998
- Serving times:
  7 days 12-2.30pm
  & 5.30-11pm
- Major credit cards
- Non-smoking area
- Licensed
- Children welcome
- 50 seats
- Starters from £2.75,
  full mezedes
  from £12.50

Omnivorous Greek Restaurant

Aphrodite Greek Taverna

Now in Croydon High Street, this restaurant won prizes in its previous location at Crystal Palace, and we reckon could do extremely well with its vegetarian set dinner for two (three courses, £12.50 per person).

Eating à la carte, you can pick from some tasty starters: giant butter beans may conjure memories of school dinners but, trust us, prepared like this – creamy and mellow in a tomato and dill sauce – they are superb. With garlic mushrooms, artichokes in lemon sauce (and plenty more to choose from) you may decide to stick with a selection of starters and come back another time to enjoy the main course briam – a vegetable casserole served with rice, chips or roast potatoes. Children are catered for with small portions from the adult menu.

Croydon

Surrey

- 322 Limpsfield Rd
  Croydon CR2 9BX
- 020 8651 1233
- Serving times:
  Tues-Sat 6-10.45pm
  Sun 6-10pm
- No credit cards
- Non-smoking
- Licensed
- Children welcome
- 36 seats
- Starters from £3

Vegan Chinese Restaurant

Veggie One

Quell the temptation to shout at the menu, it is all meat-free, despite listing prawns, chicken chop suey, fried duck and metropolitan pork. Soya beans and a little magic create the textures and flavours for a whole range of Chinese restaurant standards.

Take some non-veggie friends and wow them with one of three set dinners, or go à la carte and choose from appetisers, soups, chop sueys and chow mein, confident that you can steal a taste of anything they've ordered.

It's cheap, with starters such as eight spring rolls for £2, and also serves a couple of Japanese-influenced dishes like vegetarian sushi and udon noodles with vegetables, ginger and mushroom sauce.

The Bishop's Table

There's a separate vegetarian menu at this modern British restaurant next to Farnham's library. Vegans might struggle a little, but the meat-free dishes are inventive: roast artichoke with a rocket and tomato salad, a herby wild mushroom and poached egg salad, or a cauliflower and cumin soup are the kind of starters you can enjoy, and the mains have an Italian slant: spinach and goat's cheese ravioli, gnocchi with a carrot mousse and creamed leeks, or creamed polenta with red pepper pesto.

Vegetarian desserts aren't listed separately, so do check their credentials before ordering.

Give them a call in advance and they'll also rustle up a special if you're on a 'something-free' diet.

- 27 West St
  Farnham GU9 7DR
- 01252 710222
- Serving times:
  Mon 7-9.45pm
  Tues-Sun
  12.30-1.45pm
  & 7-9.45pm
- Booking recommended weekend evenings
- Major credit cards
- Non-smoking
- Licensed
- Children welcome
- 45 seats
- Three course lunch from £15

Surrey

The Beano

Run by a team of four cooks in an attractive Victorian building with stained glass windows, the café is open during university term time. Its loyal regulars – some of whom eat here daily – are doubtless attracted by the very reasonably priced, good, home-cooked vegetarian and vegan food.

Lunch mains can include stuffed peppers or aubergine, nut and cranberry roast, ratatouille, spinach and feta pie or a puy lentil tagine. If you fancy the full three courses, add a starter such as pumpkin or Mexican bean soup or Provençal tart, and finish with steamed chocolate pud or a strawberry pavlova, and you still won't be spending more than £8.

The menu changes daily, and they also offer outside catering. Great value.

- The Guildford Institute
  University of Surrey
  Ward St
  Guildford GU1 4LH
- 01483 562142
- Serving times:
  Term time Mon-Fri
  10.30am-3.15pm
- No credit cards
- Non-smoking
- Licensed
- Children welcome
- 60 seats
- Specials from £3

Surrey

Surrey

- 64 High St
  Kingston Upon
  Thames KT1 1HN
- 020 8546 7992
- Serving times:
  Mon-Sat 12-11pm
  Sun 12-10.30pm
- Booking recommended
  at weekends
- Major credit cards
- Non-smoking area
- Licensed
- Children welcome
- 50 seats
  & outside area
- Starters from £4.25,
  mains from £6.50

The Riverside Vegetaria

The lovely riverside location means that outdoor eating is definitely on in fine weather. The cooking is low fat without being sanctimonious, and they are not fazed by vegan, gluten-free or wheat-free requests.

Superb organic soups (which can also be taken home frozen, by the litre) include cauliflower and almond, or potato and leek. Other starter options are stuffed avocado, spicy veg balls and garlic mushrooms.

A healthy list of main courses include red lentil kedgeree – which is how it's meant to be, not the newfangled haddocky idea – divine aubergines in a peanut sauce, tofu teriayaki and a couple of nut roasts.

If you only fancy a snack, there are falafel, panini or savoury crêpes. The restaurant offers discounts to Vegetarian and Vegan Society members.

Surrey

- Terrace Gardens
  Petersham Rd
  Richmond
- 020 8948 6555
- In centre of
  the gardens
- Serving times:
  Daylight hours
  Closed Nov-Mar
- No credit cards
- Non-smoking inside
- Not licensed, BYO
  with no corkage
- Children welcome
- 20 seats and terrace
- Mains with salad
  from £5

Hollyhocks

In the heart of Terrace Gardens, which boasts one of London's finest views over the Thames, this small café serves up a delightful range of soups, quiches, bakes, falafel, jackets and daily specials with a good range of freshly prepared salads – and there's always at least one vegan and wheat-free choice.

If you've already lunched at one of Richmond's other vegetarian restaurants (don't feel disloyal, there's a good chance it's under the same ownership), arrive in the afternoon and sit on the verandah with a freshly squeezed orange juice and slice of cake, read the bargain book you just bought from their in-house secondhand charity bookshop, and don't go home till they close.

Richmond Harvest

With all-day opening from 11.30am, this is the place to go if you crave a vegetarian shepherd's pie at 4 o'clock on a wet Monday afternoon. There's also plenty of vegan choices like butter bean curry, chilli or a courgette and cashew casserole, and the wines are organic.

Mains are served with a mixed salad which can include white cabbage with carrots and sweetcorn in a horseradish sauce, the zingy tabouleh with spring onions, mint and parsley in a lemon dressing or beans with peppers and cucumber, which can also be ordered in a main course size for those in need of a serious vitamin boost.

The lunchtime special offers two courses for little more than the price of average pub grub in these parts.

- 5 The Square
  Richmond TW9 1DT
- 020 8940 1138
- Serving times:
  7 days 11.30am-11pm
- Booking recommended weekend evenings
- Major credit cards
- Smoking throughout
- Licensed
- Children welcome
- 40 seats
- Two-course lunch £8.50

Surrey

The Green Café

The perfect place to stock up for a picnic on Richmond Green, The Green Café will serve you salads and falafel in pitta bread, paninis with a choice of veg, mushroom sandwiches or a grilled aubergine baguette as well as a range of sweeter snacks including dairy-free cakes. There's also a reasonable wheat-free choice.

In the summer, choose one of their freshly pressed juices or smoothies, fair trade and herbal teas, or pop in any time for a soya cappuccino and fresh muffin.

Limited seating inside in colourful surroundings, with the possibility of some outside tables by the time you read this. The Green Café has a relaxed feel and a message board to which you're encouraged to add your favourite joke.

- 29 The Green
  Richmond TW9 1LX
- 020 8332 7654
- Serving times:
  Mon-Sat 7am-6pm
  Sun 9am-6pm
- No credit cards
- Non-smoking
- Not licensed
- Children welcome
- 10 seats

Surrey

Surrey

- 2 The Arches Riverside Richmond TW9 1TH
- Beneath Richmond Bridge
- 020 8948 8285
- Serving times:
  Daylight hours
  May close earlier in poor weather
- No credit cards
- Non-smoking inside
- Not licensed, BYO with no corkage
- Children welcome
- 80 seats including garden
- Mains with salad from £6

Tide Tables

With one of the finest riverside garden locations in the area, and set in an arch of Richmond Bridge, Tide Tables would be worth a visit even if it didn't have a comprehensive and completely vegetarian menu.

Open daylight hours seven days a week (but closing early in prolonged bad weather), this informal and friendly café offers all day light meals and snacks as well as a great range of bakes, pies, casseroles and salads with good vegan choices. Organic produce occupies a lot of menu space and there are some gluten-free options. There are freshly pressed juices, soya milk for your tea and coffee, and lots of cakes. You can also bring your own wine, with no corkage charge.

Do call to check they're not closing early if you're planning to travel there specially.

Thornton Heath

Vegetarian Indian Restaurant

Surrey

- 850 London Rd Thornton Heath CR7 7PA
- 020 8683 3344
- Serving times:
  Mon Wed Thurs 10am-8.30pm
  Fri-Sat 10am-9.30pm
  Sun 10am-1.30pm & 5-8.30pm
  Closed Tues
- Booking essential weekends
- Non-smoking
- Licensed
- Children welcome
- 50 seats
- Starters from £1.80

SWAD

Perfect night's entertainment – fall out of the bingo hall over the road and spend your winnings in here, but do book at weekends.

Cheese-filled samosas, battered and fried mashed potato (sounds almost Scottish), chickpeas and potatoes in a tamarind sauce with an onion topping are some of the tasty snacks and starters available, and the menu is extensive. There's the usual south Indian fodder, lots of vegetable curries, inventive thalis and the ubiquitous masala dosa.

If you've come here and perversely fancy Chinese, they will rustle up noodles and rice and some other Chinese standards. Worth making part of your night out and handy for the buses as well.

Café Paradiso

This bright and colourful café in the centre of Chichester is justly popular with local vegetarians.

With a completely meat-free menu, which also features some gluten-free options, there is a range of soups and snacks as well as more substantial choices.

Choose between dishes from around the world which can include falafel with mint yoghurt, guacamole and tomato and basil sauce, chilli with potato wedges, wholemeal quiche or moussaka.

There's a good range of desserts and cakes such as sticky toffee pudding, almond and pistachio pastries and vegan flapjacks, and they're licensed to serve wine and beer with meals. Café Paradiso is also open on some bank holidays, but do call to check first.

- 5 The Boardwalk
  Northgate
  Chichester PO19 1AR
- 01243 532967
- Serving times:
  Mon-Sat 9am-5pm
  Sun 10am-3.30pm
  Open some bank holidays
- No credit cards
- Non-smoking
- Licensed
- Children welcome
- 40 seats

West Sussex

Clinch's

Just a few minutes from the theatre, Clinch's is a popular spot for lunch prior to matinée performances, or for tea and cakes after a show. The blackboard menu includes soups: carrot and orange, celery and apple or lentil and tomato are often available, together with other choices such as broccoli, pepper and cashew nut quiche, cheese pasta with asparagus, or a layered potato, spinach, cheese and onion bake.

It's counter, rather than table service, and has a 14-year reputation under owner Mark Sutton for good home-cooked food. The full lunch menu is served from 11.45am, with breakfasts between 8.30am and 11am. In addition to the 75 seats inside, there's also a small patio area.

- 4 Guildhall St
  Chichester PO19 1NJ
- 01243 789915
- Serving times:
  Mon-Sat 8.30am-4pm
- Major credit cards
- Non-smoking area
- Licensed
- Children welcome
- 75 seats
- Mains from £3.80

West Sussex

West Sussex

- 3 St Martin's St
  Chichester PO19 1NP
- 01243 786715
- Serving times:
  Mon-Sat 9am-6pm
  Closed most bank
  holidays
- No credit cards
- Non-smoking
- Licensed
- Children welcome
- 140 seats
  including garden
- Full lunch from £6.95

St Martin's Organic Tearoom

In the heart of Chichester, the setting is idyllic – a pretty Grade II listed building with a lovely brick courtyard and a cottage garden full of flowers. St Martin's has had a long commitment to organic ingredients (receiving Soil Association approval for its entire menu in early 2004), there's only one non-vegetarian item on the menu, and the vegan in you will approve of the 'no butter or cream' credentials (although they do use cheese).

Expect savouries such as spinach and apple potato cakes, vegetable scones, toasted spinach and cheese sandwiches, and Welsh rarebit with salad. Sweet cakes include chocolate sponge, banana and walnut loaf, scones and flapjacks. There's also proper loose-leaf tea, freshly ground coffee and a blueberry, banana, carrot and apple smoothie.

West Sussex

- East St
  Petworth GU28 0AB
- 01798 343257
- Serving times:
  Mon-Thurs 6-10.30pm
  Fri-Sat 6-11pm
  Sun 6-10.30pm
- Major credit cards
- Licensed
- Children welcome
- 44 seats
- Mains from £5

The Vice Regal

Plenty to choose from at The Vice Regal, including takeaway, if you're in this neck of the woods. Choose your curry style from a dozen or so interesting options (helpfully labelled either sweet and creamy, sweet and tangy, mild, hot or even 'sacré bleu', if the mood takes you). There are interesting specials, adding £1 or so to the basic price, or you can order larger portions for an extra couple of quid, which sounds like a novel idea (although we don't know anyone who ever under-ordered in an Indian restaurant).

There's a reduction for children's portions, and Cobra on draught. In business for 16 years, they must be doing something very right.

east sussex
kent

east sussex • kent

East Sussex

Kent

Dartfor
Swanley

Sevenoaks

Uckfield □

Lewes
20 **21** **22**

Brighton ■

east sussex • kent

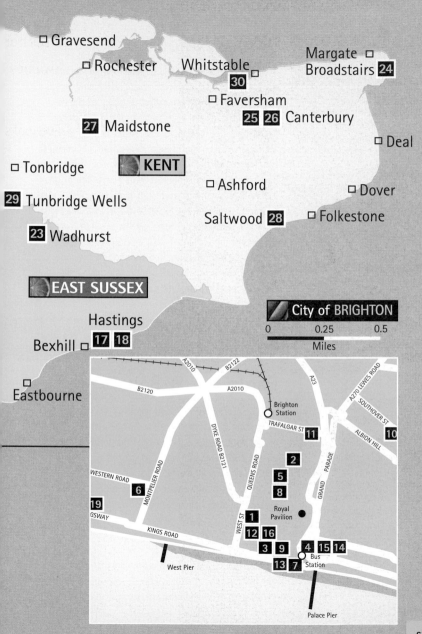

East Sussex

- 39 Ship St
  Brighton BN1 1AB
- 01273 776038
- Serving times:
  Mon-Thurs 12-11pm
  Sat-Sun 12-midnight
  Sun 12-11pm
- Major credit cards
- Non-smoking area
- Licensed
- Children welcome
- 70 seats
- Buffet £4.95

Bombay Aloo

Bombay Aloo is a justly popular Indian vegetarian restaurant that's open seven days a week, and serves a fabulous all-you-can-eat buffet throughout the day.

Settle down in a relaxed and cosy atmosphere (traditional décor with lots of wood beams, greenery and quiet Indian background music) and get ready to eat. There's all the usual bhajias, pakoras, fritters and poppadoms to start, together with a selection of dhals and half a dozen curries including Bombay Aloo's very delicately spiced korma. Finish with a fresh fruit salad or Indian rice pudding, or order from the separate à la carte dessert menu.

You can also takeaway a curry and rice for under £2, or visit between 3.15 and 5.15pm Monday–Friday for the reduced price 'happy hour' £3.50 buffet deal.

East Sussex

- 125 Gloucester Rd
  Brighton BN1 4AF
- 01273 607765
- Serving times:
  Mon-Thurs 12-9pm
  Fri 12-8pm
  Sat 12-7pm
  Sun 12-9pm
- Major credit cards
- Smoking throughout
- Licensed
- Children welcome
  upstairs till 9pm
- 75 seats
- Soup from £3.95,
  mains from £5.95

Eagle Bar & Bakery

Justly proud of their artisan bread, which you can take away, this is one of those rare places where you get enthusiastic about a sandwich. Choose cream cheese, walnut and celery, hummus and roasted pepper, cheddar and red onion – all on the bread of your choice.

Other than sandwiches, there are vegetarian bangers and mash drenched in an onion and red wine juice, baked potato, vegetarian chilli and a homemade beanburger. Check the soup and pasta of the day, they're often vegetarian.

You can snack on marinated olives, Greek salad or the great bruschetta while enjoying a properly kept real ale or glass of wine. In the trendy bit of Brighton.

Food For Friends

This casual, brasserie-style restaurant in the heart of old Brighton is visited by vegetarians from all over the world. Founded in 1981 by Simon Hope – also the author of several excellent vegetarian cookbooks – it soon won a top wholefood restaurant award with its imaginative and creative food, a tradition of excellence that continues today.

The menu changes daily and always features a great range of organic, vegan and wheat-free choices as well as an impressive selection of organic beers and wines, cocktails, smoothies and fresh juices.

The food shows influences from all over the world. Starters may include Jolly Green Giant chowder with cheesy seeds, pan-fried lemon and garlic marinated artichoke on a rocket salad, or warm pepper confit-topped blinis with dill flavoured sour cream.

The choice of mains can be even more impressive: featured on their special evening menus you may find feta and spinach boreks with onion and red wine sauce, jerked brown jolly fritters with a smoked paprika and lentil sauce, or a pesto polenta with tagliatelle, vegetables and a warm avocado and olive salad. If you can't cope with this degree of choice, don't worry, whatever you choose will be fresh, seasonal and prepared to exacting standards. Better still, go with friends and share several dishes between you – plate swapping is definitely to be encouraged.

There's a three course lunch offer for well under a tenner, and we're promised a children's menu in the near future. Extraordinarily good food and a great atmosphere. No trip to Brighton is complete without a visit.

- 17 Prince Albert St Brighton BN1 1HF
- 01273 736236
- Serving times: 7 days 11.30am-10pm
- Booking recommended Fri & Sat
- Major credit cards
- Large non-smoking area
- Licensed
- Children welcome
- 80 seats
- Mains from £7.95

East Sussex

- 2 St James's St
  Brighton BN2 1RE
- 01273 686273
- Serving times:
  Mon–Thurs 10am-8pm
  Fri–Sun 10am-10pm
- Major credit cards
- Non-smoking area
- Licensed
- Children welcome
- 38 seats
- Mains from £5

Gardenia

Over half the menu is vegan at this recently refurbished restaurant not far from the Palace Pier. You might start with the dairy-free soup of the day, try a main course of vegan vegetable pie or lasagne, and finish with an apple pudding topped with non-dairy ice cream.

Expect choices with wheat-free and organic credentials, and feed your children for just £2.50 with smaller portions of dishes from the main menu.

Organic wine, beer and soft drinks are served alongside freshly pressed juices, and you'll also find soya milk for your tea and coffee.

Oh yes, and the owner, Keith Shearing? An ex-butcher convert to the virtues of a meat-free diet. Visit on a Sunday to enjoy his (cruelty-free) roasts.

- 50 Gardner St
  Brighton BN1 1UN
- 01273 670743
- Serving times:
  Mon–Sat 10am-5pm
  Closed bank holidays
- Major credit cards
- Smoking only at
  outside tables
- Not licensed
- Children welcome
- 60 seats
- Starters from £2.70,
  mains from £5.50

Infinity Foods Café

Anyone been to Brighton and not know Infinity Foods? Just you then? Bet you've bought their products though. Part of the Infinity Foods co-op that's been running since 1975, the supermarket and bakery is just around the corner – in the North Lanes near Brighton Pavilion.

Almost all ingredients are organic, and knowledgeable staff can cater for vegan, wheat-, gluten- and sugar-free diets. Soup and salads are always vegan, as are the potato cakes and millet slices. There's a daily soup, for example pumpkin and roast red pepper, a daily main dish such as Mexican tortilla and rice, as well as desserts and lots of other tasty snacks.

Have a tasty meal and support this ethical and environmentally aware organisation.

Kambi's Restaurant

There's plenty of choice at this busy Lebanese restaurant, which is popular with large groups. Takeaway is possible, so you could put together a fine picnic if the mood took you.

Among the more unusual starters are bata kibby – potatoes stuffed with walnuts and onions; megadarra – lentils, onions and rice; or aubergine stuffed with walnuts, spices and garlic.

Mains, of which there are half a dozen to choose from, include okra with tomato, onion, lemon and rice, or split peas with dried lime, turmeric and tomato. You can also enjoy a vegetarian or even vegan meze.

Kambi's is licensed and you can also bring your own booze. It's open seven days from noon until 'good lord is that the time ...'

- 107 Western Rd
  Brighton BN1 2AA
- 01273 327934
- Serving times:
  7 days 12-midnight
- Booking recommended
  Fri-Sat evenings
- Major credit cards
- Smoking throughout
- Licensed and BYO with
  no corkage
- Children welcome
- 40 seats
- Starters from £2

East Sussex

Krakatoa

Close to the Palace Pier, this evening haunt has an upstairs section where the young or supple can sit on the floor and eat oriental-style.

There are four vegetarian starters, including a lively koh phi phi salad, with oriental leaves, mango, lime, coriander, spicy chilli oil and crushed peanuts, or delicate sweet potato fritters with soy and ginger sauce. Vegans will relish yasai udon noodles, with wakame seaweed, tofu, beansprouts, sweet potato and a nori seaweed garnish, or massaman curry from Thailand, rich with coconut milk. Old favourites like pad thai and mee goreng are reasonably priced, and dishes are prepared to order – so go with the flow and enjoy the leisurely pace.

- 7 Pool Valley
  Brighton BN1 1NJ
- 01273 719009
- Serving times:
  Mon-Sat 6-10.30pm
- Booking essential Sat
- Major credit cards
- Non-smoking area
- Licensed
- Children welcome
- 60 seats
- Starters from £5

East Sussex

- 21 Gardner St
  Brighton BN1 1UP
- 01273 679910
- Serving times:
  7 days 11am-9pm
- No credit cards
- Non-smoking
- Licensed
- Children welcome
- 25 seats
- Burgers from £2.85

Red Veg

Three cheers for Red Veg. Only two branches exist at the moment, but there are plans for more. Everything is Vegetarian Society certified, and most items can be made vegan. Let's hope they do for veggieburgers what Prêt à Manger has done for sandwiches.

This is fast food with branding – communist stars and manipulated Soviet posters of Lenin with a veggieburger wave two ketchup-smeared fingers at the Golden Arches world domination.

It's cheap as chips, or fries as we call them, and as well as tasty burgers there are falafel, wraps, breaded mushrooms and nuggets. If ease of access and price can introduce more people to eating vegetarian without shaking their fast food habit, this is the way to do it.

- 71 East St
  Brighton BN1 1HQ
- 01273 729051
- Serving times:
  Tues-Fri 12-10.30pm
  Sat 12-11pm
  Sun 12-10.30pm
- Booking recommended
  for evenings
- Major credit cards
- Non-smoking area
- Licensed
- Children welcome
- 125 seats
- Mains from £9

Terre à Terre

This buzzing restaurant and café shows an enthusiastic commitment to serving exciting, unusual food. There are nibbly appetisers like wasabi flavoured cashew nuts and tamari roasted seeds, or for something larger try the beanshoot fritters, or an unusual mustard-seed muffin with tamarind jelly. There are also Italian, Greek and Levantine breads – each coming with something delicious to dip or spread with.

Main courses are intriguingly different – even the noodles and vegetables are far above the commonplace – together with interesting chowders, soufflés and puddings. Lunch deals of soup, salad, cheese and sourdough bread are substantial and tasty, and there are organic wines and cider to wash it all down. Even the quirkily written menu is entertaining in its own right.

The Dover Castle

East meets west at the Dover Castle. Friday night is curry and stir fry night, while on Sunday lunchtimes there are roasts and barbecues – all with good vegetarian choices – and many dishes can be made vegan on request.

The regular menu features a vegetarian soup, lighter dishes like Eurasian rarebit – toasted cheese with coriander and Tabasco – or toasted garlic naan with roasted mushrooms and peppers. You can also enjoy mains such as Malaysian fried rice and vegetables, penang rojak – satay sauce with beancurd, hardboiled egg, cucumber, red onions and relishes, or the vegetarian chilli with sweet potato and mushrooms which comes with herby yoghurt and grated cheese.

Good, fresh, keenly-priced pub grub.

- 43 Southover St
  Brighton BN2 9UE
- 01273 688276
- Serving times:
  Mon-Fri
  12.30-8.30pm
  Sat 12.30-6pm
  Sun 12.30-5pm
- Major credit cards
- Smoking throughout
- Licensed
- Children welcome
- 60 seats
- Starters from £2.50

East Sussex

The George

This veggie pub has covered all the bases – family friendly, with a heated garden, they do Sunday lunch and they're not far from the station. There are loads of vegan options and the menu marks gluten-free items. No wonder they've picked up several awards.

Choose from bangers and mash, hot sausage baguette, falafel platter, and the fabulous house salad – as well as the leaves it includes veggie sausage, avocado, roast peppers, tamari-roasted seeds, garlic croutons and sun-dried tomatoes.

Saturday specials can include goat's cheese toasts with rocket pesto, frittata verde, pasta, and an aromatic tagine. Sunday adds the bonus of a nut roast with all the trimmings to an already spectacular menu.

- 5 Trafalgar St
  Brighton BN1 4EQ
- 01273 681055
- Serving times:
  Mon-Fri 12-9.30pm
  Sat 12-8.30pm
  Sun 12.30-8.30pm
- Booking recommended
  at weekends
- Major credit cards
- Non-smoking area
- Licensed
- Children welcome
  until 7pm
- 130 seats
- Starters from £3.25,
  mains from £5.50

East Sussex

East Sussex

- 13 Middle St
  Brighton BN1 1AL
- 01273 710444
- Serving times:
  Mon-Thurs 12-9pm
  Fri 12-8pm
  Sat 12-7pm
  Sun 12-9pm
- Major credit cards
- Smoking throughout
- Licensed
- 60 seats
- Mains from £4.95

The Hop Poles

A very popular pub near the front in Brighton, serving reasonably priced home-cooked food with great bread from their companion pub, The Eagle Bar and Bakery. It gets busy here, and you may have to wait at the bar for a table (shame!). Amuse yourself reading the specials menu, where the chefs and patron appear like characters out of 'Tales from the City'.

Regular dishes include tortillas, veg chilli, filled Yorkshire puds and sandwiches. The specials may include mushroom stroganoff, risotto, falafel, and stuffed peppers. Calorie-laden desserts include chocolate pecan cheesecake.

They keep real ales, children are welcome in the garden until 9pm, it's near the sea. What more could you want?

East Sussex

- 6 Little East St
  Brighton BN1 1HT
- 01273 747096
- Serving times:
  Mon 6-10pm
  Tues-Sun 12-10pm
  Closed Boxing Day to 3rd Jan
- Booking essential Fri & Sat evenings
- Major credit cards
- Non-smoking area
- Licensed
- Children welcome
- 57 seats
- Mains from £10.75

The Strand Restaurant

This modern British and Australasian establishment, near the sea front, is housed in an 18th century cottage. There's a set three course menu for around £15, or you can pick and choose from the à la carte menu.

Try the Spanish bean croquettes with smoked paprika as a starter, or head a bit further east with a spicy Indian broth. Main courses can include a shitake mushroom Wellington with redcurrants, masala gravy and Lyonnaise potatoes, or rooty-tooty lentil pie – puy lentils with rosemary and red wine, topped with winter vegetable mash and piled high with deep fried leeks. Desserts are rich and magnificent – ginger sponge with morello cherries and almonds soaked in Jack Daniels with ginger cream, plus some very boozy sorbets. Booking essential at weekends.

Trogs Café

Utterly environmentally sound, using eggs from hens rescued from battery farms, organic ingredients and a vigorous recycling policy for bottles and packaging, this splendid café is decorated in Moroccan style and is handy for Brighton Pavilion and Pier.

Special nut- or gluten-free diets can be catered for from a menu of all day breakfast, omelette and chips, potato wedges or chips with cheese, stuffed peppers, pizza slices, homity pie or a tasty halloumi, olive mint and red onion salad. All the bread comes from the Infinity Foods bakery, whose name guarantees quality. Personally, we'd have a nice blowy walk on the beach and then take Sunday lunch with Yorkshire pud, roasties, stuffing and an onion and red wine gravy.

- 24 George St
  Brighton BN2 1RH
- 01273 687821
- Serving times:
  Wed-Fri 11am-4pm
  & 7-11pm
  Sat 10am-11pm
  Sun 10am-6pm
- Major credit cards
- Non-smoking
- Licensed
- Children welcome
- 20 seats
- Snacks from £2, daily special £6.95

East Sussex

Trogs Restaurant

Brought to you by the environmentally friendly people who run Trogs Café at the same address by day, this organic restaurant on the ground floor raises the game considerably and includes plenty of vegan options.

Roasted parsnip, apple and shallot tarte tatin with a purée of pea and rosemary and a pink peppercorn and cider reduction, or sweet potato, apricot and coriander soufflé with a tomato and cumin sauce served with spicy chickpea cakes topped with grilled halloumi and orange-baked figs give just a hint of what they can do. Food is served alongside organic wine or freshly squeezed fruit or vegetable juices.

Booking recommended for Saturday nights. The menu changes monthly, visit trogsrestaurant.com for more flavours of what's to come.

- 24 George St
  Brighton BN2 1RH
- 01273 687821
- Serving times:
  Wed-Sat 7-10pm
- Booking recommended Sat evenings
- Major credit cards
- Non-smoking
- Licensed
- Children welcome
- 35 seats
- Starters from £5, mains from £13

East Sussex

East Sussex

- 42 Meeting
  House Lane
  Brighton BN1 1HB
- 01273 323824
- Serving times:
  Mon–Wed 11am–5pm
  Thurs–Sat 11am–11pm
  Sun 11am–6pm
- Major credit cards
- Smoking throughout
- Licensed
- Children welcome
- 60 seats
- Mains from £6

Wai Kika Moo Kau

In the heart of Brighton's Lanes, with a couple of pavement tables, this relaxed café's menu will take you from (a late) full breakfast to dinner, on a journey calling at an interesting and varied selection of good vegetarian food.

The Aussie burger comes fully loaded with egg, salad, beetroot, pickle and more, while the tomato tatin has caramelised, roasted tomato pieces served on seasoned mash – not a tatin as we know it, but jolly tasty all the same. House specials include leek and gruyère crown – a puff pastry case crammed with leeks, cauliflower and gruyère sauce, or there's tapas, chilli, wraps, pasta, snacks, baked potatoes and sandwiches. Movenpick ice creams as well as freshly made cakes and desserts.

East Sussex

- 50 George St
  Hastings TN34 3EA
- 01424 429092
- Serving times:
  Tues–Wed
  11am–2.30pm
  Thurs–Sun
  11am–2.30pm
  & 7–10pm
  Closed on Mondays
  except bank holidays
- No credit cards
- Non-smoking area
- Licensed
- Children welcome
- 30 seats
- Starters from £2,
  mains from £4.95

East 2 West

Handy for the crazy golf on the sea front, this international restaurant ranges across Mexican, Chinese and Italian cooking, but is weighted towards Indian. Everything is homemade and can be adapted to your preferences. There are daily specials and the menu is comprised of the owners' family favourites. Vegans are well catered for.

You can have light meal or go the whole hog: tacos, bhajis or spring rolls to start, bhel poori, vegetable curries, enchiladas or pasta as a main. Quite which wine to choose with this combination is, er, difficult. Answers on a postcard please. Round off with a matka kulfi (saffron, pistachio, cardamom) and you get to keep the pot.

Heaven & Earth

This small Hastings café, just a few hundred yards from the pier, is the only completely vegetarian restaurant in town, and offers a small but interesting range of food using organic produce wherever possible.

In addition to the self-service salad bar, choose from vegetable terrines, quiches and lasagne as well as daily specials (which are often vegan) such as curry, goulash and sweet and sour dishes.

They also serve a selection of cakes and teas, and there's always a drop of soya milk if you prefer it.

Park yourself on one of the outside tables to watch Hastings life go by (if you're not trying to warm up during a typical British bank holiday weekend).

- 37 Robertson St Hastings TN34 1HT
- 01424 712206
- Serving times: Mon-Sat 10am-5pm
- No credit cards
- Non-smoking area
- Not licensed
- Children welcome
- 25 seats
- Snacks from £1.20

East Sussex

The Sanctuary

A relaxed and friendly café, open till 11pm – stylish, arty and with a basement for private parties and intimate gigs. Mainly vegetarian, it's great for toasted bagels or baguettes, and a scrambled egg or pain au chocolat breakfast.

The daily specials feature a vegan option, and there are vegetarian and vegan Sunday lunches as well. Samples from the menu include a Jamaican coconut curry with plantain, sweet potato, carrots, green beans and courgette on sticky yellow rice, the vegan roasted butternut squash and red onion soup with soda bread, or spinach, roasted veg and halloumi baked wraps with dill and crème fraiche.

Half of the wines are organic, and there are organic pressés, ginger beer and old-fashioned lemonade.

- 51-55 Brunswick St East Hove BN3 1AU
- 01273 770002
- Serving times: 7 days 9am-10pm
- Major credit cards
- Non-smoking area
- Licensed
- Children welcome
- 75 seats
- Snacks from £2.50

East Sussex

Vegetarian Restaurant & Tearoom

- 199 High St
  Lewes BN7 2NS
- 01273 473968
- Serving times:
  Tues-Sat 10am-5pm
  Full menu
  11.45am-4pm
- No credit cards
- Non-smoking
- Not licensed, BYO
  with no corkage
- Children welcome
- 40 seats
- Mains from £4.95

East Sussex

Seasons Restaurant

In the basement of a listed building, Seasons has been here for almost 15 years. Mostly organic, everything is cooked fresh daily and they don't own a microwave.

There's plenty of vegan choice – nut roasts, bean burgers, casseroles or lentil and buckwheat slice. Other mouthwatering options can include nutty parsnip or leek and potato soup, cashew and mushroom roast, red bean goulash, mushroom and tofu stroganoff, or spinach, cheese and potato pie. They also do individual frozen vegetarian meals to take home, which from a range like this is a bit of a bonus.

Desserts can include apple and apricot crumble, apple bakewell or carrot cake. Bring your own wine, try their organic elderflower or ginger beer, or enjoy tea and coffee – with soya milk if you prefer.

Omnivorous Pub & Restaurant

- South St
  Lewes BN7 2BU
- 01273 471018
- Serving times:
  Mon-Fri 12-3pm
  & 5-9pm
  Sat-Sun 12-4pm
  & 5-9pm
- Major credit cards
- Non-smoking area
- Licensed
- Children welcome
- 70 seats

East Sussex

Snow Drop Inn

Winners of a Vegetarian Pub of The Year award under the previous landlords, the Snow Drop Inn has retained its strong vegetarian bias with chef Sian Edwards.

More than half the menu is vegetarian, organic foods feature, and their pizza bases are vegan. Choose from spicy carrot or chickpea, lemon and garlic soup, or opt for the vegetarian meze platter to start. Main courses can include a chestnut, mushroom and red wine en croûte or courgette and sweet potato fritters with a wild mushroom sauce.

As you would expect there's a wide range of drinks, including real ales and, in addition to the garden and patio, there's a newly refurbished function room to host and cater for your vegetarian party.

The Garden Room

The Garden Room is a small and friendly café-tearoom and gallery, so there's always something to see. Just two minutes from the railway station, idle away your waiting time here in pleasant surroundings.

There's fresh homemade soup – always with a vegetarian choice, as well as vegetarian pâté or hummus, while main courses can feature a nut roast served with apricot sauce, spinach pies, pasta bakes and quiches. They also work hard to accommodate special diets.

Homemade chocolate fudge and carrot cakes, and good tea and coffee or wine and beer available. Children are very welcome and there's a small walled garden with an extra dozen seats.

- 14 Station St
  Lewes BN7 2DA
- 01273 478636
- Serving times:
  Mon-Sat
  10am-4.45pm
- No credit cards
- Small smoking area
- Licensed
- Children welcome
- 24 seats and
  walled garden

East Sussex

Wealden Wholefoods

This vegetarian café in the wholefood shop of the same name is operated by a small co-operative specialising in organic, local and fair trade produce. Lunch is served between 12 and 3pm – choose from daily homemade organic soups, vegetarian pies, quiche and nut roasts or the vegan lentil and buckwheat slice. At other times there's a range of savoury snacks and a wide selection of cakes. Fair trade coffees include Café Direct, Percol, Mount Hagen and a Mexican decaf.

The building dates from the 17th century, and there's a cottage garden, ideal for a refreshing summer drink. In the winter, grab a table by the wood-burning stove and warm up with one of their top-notch organic hot chocolates.

- High St
  Wadhurst TN5 6AA
- Serving times:
  Mon-Sat
  9.30am-4.45pm
  Closed bank holidays
- No credit cards
- Non-smoking
- Licensed
- Children welcome
- 14 seats
- Lunch with salad
  from £3.50

East Sussex

Kent

- 92 High St
  Broadstairs CT10 1JJ
- 01843 602454
- Serving times:
  Summer opening
  Sun-Mon
  8.30am-6pm
  Tues-Sat
  8.30am-10pm
  Winter opening
  Mon-Sat 10am-4pm
- Major credit cards
- Non-smoking
- Licensed
- Children welcome
- 30 seats

Daisy's Café Bar

Busy with local trade and holidaymakers, Daisy's café bar is part coffee shop and part restaurant, and they're quite happy just to serve you just coffee and homemade cake if you're not hungry enough for one of their more substantial vegetarian dishes.

The usual fare of paninis, jackets, salads and sandwiches are complemented with daily specials such as a mild vegetable korma, or ricotta and spinach or chestnut and ricotta parcels. Smaller portions are available for children. You can enjoy a glass of wine with your meal, or choose from Pago juices and an extensive selection of regular and fruit teas.

Daisy's is open seven days a week during the busy summer period, and their walled garden doubles the dining space in good weather.

Kent

- St Alphege Lane
  Canterbury CT1 2EB
- 01227 457009
- Serving times:
  Tues-Sat 10am-4pm
- No credit cards
- Non-smoking
- Licensed
- Children welcome
- 40 seats
- Mains from £2.50

Environment Centre Café

This café, part of an environment centre in a medieval church, has a range of reasonably priced meals such as potato and cheese pie, quiche, various pasta dishes, hot vegetable bakes and salads. Much of the food is organic. If you're still feeling peckish or just fancy a treat, pick from a choice of homemade cakes, fruit crumbles, ice creams, bakewell tarts or fruit. Children can have small portions from the main menu, or pizza and beans or a baked potato.

You can enjoy a glass of wine or a beer with your meal and, in summer, there are also freshly squeezed juices. Visit the centre itself to find out more about Canterbury's history.

Canterbury

Canterbury Wholefoods

On the first floor of a converted foundry, the café offers lunches such as sesame flan, or falafel with hummus in pitta, both served with salads. Alternatively you could try a slice of freshly baked carrot cake, chocolate brownies or an apricot slice. Breakfast ranges from muesli with fresh fruit and honey to scrambled tofu with pesto.

Vegans will find plenty of choice both from the regular menu and on the daily specials board such as vegan 'cheese' filled baguettes or tofu pie with sweet potato topping. The children's menu features fishless fishcakes or veggieburgers, both served with beans. There's a huge range of coffees, teas and herbal teas, as well as juices and cordials, and soya milk is available.

- 1 Jewry Lane
  Canterbury CT1 2NR
- 01227 464623
- Serving times:
  Mon-Sat
  10am-4.30pm
  Closed bank holidays
- Major credit cards
- Non-smoking
- Licensed
- Children welcome
- 40 seats

Maidstone

Blackthorn Garden

Unusually situated behind a medical centre, and quite possibly Maidstone's best-kept secret, Blackthorn Garden is a charity helping people with long-term illness. The café has a brief lunch opening during the week, and the aim is to use organic and biodynamic produce grown in their garden. The set menu changes daily and offers delights such as squash and vegetable curry, basil and vegetable soup and chocolate praline pudding, or vegetable soup, a veggie mince and potatoes, and rice pudding.

Fruit cordials, apple juice and Blackthorn elixir are all made from their own fruit, and soya milk is available. Have a good lunch in this unassuming café, and support a worthwhile project.

- St Andrews Rd
  Maidstone ME16 9AN
- Rear of Blackthorn
  Medical Centre
- 01622 725585
- Serving times:
  Mon-Fri lunch
  12-1.45pm
- No credit cards
- Non-smoking
- Not licensed
- Children welcome
- 40 seats

Saltwood

- Sandling Rd
  Saltwood CT21 4HL
- 01303 266327
- Serving times:
  7 days 11am-4.30pm
  (March-October)
- No credit cards
- Not licensed
- Children welcome
- 100 al fresco seats
- Burgers from £1.50

Brockhill Country Park Café

This outdoor café is open seven days a week from spring through autumn and is set in a lovely park with a lake, valley and a play area, handy for the beach and the Channel Tunnel (convenient if you've just toughed out a week's veggie catering in France).

Choose from various homemade vegetarian burgers, salad rolls, stuffed pitta and cheap chips. There are dairy-free ice creams as well as the regular kind. They will also fix a vegetarian or vegan pre-packed picnic given a bit of notice.

The simple finger-food approach is good value and you won't break the bank if you take a posse of children there in the school holidays.

Tunbridge Wells

- 15 Ritz Buildings
  Church Rd
  Tunbridge Wells
  TN1 1HP
- Opposite Town Hall
- 01892 512215
- Serving times:
  Mon-Sat
  10am-5.45pm
- Major credit cards
- Non-smoking
- Not licensed, BYO
  with no corkage
- Children welcome
- 25 seats
- Snacks from £2.50

Continental Flavour

Queue up at the counter in the health food shop and head upstairs with your tray, or take away. Sandwiches (including that rare but simple choice, a salad sarnie) come plain or garnished and are a similar price to hot baked goods like curried vegetable pasties or aubergine and wild rice bake. There's also jacket potatoes with various filling, daily savouries and soup – check the board for the day's options.

Cheese or fruit scones, a selection of cakes and a changing choice of desserts like pear and almond flan, trifle, crumble, pavlova or cheesecake and local ice cream make this a good stop for refuelling at any time of the day. Pots of coffee or tea – with soya milk if you prefer – and Pago brand juices wash it all down.

Seasalter

A traditional omnivorous seaside café by day but, wait for it, one that transforms into a completely vegetarian restaurant for Friday and Saturday evenings.

Expect the sauce bottles to be replaced with candles, and a fine menu with starters such as asparagus with a lime and crème fraiche butter topped with a poached ducks egg, and mains that can include an aromatic stir fry spiced with coriander, garlic, chilli and lime. Finish with the vegetarian cheeseboard or a lemon, cinnamon and clove-flavoured mixed fruit compôte.

There are some outdoor tables if you're visiting the daytime omnivorous café (weekend opening only). Pop in for a free range fried egg buttie.

- 400 Faversham Rd
  Seasalter
  Whitstable CT5 4BW
- 01227 273366
- Serving times:
  Café
  Sat-Sun 10am-4pm
  Restaurant
  Fri-Sat 7-10pm
- Major credit cards
- Non-smoking
- Not licensed, BYO
  with no corkage
- Children welcome
- 18 seats

Kent

gloucestershire
herefordshire
warwickshire
worcestershire

gloucestershire • herefordshire
warwickshire • worcestershire

Gloucestershire

Herefordshire

Warwickshire

Worcestershire

Bearwood
Kington 16   11

 **HEREFORDSHIRE**

gloucestershire •

□ Nuneaton

WORCESTERSHIRE

Kidderminster □

Ryton-on-Dunsmore 18   17 Rugby

19 Bromsgrove

□ Droitwich

Warwick □   □ Leamington Spa

Bromyard
12
15 Hope under Dinmore

23 Worcester

□ Stratford-upon-Avon

20 21 22 Great
Malvern

□ Evesham   **WARWICKSHIRE**

3 14 Hereford

□ Tewkesbury

□ Stow-on-the-Wold

1 2 Cheltenham

4 5 Gloucester

7 8
9 10 Stroud

Nailsworth 6

3 Cirencester

GLOUCESTERSHIRE

herefordshire • warwickshire • worcestershire

- 127-9 Bath Rd
  Cheltenham GL53 7LS
- 01242 581411
- Serving times:
  Mon-Sat 12-2pm
  & 6.30-10.30pm
- Major credit cards
- Non-smoking
- Licensed
- 140 seats
- Mains from £9

Morans Eating House

This stylish restaurant on Cheltenham's Bath Road is accessed through the popular wine bar, and offers a good choice for vegetarians on both the regular and the specials menus.

Start with Mexican three-dip platter (salsa, roasted spicy aubergine and sun-dried tomato with cannellino beans and tostadas) or a green pea, mint and cauliflower terrine – or check the day's specials and hope the deep-fried Brie with cranberry dressing is on. Regular mains include asparagus and wild mushroom risotto cakes served with spicy couscous – while the specials (two veg and three non-veg choices) have featured a mixed pepper, artichoke and rocket flan or Thai green curry. No bookings, except for parties of six or more, and there may be a bit of a wait at weekends.

- 317 High St
  Cheltenham
  GL50 3HW
- 01242 234232
- Serving times:
  Mon-Thurs 10am-3pm
  Fri-Sat 10am-9pm
- Major credit cards
- Non-smoking area
- Not licensed, BYO
  with no corkage
- Children welcome
- 45 seats
- Mains from £5

The Orange Tree

The bright and welcoming Orange Tree is a place that takes special diets seriously. 100% vegetarian, they clearly mark which dishes are vegan and wheat-free. The restaurant caters for all appetites, whether you fancy a light snack (pitta sandwiches, pasties, jackets) or a main meal (which can include nut roast with onion gravy, asparagus and leek tart, Thai green curry or chilli enchiladas). Whatever you choose, leave room for dessert – they serve dairy-free ice cream, wheat-free chocolate and almond cake and – how could we resist? – the most enormous slices of vegan chocolate cake.

It's open until 9pm on Friday and Saturday evenings for dinner and, although it's not licensed, you're welcome to bring your own wine.

Gloucestershire

Gloucestershire

Cirencester

The Organic Farm Café

There's a 15 acre organic vegetable garden around this café in an organic farm shop, which is constructed of green oak from a nearby wood. All eggs, honey, vegetables, soft fruit and chutneys are their own garden produce, and there's a small play area for children, outdoor seating, and a woodland walk.

The menu changes daily, with specials inspired by the Soil Association certified kitchen garden. Children can enjoy smaller portions, or a plate of bits and bobs from a selection of fruit, veg and cheese. There are also organic juices and a wide range of herbal teas.

Follow the signs to the organic farm shop on the B4425 to the north-east of Cirencester.

- Abbey Home Farm
  Burford Rd
  Cirencester GL7 5HF
- 01285 640441
- Serving times:
  Tues-Fri 9am-4pm
  Sat 9am-3.30pm
  Lunch menu served
  12-2.30pm
- Major credit cards
- Non-smoking
- Not licensed
- Children welcome
- 60 seats
- Starters from £3.50

Gloucester

Gloucester Guildhall Café

This virtually vegetarian café is inexpensive, and food is freshly prepared each day. The menu standards are sandwiches, toasties or baked potatoes with side salad, together with daily specials which cross continents to bring you dishes such as vegetable goulash, chilli stuffed peppers and risotto. The soups can be a homely leek and potato or shurit ads – a comforting Egyptian lentil soup – both served with crusty bread.

Tea and coffee are very reasonably priced and they serve decent hot chocolate as well as a range of beers and wine. The full lunch menu is served between 11.30am and 2.30pm, and the café opens as a bar (but doesn't serve food) in the evenings.

- 23 Eastgate St
  Gloucester GL1 1NS
- Opposite Woolies
- 01452 396378
- Serving times:
  Tues-Sat 10am-3pm
  Lunch menu served
  from 11.30am
  Closed early July
  to early Sept
- No credit cards
- Non-smoking
  during the day
- Licensed
- Children welcome
- 32 seats
- Snacks from £1.50

Gloucester

Vegetarian Chinese Café

- 42 Southgate St
  Gloucester GL1 2DR
- 01452 502147
- Serving times:
  Mon 9.30am-6pm
  Tues-Sat 9.30-9.30pm
- Major credit cards
- Non-smoking
- Not licensed
- Children welcome
- 18 seats
- Mains from £3

Kings Café

Imagine – a totally vegetarian Chinese café just two minutes' walk from the main shopping street in the centre of Gloucester.

Kings Café is a small (18 seat) eatery with an enormous menu featuring veg-beef, veg-chicken and veg-duck – alongside more traditional bean curd and chow mein dishes. There are set meals (under £20 for four people), and they also have a busy takeaway trade. If that's not enough, you can also pop in for breakfast (potato jacks, steamed veggies, fried egg and veggie sausage) or invent your own combination from their freshly squeezed juices. Between 11am and 2pm they offer lunchtime specials – two simple set meals if you simply haven't time to peruse the vast choice.

Nailsworth

Virtually Vegetarian Café

- Old Bristol Rd
  Nailsworth GL6 0LA
- 01453 837514
- Serving times:
  Tues-Sun 11am-4pm
  Lunch served
  12.45-2.30pm
  Sundays: only drinks
  and cakes served
- No credit cards
- Non-smoking
- Not licensed
- Children welcome
- 34 seats
- Snacks from £2

Ruskin Mill

You'll find this pleasant café in an old woollen mill which has been converted into a further education centre for young adults with learning difficulties. Drinks and cakes are available either side of lunch, and there's a balcony which doubles the size of the available dining area in fine weather.

As well as vegan, wheat- and dairy-free options, many dishes include organic produce they've grown themselves. The menu changes daily, but expect to find decent home-cooked food such as sweet potato and butternut squash soup, chilli cheese tortilla with fresh tomato salsa, couscous with roast vegetables, and puddings like pear and almond tart.

You can also stock up on organic produce in the Mill's craft and vegetable shop.

Balti Spice

Definitely a cut above your average balti house, Stroud's Balti Spice comes Curry Club recommended, together with other honours, so expect the best kind of high street Indian.

Open evenings only, booking is advisable for Friday and Saturday nights. They offer a vegetarian set menu for 2 or 4 people, but if you're ordering individually there are some lovely vegetable dishes with coconut or lemon complementing the spicing, or a tangy potato tamboda with lemon juice and tamarind. There's a great selection of vegetarian balti dishes, well-flavoured rice dishes and bhajee (dry curry) side dishes.

Wine, beer and spirits are on offer but, if you must, bring your own aged claret, subject to £3.50 corkage. Takeaway available.

- 17 Gloucester St
  Stroud GL5 1QG
- 01453 766454
- Serving times:
  Mon-Thurs 6-11.30pm
  Fri-Sat 5.30-midnight
  Sun 6-11.30pm
- Booking advisable
  Fri & Sat
- Major credit cards
- Non-smoking area
- Licensed
- Children welcome
- 64 seats

Gloucestershire

Mills Café

Everything is freshly prepared at Mills (using locally sourced organic ingredients, wherever possible) – there are no microwaves here. It's a cross between a café-bar and bistro, with a lovely outside courtyard seating area when the weather's kind. The lunch menu changes daily, and around half the choices are vegetarian – which can include dishes such as hazelnut rissoles with apple sauce or a toasted aubergine, mushroom, garlic and cheese baguette – and there's always help-yourself salads. You can also choose from the temptingly long cake list for afternoon tea.

Serving fresh home-cooked food for nearly 20 years, Mills has a loyal following of local regulars.

- 8 Withey's Yard
  High St
  Stroud GL5 1AS
- 01453 752222
- Serving times:
  Mon-Sat
  8.30am-4.30pm
  Lunch from midday
  Closed bank holidays
- Major credit cards
- Non-smoking area
- Licensed
- Children welcome
- 55 seats and large
  courtyard
- Specials from £6.50

Gloucestershire

Vegetarian Café

- 2 Bedford St
  Stroud GL5 1AY
- 01453 758202
- Serving times:
  Mon-Sat 9am-4.30pm
  Closed bank holidays
- Major credit cards
- Non-smoking
- Not licensed
- Children welcome
- 36 seats
- Mains from £5.50

Gloucestershire

Mother Nature

Situated inside a health food store, the owners of Mother Nature take catering for special diets seriously – there are yeast-, sugar- and gluten-free options as well as some interesting vegan choices.

The menu features proper homemade soup and daily specials such as cashew nut risotto, vegetable rosti or a brown lentil hotpot with garlic roast potato topping – all served with a couple of interesting freshly prepared salads which are also available individually. There are cakes, ice cream, flapjacks and baked puddings, freshly pressed juices, and soya milk. Children are welcome and can choose smaller portions from the main menu, and there are a few tables outside if you're there on a sunny day.

Virtually Vegetarian Café

- 24 High St
  Stroud GL5 1AJ
- 01453 759195
- Serving times:
  Mon-Sat 9am-5.30pm
  Lunch menu served
  from midday
  Closed bank holidays
- No credit cards
- Non-smoking
- Licensed
- Children welcome
- 60 seats
- Snacks from £3

Gloucestershire

Woodruffs Organic Café

Three cheers for Britain's first totally organic café. Everything is homemade and uses local produce where possible. With a family room, high chairs and toys, this place is very child-friendly. The menu changes daily, and special diets are taken in Woodruff's stride.

Open for breakfast, try the fried mushrooms in cream and tamari with black pepper. Lunch is available from midday with a couple of specials as well as decent open sandwiches with lots of goat's cheese, brie, hummus, feta and grilled veg options. Baked potatoes come with salad and various toppings and there are filled omelettes as well. They are conscientious about wheat-free and vegan diets, and there is a good children's menu as well as a daily selection of home-baked cakes.

The Cider House

If you've been visiting the picturesque black-and-white villages of Weobley, Pembridge and Eardisland, take lunch at this high quality restaurant in a converted barn, with its outlook onto the rural Herefordshire landscape.

The short menu changes regularly, and can feature starters of beetroot and apple soup with home-baked bread or a warm mixed bean salad, and main courses such as a local cheese, courgette and walnut tart, or sweet potato cakes served with a spinach and lentil purée. Our recommendation? Order a glass of their organic cider, grab a table on the terrace, and settle in for some scrummy and beautifully presented food.

The Cider House is well signposted from both Pembridge and the A4112.

- Dunkerton Cider
  Bearwood
  near Pembridge
  HR6 9ED
- 01544 388161
- Serving times:
  April-Sept Wed-Sat
  12-2.30pm
  Open bank holidays
  and occasional
  Mon & Tues
- Booking recommended
- Major credit cards
- Non-smoking area
- Licensed
- Children welcome
- 60 seats
- Mains from £10

O'Malleys Public House

Visit O'Malleys for a good choice of vegetarian food that goes way beyond ordinary pub grub.

There's a couple of quorn variations – piri piri or en croûte – stuffed bell peppers and a cheese-topped casserole, veg sausages and champ (mash with buttery cabbage), or butternut squash and sweet potato patties. If you don't fancy the full monty (and you do get quite a plateful with the mains), there are soups such as parsnip and onion, brie wedges or garlic mushrooms. There are also children's choices in the vegetable and cheese country bake, cheese and tomato pizza or quorn sausages.

O'Malley's gets busy in the summer – book to be sure of a seat.

- Stourport Rd
  Bromyard HR7 4NT
- 01885 488881
- Serving times:
  Tues 7-9pm
  Wed-Fri 12-2pm
  & 7-9pm
  Sat 12-2pm & 7-10pm
  Sun 12.30-3pm
  & 7-8.30pm
  Open bank holidays
- Major credit cards
- Non-smoking
- Licensed
- Children welcome
- 60 seats
- Mains from £9.50

- All Saints Church
  High St
  Hereford HR4 9AA
- Next to Boots
- 01432 370415
- Serving times:
  Mon-Sat
  8.30am-5.30pm
  Full lunch
  menu served
  11.30am-2.30pm
  Closed bank holidays
  and Easter weekend
- Major credit cards
- Non-smoking
- Licensed
- Children welcome
- 90 seats
- Sandwiches from
  £3.65

Café@All Saints

Café@All Saints is innovatively and sympathetically incorporated into the South Chapel of Hereford's All Saints Church, where writer and restaurateur Bill Sewell – also the owner of the highly regarded 'The Place Below' in St Mary Le Bow Church in London – has created an award-winning restaurant serving extraordinarily good modern British food.

Bill has forged strong relationships with numerous local suppliers, and fresh Herefordshire produce naturally features significantly on the daily-changing menu. If it's being served on the day you visit, try the field mushroom and ale pie with smoked cheddar mash, or roast pumpkin, spinach and Little Hereford cheese quiche.

Salads can include goat's cheese with asparagus (from the local farm at Tillington), new potatoes, roast spring onions and mixed leaves, or courgette and roast pepper with olive oil, lemon and flat parsley. All the sandwiches are made from bread baked daily on the premises: choose from fillings such as roast leek, gruyère and mustard, or the vegan mushroom and roasted tofu.

The coffee and cakes are no less exceptional, some favourites (all homemade, of course) include Hereford cider and apple tart, lemon and lime cream pie, and cranberry and marzipan cake.

Open for breakfast and coffee from 8.30am, the lunch menu is served between 11.30am and 2.30pm, with sandwiches available until 5pm. The café also opens for occasional seasonal evening dinners during the autumn, and is available for private evening party bookings – minimum numbers apply.

Nutters

A vegetarian café tucked away in a small courtyard off Church St, which is a narrow road leading to the Cathedral from the centre of town.

There's up to a dozen daily specials such as homity pie or watercress and potato bake, tomato and lentil or parsnip and apple soups, and vegans aren't forgotten with the likes of spinach and potato slice and spicy bean Provençal. Cake lovers won't be disappointed with a wide range of sweeter options: as well as standards like carrot or chocolate, there can be a vegan date and apricot slice or the locally-inspired apple and cider cake.

With only a few tables inside, they double their capacity in warmer weather with around 20 extra seats in the courtyard itself. Perfect.

- Capuchin Yard
  Church St
  Hereford HR1 2LR
- 01432 277447
- Serving times:
  Mon-Sat 9am-5pm
- No credit cards
- Non-smoking except courtyard
- Licensed
- Children welcome
- 20 seats and courtyard
- Mains from £5.00

Orangery Restaurant

A light and airy restaurant and tearoom in the grounds of Herefordshire's Hampton Court, the Orangery offers an exceptional vegan and vegetarian choice including fruit and veg from the estate's organic gardens.

The homemade soup is always vegetarian, or choose snacks and starters such as roast red pepper pâté, hummus, herbed olives, and stilton mushrooms.

As well as a great range of salads, there's up to half a dozen daily mains including vegan options like nut roast, lentil bake or smoked tofu kebab. Lunch is served until 3pm, with teas and cakes until the 4.30pm close.

There is an entrance charge to Hampton Court, but with a range of well-signed walks and beautiful grounds, it's good value. Visit in the spring to see the stunning tulip gardens.

- Hampton Court Estate
  Hope under Dinmore
  HR6 0PN
- 01568 797676
- Serving times:
  Easter-Dec
  11am-4.30pm
  Closed Jan-March
- Major credit cards
- Non-smoking
- Licensed
- Children welcome
- 76 seats & large garden

Herefordshire

- Penrhos Court
  Kington HR5 3LH
- 01544 230720
- Serving times:
  Seasonally and
  weekends 7–8.30pm
- Booking essential
- Major credit cards
- Non-smoking
- Licensed
- 30 seats
- 4 courses £30

Penrhos Court

Close by Offa's Dyke, Penrhos Court is a highly regarded hotel and restaurant serving organic food and wine, with some stunning vegetarian options in the four course evening meals.

The first and second courses – such as fennel and almond or tomato and basil soup followed by a roast butternut squash and feta salad or sundried polenta with roasted red pepper – are always vegetarian, as are two of the four daily mains. Expect choices like roast leek, mascarpone and thyme frittata, linguine with pesto and roast vegetables or curried mushrooms with red rice.

The hotel is in a restored manor farm, with a medieval Cruck Hall housing the restaurant. Penrhos Court opens seasonally during the week plus many weekends and booking – well in advance – is essential.

Warwickshire

- 27 High St
  Rugby CV21 3BP
- 01788 543223
- Serving times:
  Mon-Sat
  9am-4.30pm
  Lunch served
  from 11am
  Closed bank holidays
- Major credit cards
- Non-smoking
- Licensed
- Children welcome
- 110 seats
- Mains from £6

Summersault

Housed in one of the original terracotta-fronted Boots the Chemists dating from 1895 and retaining some of the original fittings, there's also a rooftop conservatory and garden at this long-established and popular vegetarian restaurant.

Summersault uses a lot of organic produce and can cater for many special diets. Soups are always vegan, together with a number of mains like chestnut pie or courgette bake. If you're not resolutely dairy-free, try the leek and cream flan with toasted pine nuts and sundried tomatoes. All mains come with a choice of salad.

Good desserts, pavlova, baklava and fruit crumbles, and children can enjoy smaller portions from the adult menu. Open for coffee, lunch and afternoon teas.

Ryton Organic Gardens

The gardens and vegetable kingdom here are worth a visit in their own right – educational, beautiful and extensive – but you won't be charged admission to the waitress service restaurant and coffee shop if you're not going to do the whole experience.

As you would expect, all produce is organic – and vegan, wheat-free and other special diets are catered for. You can enjoy starters, snacks and sandwiches, or opt for a main dish with choices such as spinach and wild mushroom jalousie, butternut squash ravioli with hazelnut butter, vegetable and bean chilli, or baked courgette with a chickpea filling.

The entire menu is interesting and ambitious, and it might be an idea to book if you're visiting on Saturdays or Sundays.

- Wolston Lane
  Ryton on Dunsmore
  CV8 3LG
- 024 7630 3517
- Serving times:
  7 days 11am-3pm
  Closed Xmas – 1st Jan
- Major credit cards
- Non-smoking
- Licensed
- Children welcome
- 80 seats
- Mains from £7

Warwickshire

Maekong Thai

Vegetarian choices are clearly indicated at this Thai restaurant, and there's a more than respectable selection of around 20 meat-free dishes. Although there's nothing marked vegan per se, they will cater for dairy- and egg-free diets with a bit of notice.

There are two vegetarian set meals, otherwise choose from a couple of hot and sour soups, satay, spring rolls or sweetcorn cakes and a variety of stir fried vegetables, tofu and curries. The chilli heat of most dishes is made clear; useful for those of us lacking asbestos tongues.

There's also a special lunch menu deal – a main course for around a fiver, or add a starter as well for just a couple of quid more.

- 12 Worcester Rd
  Bromsgrove B61 7AE
- 01527 578888
- Serving times:
  Mon-Sat 12-2.30pm
  & 6-11pm
- Booking recommended
  Fri & Sat evenings
- Major credit cards
- Non-smoking except
  bar area
- Licensed
- Children welcome
- 76 seats
- Starters from £4

Worcestershire

Worcestershire

- Great Malvern
  Railway Station
  Great Malvern
  WR14 3AT
- 01684 893033
- Serving times:
  Mon-Sat 9am-6pm
- No credit cards
- Non-smoking
- Licensed
- Children welcome
- 28 seats
- Lunch specials
  from £3.35

Lady Foley's Tearooms

This prize-winning tearoom is in a restored Victorian railway station. You really won't mind a cancelled train in the middle of the day if you can console yourself with homemade cauliflower cheese or a ginger vegetable stir fry from the specials' board. There are proper sandwiches – on your choice of bread – tea and crumpets (all too rarely available in public), homemade soup, plus the usual scones, coffees, milkshakes, beer and wine. There's always something for vegans to enjoy as well.

Lady Foley's special blend of tea completes this very English experience – hopefully more 'Railway Children' than 'Brief Encounter'.

As well as seating inside, there are more tables on the platform.

Worcestershire

- 4 St Ann's Rd
  Great Malvern
  WR14 4RG
- 01684 564787
- Serving times:
  Mon-Fri 12-2.30pm
  & 6-9.30pm
  Sat-Sun 12-9.30pm
  bank holidays
  12-9.30pm
- Major credit cards
- Non-smoking area
- Licensed
- Children welcome
- 100 seats
- Starters from £3.50,
  mains from £7

Red Lion

The Red Lion is a traditional English pub in stunning surroundings with a buzzy atmosphere and decent vegetarian dishes on the menu. Vegans can enjoy the vegetable chilli, and the pub will also do their best to accommodate special diets. Food is cooked to order and there are no pre-bookings unless you are bringing a large party.

There's a range of pastas, risotto, stroganoff and salads as well as more unusual dishes like an African vegetable stew. Smaller children's mains are available for £4 (there's more than one choice and they're all served with chips, so you stand a reasonable chance of avoiding a tantrum) and if you've not got time to stop for long, try one of their baguettes.

St Ann's Well Café

800 feet up on the Worcestershire Beacon, there's seating for 20 inside and an almost unlimited number outside. The café serves 120 teas and 20 coffees as well as letting you BYO without a corkage charge and, best of all, you can have free Malvern water straight from their spring. We wonder if you can bring your own five gallon drum? Food is available between 12 and 3pm, and there's a good vegan choice: corn on the cob, aubergine and mango curry, soup, spicy burgers, nut burgers and baked potatoes as well as a vegan chocolate dessert, sugar-free fruit cake, and good old sticky toffee pudding.

Open weekends all year round, weekdays from Easter to September. Worth climbing the hill for.

- St Ann's Rd Malvern WR14 4RF
- 01684 560285
- Serving times: Easter-September 7 days 10am-6pm Full menu served 12-3pm Winter opening weekends only
- No credit cards
- Non-smoking inside
- Not licensed, BYO with no corkage
- 20 seats and large outside area

Natural Break

This is a longstanding (25 years) family-run business with an outside catering division. There are some good daily lunch deals, and they always have something vegan – baked potato and mushrooms à la grecque, for example. The old standards – cauliflower cheese with nutmeg, tomato, courgette and cheese bake – are there, but they ring the changes with brie and potato pizza, a splendid choice of salads (beetroot, apple and celery, or sweetcorn, courgette and radish are just two of the many examples) and tasty savoury flans.

The excellent Pago brand of fruit juices is also available, there's a neat courtyard area and the café is close to the station.

- 4 The Hopmarket Worcester WR1 1DL
- 01905 26654
- Serving times: Mon-Sat 9am-5pm
- No credit cards
- Non-smoking
- Not licensed
- Children welcome
- 50 seats
- Daily special from £5.50

berkshire

buckinghamshire

oxfordshire

Berkshire

Buckinghamshire

Oxfordshire

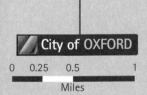

City of OXFORD

0   0.25   0.5   1

Miles

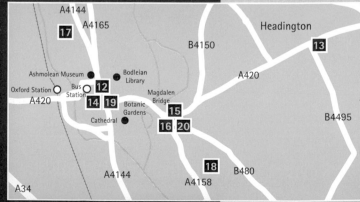

berkshire • buckinghamshire • oxfordshire

BUCKINGHAMSHIRE

□ Banbury

OXFORDSHIRE

8 9 10 Milton Keynes
7 Bletchley

□ Bicester

11 Kidlington

6 Aylesbury

□ Witney

■ Oxford

□ Abingdon

Amersham □

High Wycombe □

□
Beaconsfield

Maidenhead □

4 Slough

5 Windsor

BERKSHIRE

1 2 3 Reading

□ Newbury

Berkshire

- 11 St Mary Butts
  Reading RG1 2LN
- 0118 958 1357
- Serving times:
  Mon-Thurs 11am–
  10.30pm
  Fri-Sat 11am-11pm
  Sun 12-6pm
- Major credit cards
- Non-smoking area
- Licensed
- Children welcome
- 40 seats
- Mains from £4.50

Café Iguana

Berkshire's only completely vegetarian eaterie is just a few minutes walk from Reading's Oracle centre.

Great fillings for the baguettes, pitta and ciabatta include smoked cheese, tofu and cashew nut pâté with watercress, while starters and sides range from a dish of large olives to Cajun-style potatoes with salsa and sour cream. An all day breakfast competes for your attention alongside Mexican-style mains of nachos, fajitas and quesadillas, and there are daily specials like nut roast with all the essential extras, decent salads and interesting, freshly prepared soups. Huge vegan choice, and what isn't already dairy- and egg-free can often be adapted. Fresh fruit smoothies and juices, fair trade tea and coffee (including soya options), vegan wine and bottled organic beer.

Berkshire

- 35-39 London St
  Reading RG1 4PS
- 0118 958 3555
- Serving times:
  Tues-Sat 12-3pm
  & 6-9pm
  Bar open till 11pm,
  1am on Fri & Sat
- No credit cards
- Non-smoking area
- Licensed
- Children welcome
- 50 seats
- Snacks from £3

Global Café

Part of Reading's International Solidarity Centre, The Global Café offers a largely vegetarian menu, with plenty of choice for vegans in a relaxed family-friendly café bar environment. Open Tues-Sat, you can snack on a ciabatta sandwich, jacket or salad bowl, drop in for a drink, or leave it till later and explore the evening menu which can include the irresistible (and vegan) squashed nut bombe.

It's a favourite meeting place, with a full bar (including organic cider), and you can also enjoy a soya latte. There's internet access and chill-out sofas in the smoking area at the back. Special events include salsa dancing and quiz nights, but beware – Friday night is fish night, though veggie choices are still on the menu.

Omnivorous Chinese Restaurant

Le Shanghai

Just over the bridge from the centre of Reading into Caversham, Le Shanghai serves food from several regions of China – along with some Thai dishes – in a modern, stylish setting. It has an extensive menu, of which about a quarter is the vegetarian section.

Start with grilled vegetarian dumplings or sweet and sour vegetarian won tons, and then move on to a choice of 11 mains, including Kung Po deep-fried bean curd and sizzling mixed vegetables in blackbean sauce. Many dishes are suitable for vegans or can easily be adapted – and the staff are also able to help you select gluten-free options. Le Shanghai holds regular dinner/dance evenings, normally on Wednesdays.

- 32 Church St
  Caversham
  Reading RG4 8AU
- 0118 947 2097
- Serving times:
  7 days 12-2pm
  & 6-10.30pm
- Booking recommended weekend evenings
- Major credit cards
- Smoking throughout
- Licensed
- Children welcome
- 68 seats
- Mains from £4

Berkshire

Omnivorous Indian Restaurant

Barn Tandoori

This is one of those places that you drive past late at night, catch out of the corner of your eye, and wake up the following morning wondering if you dreamt it. In a early 1900s council building – but looking more like an ornate cricket pavilion than office or restaurant – Barn Tandoori is in the middle of Salt Hill Park, to the west of the town centre.

Enjoy a decent selection of well-cooked Indian vegetarian food, from starter favourites such as samosas, onion pakoras and masala dosa, through a variety of mains-size portions of vegetable curries, dhals and bhajis.

The restaurant itself is spacious and pleasant, with charming staff. The place to go for a curry if you're in this neck of the woods.

- Salt Hill Park
  Bath Rd
  Slough SL1 3SR
- 01753 553072
- Serving times:
  7 days 12-2.15pm
  & 6-11.15pm
- Major credit cards
- Non-smoking area
- Licensed
- Children welcome
- 75 seats
- Starters from £2

Berkshire

Berkshire

- 27 St Leonards Rd
  Windsor SL4 3BP
- Serving times:
  Mon–Thurs
  12–2.30pm
  & 6.30–10.30pm
  Fri–Sat 12–2.30pm
  & 6.30–11pm
  Closed some bank
  holidays
- Booking
  recommended
- Major credit cards
- Non-smoking area
- Licensed
- Children welcome
- 70 seats
- Starters from £2.95,
  mains from £8.50

Al Fassia

Book ahead for Royal Moroccan cooking within scampering distance of Windsor Castle. The food is warmly spiced with ginger, saffron, cumin and coriander, sharpened with lemon and olives. Even the odd cove who says he doesn't like spicy food will be delighted.

There are delicious vegetable stews in starter sizes, shorba (a veg soup with thread pasta), moreish garlic dips, and tabouleh – fresh and full of texture.

Mains include a white bean tagine, various couscous dishes and bastilla – homemade (mark you) filo pastry with vegetables and noodles, served with salad and saffron rice. Finish with a juicy, refreshing orange and cinnamon salad, honey pancakes or sweet pastries.

Buckinghamshire

- 11 Temple St
  Aylesbury HP20 2RN
- 01296 421228
- Serving times:
  Mon–Thurs 8am–10pm
  Fri–Sat 8am–10.30pm
  Sun 8am–3pm
- Major credit cards
- Smoking throughout
- Licensed
- Children welcome
- 70 seats
- Mains from £8

Carlo's

This candlelit restaurant in a former gentlemen's club is open all day, and they hold regular dinner-dances and fado nights (wonderful, melancholy Portuguese songs) for which you must book.

Some of the fresh produce is sourced from the owners' parents' farm, and the wines are almost exclusively Portuguese.

Main courses are richly sauced: ratatouille pancakes with white wine sauce and grilled cheese, mushrooms en croûte with ricotta, mascarpone, mozzarella, peppers and olives in flaky pastry, or a bean-pot piri piri. Dishes don't have to be finished with cheese, so do ask, and there is also an on-menu vegan choice of vegetables in a basil and tomato sauce with pine nuts and olives.

Veggie World

This restaurant also has a thriving wholesale and retail side where you can buy a vast range of 'meat'- and 'fish'- style soya protein. The intention is to give vegetarians a wider choice of dishes, and to attract non-vegetarians to a cruelty-free diet without denying them familiar shapes and flavours.

The vast majority of dishes in the restaurant are vegan, and the menu is clear and wonderfully simple for such a comprehensive choice. The day's specials are marked on the board.

Starters include butterfly prawns, grilled veggie dumplings, salt and pepper aubergine and soups. You can then sample sweet and sour dishes, roast duck and chicken (don't panic, it's all vegetarian), noodles and rice. For those who want to invent their own combination, you can also choose any 'meat' style protein and add your own choice of sauces which are marked for heat and their vegan-friendly credentials. Fancy prawns in Szechaun sauce, steak with green pepper and black bean, or chicken with cashew nuts and vegetables? As they say in establishments far inferior to this one – 'you got it' .

Set meals for two to five people are very competitively priced and offer a great guided tour of the menu.

Veggie World serves soft drinks and China tea in various flavours, but charges just £1 per person corkage if you bring your own wine. Open for lunch and dinner – eat here with confidence, knowing you won't end up with an inadvertent mouthful of animal fat or oyster sauce.

- 150-152 Queensway Bletchley MK2 2RS
- 01908 632288
- Serving times:
  Tues–Sun
  11.30am-2.30pm
  & 5-10pm
- Major credit cards
- Non-smoking
- Not licensed, BYO with corkage £1 per person
- Children welcome
- 35 seats
- Starters from £1.50

Buckinghamshire

Buckinghamshire

- Camphill Community
  Japonica Lane
  Willen Park South
  Milton Keynes
  MK15 9JY
- 01908 235505
- Serving times:
  Mon-Fri
  10am-4.30pm
  Closed bank holidays
- No credit cards
- Non-smoking
- Not licensed
- Children welcome
- 36 seats
- Snacks from £1

Camphill Café

This rustic café is run for the support of the Camphill Community for people with special needs. There are a couple of nice patio areas overlooking the gardens where a lot of the vegetables are grown, and everything is organic.

Choose from the fresh daily soup with homemade rolls, and a different special each day which can include nut roast, stroganoff, vegetable tacos, pasties and a variety of bakes.

If you're only popping in for a snack, have tea and crumpets or select something from the cake counter. Whatever you fancy, you'll eat here at very reasonable cost, knowing that you're supporting a hugely worthwhile project at the same time.

Buckinghamshire

- Christ Church
  Purbeck
  Stantonbury Campus
  Milton Keynes
  MK14 6BL
- 01908 315627
- Serving times:
  Mon-Fri 12-2pm
  term time only
- No credit cards
- Non-smoking
- Not licensed
- Children welcome
- 150 seats
- Mains from £3.20

Eating Point

You can't complain about a place that does a simple main course for £3.20, and jacket spuds for even less. Open during term times only, Eating Point is a no-frills café based in a church, mainly catering for a busy school campus whilst providing valuable work experience for young adults.

Everything is prepared fresh daily, so the menu changes regularly. Expect some good soups such as vegetable and barley, or butter bean and tomato, and mains like macaroni cheese with vegetables, cheese and potato pie, ratatouille or lentil curry. Desserts (from under a pound) can feature apple, redcurrant and blackberry crumble as well as a selection of cakes.

There are generally vegan options, and they also run an outside catering service.

Fortune Palace

Ever felt a bit left out when you go for a Chinese and you're presented with a few bits of veg in a sauce of uncertain origin? If so, and you're in Milton Keynes, head for Fortune Palace close to the station for something refreshingly different.

Using soya protein to mimic the texture and taste of meat, these clever chefs prepare a great selection of Chinese favourites from starters of satay 'chicken' or crispy 'duck' (and even sweet and sour 'ribs'...) to main courses of 'beef' in black bean, Kung Po 'chicken' and 'duck' in a lemon sauce.

There's a vegetarian set meal for two (or more), so why not rustle up a few veggie friends and make a night of it?

- 600 Elder Gate
  Milton Keynes
  MK9 1BE
- 01908 325588
- Serving times:
  7 days 12-2.30pm
  & 5-11pm
- Major credit cards
- Non-smoking area
- Licensed
- Children welcome
- 60 seats
- Mains from £4.50

Buckinghamshire

Tiffins Tandoori

A favourite with the Oxford area vegetarian in the know, Tiffins gives you a decent and keenly priced selection of vegetarian food and has received honourable press mentions.

As well as the usual suspects in the side order department, there's a comprehensive range of curries ranging from the mild to the 'definitely not for beginners' variety, and an extremely good value vegetarian set meal of around eight items for little more than a tenner a head. A friendly, comfortable, candlelit restaurant of the sort we all wished we had just around the corner, they assure us that everything is GM-free. There's also a thriving takeaway section with free local delivery subject to a minimum order.

- 63 High St
  Kidlington OX5 2DN
- 01865 372245
- Serving times:
  7 days 6-11.30pm
- Booking recommended
  Fri & Sat evenings
- Major credit cards
- Non-smoking area
- Licensed
- Children welcome
- 36 seats
- Mains from £3.50

Oxfordshire

- 89 The Covered Market
  Oxford OX1 3DU
- 01865 250499
- Serving times:
  Mon-Sat 11am-4pm
- No credit cards
- Non-smoking
- Not licensed
- Children welcome
- 12 seats

Alpha Bar

The majority of Oxford's Alpha Bar trade is takeaway, but if you're lucky enough to grab one of their seats, it's a good place to catch your breath on that whistle-stop tour of Oxford.

Predominately vegetarian, with good vegan options, try one of their vegetable stews or chillis or enjoy a roast tofu, falafel, or carrot and seaweed sandwich. Many visit just for the fruit smoothies and freshly squeezed fruit and vegetable juices, so you could always just pop in and get your five portions of fruit and veg in a single hit.

A short word of warning though – the market was originally constructed to house Oxford's thriving butchery trade, and some butchers are still there. Not for the squeamish.

- 146 London Rd
  Headington
  Oxford OX3 9ED
- 01865 761106
- Serving times:
  Mon-Thurs
  11.30am-10.30pm
  Fri-Sat 11.30am-11pm
  Sun 11.30am-10.30pm
- Major credit cards
- Non-smoking area
- Licensed
- Children welcome
- 80 seats

Bar Meze

Bar Meze is a very attractive restaurant with a glazed roof, which invites lunchtime dining. The place is elegantly comfortable.

You'll do best ordering off the cold meze menu, and go for the varieties. If you order a single dish it's £5 for a starter or £9 as a main, which is an awful lot of stuffed vine leaves where we come from. It's better to have a platter of three for £8 – beans plaki, grilled cheese and artichoke hearts, for example.

For the main course choose from stuffed aubergine or char-roasted vegetables, or dive into three or four choices from the hot meze menu.

Nice, sticky, super-sweet desserts and coffee.

Chiang Mai

This one is special. Tucked away down an alley in a 17th century timber framed building, their kitchen imports spices and herbs from Bangkok every week.

There's a substantial vegetarian menu of delicious dishes: a piquant tom kha het soup – mushrooms in a coconut soup with lemon grass and chilli, pak krau chiang mai – the house-style vegetables with a spicy peanut sauce, and there's always a vegan choice. Desserts are similarly appealing including sticky coconut rice with banana.

Chiang Mai can cater a romantic dinner for two or a bigger celebration, in separate rooms. This is sophisticated, special occasion dining of the first order, and it's essential to book.

- 130a High St
  Oxford OX1 4DH
- Down alley opposite Whittards
- 01865 202233
- Serving times:
  Mon-Sat 12-2.30pm
  & 6-10.30pm
  Sun 12-3pm & 6-10pm
  Closed bank holidays
- Booking essential
- Major credit cards
- Non-smoking area
- Licensed
- Children welcome
- 80 seats

Oxfordshire

Hajduczek

The main attraction here is the 40 types of vodka. You can drink it throughout the meal and not make a beast of yourself. Tiny, intensely flavoured icy shots complement the rich savoury Slavic cooking. It's a civilised, grown-up way of dining.

Poland is not famous for its vegetarian cooking but you can eat well here. Start with barscz – beetroot soup, pierogi – little pastries stuffed with cabbage and white cheese, kopytka – herbal dumplings with cream and breadcrumbs, or a vegetarian bigos – sauerkraut stew.

The mains are bigger portions of the starters, plus lovely sweet pancakes with cream cheese, cherries and chocolate sauce. Make an evening of it, savour the richness and don't stint on the vodka.

- 84 Cowley Rd
  Oxford OX4 1JB
- 01865 243390
- Serving times:
  7 days 12-2.15pm
  & 6-10.30pm
- Major credit cards
- Non-smoking area
- Licensed
- Children welcome
- 50 seats
- Mains from £6.50

Oxfordshire

Oxfordshire

- 68-70 Cowley Rd
  Oxford OX4 1JB
- 01865 725984
- Serving times:
  Mon-Sat 12-2pm
  & 7-11.30pm
  Sun 12-2pm
  & 7-11.00pm
- Booking
  recommended
  weekend evenings
- Major credit cards
- Non-smoking area
  during lunch
- Licensed
- Children welcome
- 60 seats
- Starters from £2.50,
  mains from £5

Hi-Lo Jamaican Eating House

It's a delight to find that there's a reasonable amount of good scoff available on the menu at this popular Caribbean-cuisine venue, known as much for its music and atmosphere as the food. This is a long lunch or night out occasion.

Make a hog of yourself with starters or snacks (at £2.50 or less!) which include soup, baked sweet potatoes, fried plantain and buttered breadfruit. There's generally just one vegetarian main of the day, but the selection of extras it's offered with – rice and peas, yam, sweet potato and turned cornmeal with veg – means you won't feel hard done by. Have a sticky dessert and a shot of rum from the considerable choice to finish off.

Oxfordshire

- 110 Magdalen Rd
  Oxford OX4 1RQ
- 01865 794604
- Mon-Sat 10am-6pm
  Lunch served
  from midday
  Closed bank holidays
- No credit cards
- Non-smoking
- Not licensed
- Children welcome
- 50 seats
- Lunch special
  from £4.75

The Magic Café

This friendly neighbourhood café is open for breakfast and lunch six days a week, and you can chill out at a pavement table in the summer.

Everything is freshly prepared on the premises, from the savoury pies to the hazelnut and orange custard tarts. Breakfast buns come filled with mushrooms fried in butter or two fried eggs – or both, if last night was a heavy one. You can soothe yourself from the choice of herbal, Indian and China teas or indulge with an iced coffee latte.

Lunch, served from noon, has chef's specials from the board, soup and a roll or a savoury pie and salad, homemade ice cream and cakes. Bring on the cherry vanilla tarts.

The Garden Kitchen

This restaurant is in the Jericho area of Oxford, in the Gardener's Arms pub which itself has a pool room, garden and a good comfortable bar. You'll find a relaxed and friendly atmosphere here, with a keen student following.

The style of cooking is high quality traditional British, with some other influences and many dishes are vegan – including a dairy- and egg-free Sunday roast. Owner Andy Skinner will also provide buffets for special events or cater for your own party

Most main courses are under £6, and the menu changes regularly. Sample dishes include homemade shepherds pie – a thick layer of mince and gravy topped with mashed potato finished under the grill; mushroom and pea stroganoff – onions, mushrooms and peas cooked with rice in a white wine and cream sauce, or winter potatoes – fried new potatoes with green beans in a wine and cheese sauce. For something lighter, try bar snacks along the lines of veggieburgers, ciabatta, pizza, garlic bread or tortilla wraps.

Desserts include (vegan) Swedish Glace ice cream with hot chocolate sauce, and Andy's planning to serve a wider range of homemade puddings soon.

Food is available from Wednesday to Sunday (all-afternoon opening on Saturday and Sunday), and they can get busy. Do book if you're in a large group, and note that there is another Gardener's Arms pub not far away – you'll be wanting the one on Plantation Road, between Walton Street and Woodstock Road.

- The Gardener's Arms
  39 Plantation Rd
  Oxford OX2 6JE
- 01865 559814
- Serving times:
  Wed-Fri 12-2.30pm
  & 5-9pm
  Sat 12-9pm
  Sun 12-6pm
- Major credit cards
- Smoking throughout
- Licensed
- 60 seats & garden area
- Mains from £5

Oxfordshire

- 6-8 St Michaels St
  Oxford OX1 2DU
- Next door to Arcadia
- 01865 721033
- Serving times:
  Mon-Thurs
  11.30am-9.45pm
  Fri-Sat
  11.30am-10.15pm
  Sun 11.30am-8.45pm
- Major credit cards
- Non-smoking
- Licensed
- Children welcome
- 52 seats
- Mains from £6.50

The Nosebag

The Nosebag is a counter-service restaurant in a 16th century building which has been running since the 1970s. Everything is homemade on the premises, there's plenty of vegetarian choice, and they can usually cope with vegan or wheat-free requests.

Try a lunchtime lasagne of green vegetables and pesto, a black-eyed and red bean chilli or a lentil and vegetable moussaka. Smaller dishes include baked potatoes, soup and quiche. In the evenings pumpkin, lemon and sage risotto with salad and garlic bread, or an Indonesian vegetable curry often put in appearances.

Wash it all down with a beer, glass of wine, organic cider or Benson's apple juice and finish off with one of the very fine desserts.

- 43 St Clements St
  Oxford OX4 1AG
- 01865 202787
- Serving times:
  Mon-Sat 12-1.30pm
  & 6-11pm
  Sun 6-11pm
- Booking recommended
  Fri & Sat
- Major credit cards
- Smoking throughout
- Licensed
- Children welcome
- 60 seats
- Mains from £6

The Pink Giraffe

This is a good value, fairly central, Chinese restaurant with a clearly marked selection of vegetarian dishes making innovative use of soya to replace the meat in dishes such as Szechaun shredded beef and chicken with cashew nut in yellow bean sauce. You can specify no MSG in many dishes if you let them know in advance.

It's essential to book on Friday and Saturday – not surprisingly, as one of their bargain deals is an all-you-can-eat offer from a set menu, and one with good vegetarian options on it.

There are also a couple of vegetarian set dinners for two or more, as well as a comprehensive takeaway menu. And if you're looking for something out of the ordinary to go with all this, there are plenty of cocktails and non-alcoholic punches.

middlesex

middlesex

Middlesex

middlesex

Stanmore ☐

1 Edgware

☐ Harefield

☐ Pinner

2 **3** Harrow
4 **5**

☐ Ruislip

☐ Ickenham   Sudbury ☐

8 **9** **10** **11** Wembley
12 **13** **14** **15** **16**

☐ Uxbridge

☐ Hillingdon

☐ Greenford

17   Hayes ☐

6 Southall

☐ West Drayton

☐ Harmondsworth

☐ Brentford

Hounslow ☐   ☐ Isleworth

☐ Stanwell

7 Twickenham

☐ Feltham

☐ Staines ☐ Ashford

☐ Teddington

☐ Hampton

☐ Sunbury

MIDDLESEX

- 236 Station Rd
  Edgware HA8 7AU
- Close to Edgware
  underground
- 020 8905 3033
- Serving times:
  Mon- Fri 12-2.30pm
  & 6-11.30pm
  Sat 12-3.30pm
  & 6-11.30pm
  Sun 12-11.30pm
- Booking recommended
  Sat evening
- Major credit cards
- Smoking throughout
- Licensed
- Children welcome
- 55 seats
- Mains from £4.00

Chai

This contemporary restaurant nails its colours to the mast and declares itself 100% strictly vegetarian. If you've ever worried about hidden stock cubes or oyster sauce, you can eat here with confidence and greed, as could any visiting vegan.

Open daily for lunch and dinner, it's nice to be spoiled for choice. Dive into their lunch buffet, or make a beast of yourself for £9.90 with unlimited ordering from the à la carte evening menu, including loads of tofu dishes, Thai curries, mock duck and mixed vegetables – or order a special meal for two.

Rather quaintly, children can eat for £5.90 subject to a height restriction of 120cm. Don't sit up straight Nigel, slump those shoulders.

- 156 Kenton Rd
  Harrow HA3 8AZ
- 020 8909 2232
- Serving times:
  Tues-Sun 12-3pm
  & 6-10pm
- Booking recommended
  weekends
- Major credit cards
- Non-smoking
- Not licensed
- Children welcome
- 110 seats
- Starters from £1.50

Pradips

There's plenty of vegan choice on this menu, which can also cater for other special requirements. Booking is advisable at the weekend, but you should get a table during the week without planning ahead.

There's a healthy eating range on this menu, which includes a selection of dishes that are boiled rather than fried, and they run a buffet on Friday to Sunday, where you can indulge in unlimited starters and main courses with a complimentary soft drink. This glutton's licence costs under £8.

If you just want a couple of dishes, order à la carte, as it's hard to find anything costing more than £3, and most dishes are much less. Desserts include an unusual east Indian deep fried paneer dipped in a sugary syrup.

Ram's

Success came quickly to Ram's, which opened in 2001 to much favourable press comment, not to mention the odd award the following year. The predominately Gujarati clientèle gives further indication of the quality and authenticity of the cuisine on offer.

Vegan and Jain diets are well catered for, and every weekend there are specials to demonstrate Surti cuisine – the undhiu of aubergine, three sorts of potato, banana and peas is in itself probably worth making the trip for. Traditional favourites like spinach aloo and vegetable korma aren't missing from the menu, but do try one of the specialities as well.

The open plan restaurant is licensed, but also serves fresh lassi made with homemade yoghurt, passion fruit juice, faluda and milkshakes.

- 203 Kenton Rd
  Harrow HA3 0HD
- 100 yards from Kenton
  Road tube
- 020 8907 2022
- Serving times:
  7 days 12-3pm
  & 6-10.45pm
  Open bank holiday
  Mondays
- Booking advisable
  at weekends
- Major credit cards
- Non-smoking
- Licensed
- Children welcome
- 75 seats
- Mains from £3.50

Middlesex

Sakonis

Sakonis in Harrow is, like their other London branches in Wembley, Tooting and Forest Gate, a family-friendly and alcohol-free café and restaurant with a great value all-vegetarian lunchtime and evening buffet.

With well over 150 seats it can be a bustling venue especially on weekend evenings but, if you're on a budget and want to sample a whole selection of Indian and Indo-Chinese dishes – and go back for the ones you particularly enjoyed a second time – Sakonis buffet is quite definitely for you.

This all-you-can-eat feast is served between 12 and 3pm, and 7 and 9.30pm – £5.99 at lunch, £7.99 in the evenings. Order from the menu between 3 and 7pm.

- 5-8 Dominion Parade
  Station Rd
  Harrow HA1 2TR
- 020 8863 3399
- Serving times:
  Mon-Tues 12-9.30pm
  Thurs 12-9.30pm
  Fri-Sat 12-10pm
  Sun 12-9.30pm
- Major credit cards
- Non-smoking
- Not licensed
- Children welcome
- 170 seats
- Lunch buffet £5.99

Middlesex

Middlesex

- 123 Headstone Rd
  Harrow HA1 1PG
- 020 8863 6144
- Serving times:
  Mon 12-2.15pm
  & 6-10.45pm
  Wed-Sun 12-2.15pm
  & 6-10.45pm
  Closed Tuesdays
- Major credit cards
- Non-smoking
- Not licensed, BYO
  £1 per person corkage
- Children welcome
- 30 seats
- Starters from £3

Veggie Inn

Veggie Inn is a delightful, recently opened vegan Chinese restaurant which cleverly prepares soya protein to mimic the texture and taste of the ingredients in traditional Chinese dishes such as Kung Po chicken, crispy duck or even king prawns.

Construct your own à la carte selection from the comprehensive menu, or settle in for the night with one of three set menus featuring up to dozen inspired dishes. Bring your own bottle for nominal corkage, enjoy fresh apple or carrot juices, or try their freshly pressed (yes, you read that right) soya milk.

Modern, clean, attractive premises, and they're only a few minutes up the Headstone Road from Harrow's multiplex. You'll know you're close when you catch a glimpse of the fairy lights covering their awning.

Southall

Vegetarian Indian Café

Middlesex

- 17 South Rd
  Southall UB1 1SU
- Opposite Himalaya
  cinema
- 020 8571 3110
- Serving times:
  7 days 10am-8pm
- No credit cards
- Non-smoking
- Not licensed
- Children welcome
- 38 seats
- Snacks from £1

Shahenshah

Homely Indian vegetarian café, just a few yards off Southall's High Street. Expect canteen-style tables and seating with a view of the kitchen and the sweet counter, and a good selection of snacky – and more substantial – home-produced fare.

The daily thali at just £4 is excellent value, and you can also order a takeaway, grab a samosa for just 30p, or pop in for tea or coffee. If you can't wait for lunch, enjoy a late breakfast from 10am or, if hunger pangs aren't going to let you get through the afternoon without being satisfied, try a kulfi or some of those irresistible Indian sweets.

Pallavi

With more than half the menu vegetarian, including some Malabar specialities, biriyanis and exotic starters, you're going to find yourself spoilt for choice at this south Indian restaurant specialising in Keralan cuisine.

There are crisp roasted pancakes stuffed with potato curry, lentil cakes, vegetable samosas and irresistible cashew nut pakodas in the nibbly starter section, together with interesting curry choices in the mains. Try green bananas with spices and onions, cabbage with coconut, onion and carrot or kalan – mango and yam cooked with fresh coconut, yoghurt, cumin and green chillies.

Pallavi is keenly-priced, and also offers take away or free home delivery if you're local with a large-ish order.

- Unit 3
  Cross Deep Court
  Heath Rd
  Twickenham TW1 4AG
- 020 8892 2345
- Serving times:
  Mon-Thurs 12-3pm
  & 6-11pm
  Fri-Sat 6-11pm
  Sun 12-3pm & 6-11pm
- Booking recommended weekend evenings
- Major credit cards
- Non-smoking area
- Licensed
- Children welcome
- 65 seats
- Starters from £2.50

Africana Restaurant

Superb value, simple menu and the option to buy samosa, kachori and spring rolls for home cooking – we just wish this family-run restaurant had a branch in every high street.

There's a choice of 20 starters between £2 and 3.50, including samosas (four for £2!), bhel and bhajias, and 11 specialities, from biryani, vegetable curry, rice and dhal or some belt-bursting thalis, plus side dishes and breads and desserts. Alcohol isn't served, or welcome, but when there's fresh passion fruit juice, fresh carrot, or lassi on offer, who needs it?

There's a warm and friendly feel to the restaurant, and a real willingness to make you welcome.

- 224 Ealing Rd
  Wembley HA0 4QL
- Opposite Chequers pub
- 020 8795 2455
- Serving times:
  7 days 12-10pm
- Booking recommended weekend evenings
- No credit cards
- Smoking throughout
- Not licensed
- Children welcome
- 50 seats
- Starters from £2.50, mains from £3.50

Middlesex

- 533 Wembley High Rd
  Wembley HA0 2DJ
- 020 8902 6000
- Serving times:
  Tues-Thurs 12-10pm
  Fri-Sat 12-11pm
  Sun 12-10pm
- Major credit cards
  over £10
- Non-smoking
- Not licensed
- Children welcome
- 60 seats
- Buffet from £5

Ahimsa

All-you-can-eat Chinese-Thai vegetarian buffets have been the flavour of the month for some time, with up to a dozen having sprung up over the last few years.

Ahimsa is decorated in a more minimalist style than many – plain white walls, large mirrors, pine (think IKEA rather than MFI) tables and chairs and, of course, a large stainless steel buffet stuffed with dozens of soya-based faux meat dishes such as 'beef' in blackbean sauce and sweet and sour 'chicken', as well as noodles, veg, rice, deep-fried aubergine and sweet potato. There can also be a small choice of Indian-style options, and hot and sour Thai soups.

Grab a plate, fill it up, and keep going back for more until you've bid farewell to your diet in spectacular (and inexpensive) style.

- 420 High Rd
  Wembley HA9 6AH
- 020 8900 1466
- Serving times:
  Tues-Fri 12-3pm
  & 6-10.15pm
  Sat-Sun 1-10.15pm
  Open bank holiday
  Mondays
- Major credit cards
- Non-smoking area
- Licensed
- Children welcome
- 80 seats
- Starters from £2.40

Chetna's Bhel Poori House

On Wembley's busy High Road, Chetna's Bhel Poori House offers a comprehensive pizza menu alongside its Bombay and Gujarati cuisine. With thalis for under a fiver, the menu also features their famous dosas and a wide range of curries as well as other popular Chetna dishes, which can be ordered omitting the onion and garlic if you prefer.

As well as the usual suspects in the beer and wine ranges, try their mango lassi or the signature falooda: a rose flavoured milkshake with takmaria topped with ice cream and pistachios – an excellent accompaniment to many of the spicier curries.

Normally closed on Mondays, they do open for bank holidays but are then shut on the following Tuesday.

Vegetarian Restaurant

Jashan

In their own words, this is a semi-fast food restaurant, but don't let that put you off – there's an extensive menu, including some Chinese, Thai and Indian/Italian dishes. Try the lunchtime buffet during the week for £4.99 per person – but it won't break the bank at weekends, either.

There's a quick bites selection of dosas, puris, pakoras and samosas, and dozens of dishes of different vegetables, biryanis, Indian breads and desserts. Jashan market themselves as "a taste of India for the homesick or an introduction to it as good as a visit."

Vegan food is easy here, together with garlic- and onion-free diets.

- 1-2 Coronet Parade
  Ealing Rd
  Wembley HA0 4AY
- Next to library
- 020 8900 9800
- Serving times:
  Mon-Fri 12-3.15pm
  & 6-10.45pm
  Sat-Sun 12-11pm
- Major credit cards
- Non-smoking
- Licensed
- Children welcome
- 100 seats
- Snacks from £2.75

Vegetarian Café

Wembley

Maru's Bhajia House

We would hate to be dictatorial, but stick with us just this once. When you visit Maru's there are two must-have items on the short, predominately snacky menu: Maru's bhajia – the deliciously-spiced deep-fried potato and gram flour snack which comes with its own chutney – and a glass of their freshly squeezed passion fruit juice.

You can also enjoy dishes like bhel poori, kachoori and spring rolls and, if you can't persuade the little ones to join you in these spicy delights, order them chips and beans or a toastie from the children's section.

And what's in the large, transport café-style sauce bottle on your table? Tamarind sauce – the ideal accompaniment to that second round of bhajia you're about to order...

- 230 Ealing Rd
  Wembley HA0 4QL
- 020 8902 5570
- Serving times:
  Mon-Thurs
  12.30-8.30pm
  Fri-Sun 12.30-9.30pm
- Booking recommended
  weekends
- Major credit cards
- Non-smoking
- Not licensed
- Children welcome
- 28 seats
- Snacks from £1.60

Middlesex

- 129 Ealing Rd
  Wembley HA0 4BP
- 020 8903 9601
- Serving times:
  Mon-Fri 12-9.30pm
  Sat-Sun 9am-10pm
- Booking recommended
  evenings
- Major credit cards
- Non-smoking
- Not licensed
- Children welcome
- 120 seats
- Buffet from £5.99

Sakonis

In the heart of the Ealing Road shopping area – where the grocers, clothes and CD shops spill, market-style, onto the pavement – you'll find this large, highly regarded café and restaurant offering a popular lunch and evening buffet featuring a choice of over thirty Indian and Indo-Chinese dishes.

The usual curries, rice, dhals and bread jostle for space with up to ten daily-changing buffet specials, and while you're loading your plate with this well-prepared fare you get a good view of the open plan kitchen area (always guaranteed to inspire confidence).

You can also enjoy a breakfast version – served 9-11am at weekends – but we recommend you arrive on the early side as the restaurant can be full by 10am.

Middlesex

- 549 High Rd
  Wembley HA0 2DJ
- 020 8902 1515
- Serving times:
  Mon-Fri 12-10.30pm
  Sat 12-11pm
  Sun 12-10.30pm
- Major credit cards
- Non-smoking
- Not licensed
- Children welcome
- 60 seats

Sarashwathy Bavans

Limber up your lips just by saying the name and then indulge in some wonderfully aromatic authentic south Indian dishes. You're probably not going to be able to resist the bhel poori, and then find yourself torn between the dosas, ginger cauliflower or the paneer mushrooms. A choice of two massive thalis eases the pain of deciding from a long menu, which includes a small Chinese section. Complement the superb spicing with a sweet lassi.

Lunchtimes Mon to Thurs offers up the bargain mini thali for £2.75 to take away, if you're lucky enough to work in the area. Open throughout the day and evening, home deliveries and party cooking can be arranged. The clientele are predominantly Indian and Sri Lankan, testament to fine cooking from Mr Dayalan's team.

Tulsi

An upmarket 240 seat vegetarian restaurant which opened in January 2004, Tulsi has a stylish and simply decorated interior – don't expect bench seats and flock wallpaper. The food is predominately south Indian with some other regional specialities, together with a large Indo-Chinese section – including the now seemingly compulsory chilli paneer.

Visit at the weekends if you're a fan of all-you-can-eat buffet dining, or try one of their thalis.

The first floor opens at busy times, but has also been designed to provide a separate dedicated party area, complete with a small dance floor and its own bar. Book it for your birthday bash or wedding reception, but make sure you bring a few friends – it seats 120.

- 22 Ealing Rd
  Wembley HA0 4TL
- 020 8900 8526
- Serving times:
  Tues-Sun 11am-11pm
- No credit cards
- Non-smoking downstairs
- Licensed
- Children welcome
- 240 seats
- Starters from £3

Middlesex

Woodlands Restaurant

Woodlands in Wembley shares its south Indian cuisine with three other Woodlands restaurants in London, and they claim that their chefs have at least fifteen years' previous experience at branches in India and Singapore.

Not a place to go for fiercely hot vindaloos and several pints of lager, Woodlands food is more subtly spiced and includes traditional south Indian starters such as idli and pakoda, snacky street food like bhel poori and aloo tikki, and mains of dosas, uthappams and a range of delicately flavoured curries.

Slightly less expensive than the other Woodlands venues (there's a lot of competition round here) the lunchtime takeout box of masala dosa, korma and rice is available for just £3.50.

- 402 High Rd
  Wembley HA9 6AL
- 020 8902 9869
- Serving times:
  7 days 12-2.45pm
  & 6-10.45pm
- Major credit cards
- Smoking throughout
- Licensed
- Children welcome
- 55 seats

Middlesex

Middlesex

- 131 High St
  Yiewsley
  West Drayton UB7 7QL
- 01895 422464
- Serving times:
  Mon-Fri 12-2.30pm
  & 6-11pm
  Sat 6-11pm
  Sun 12-3pm
  & 6-10.30pm
- Booking recommended
- Major credit cards
- Non-smoking area
  on request
- Licensed
- Children welcome
- 160 seats
- Starters from £3.50

Water Palace

This is a modern fine-dining Chinese restaurant with creative and seasonal menus. There's a good choice of vegetarian appetisers and mains, and you can order off menu if can't find exactly what you want.

Vegetarian appetisers include the Chinese standards of spring rolls and vegetable dumplings, but with the addition of more interesting dishes like veggie crispy 'duck' and salt and chilli runner beans. Main courses feature tofu and veggie 'chicken' options, asparagus with garlic and spring onions, Japanese shitake mushrooms, and sea spice aubergine in hot chilli sauce.

You can also enjoy the gourmet vegetarian set meal of around ten dishes, with gluten standing in to create some traditional Chinese favourites. Booking recommended, especially Fridays and Saturdays.

bedfordshire
cambridgeshire
hertfordshire

bedfordshire • cambridgeshire
hertfordshire

Bedfordshire

Cambridgeshire

Hertfordshire

Wisbech

Peterborough **7**

March

CAMBRIDGESHIRE

Ely

Huntingdon

BEDFORDSHIRE

St Neots
8

4 5 6 Cambridge

2 Bedford

Biggleswade

Royston

11 Heydon

1 Ampthill

12 13 Letchworth

Hitchin

Leighton Buzzard

Stevenage

Dunstable **3**   Luton

10 Bishop's
Stortford

Harpenden

Hertford   **15** Ware

St Albans **14**

Hatfield

HERTFORDSHIRE

Watford

9 Barnet

bedfordshire • cambridgeshire • hertfordshire

Bedfordshire

- 91 Dunstable St
  Ampthill MK45 2NG
- 01525 404666
- Serving times:
  Tues-Fri 12-2pm
  & 6-10pm
  Sat 6-10.30pm
  Closed Sun & Mon
- Booking essential
  at weekends
- Major credit cards
- Large non-smoking
  area
- Licensed
- Children welcome
- 80 seats
- Starters from £3.50,
  mains from £9.00

Donatello's

This traditional Italian pizzeria also lists a range of pastas, salads and side dishes. There are relatively few completely vegetarian dishes, but the proprietors are so willing to adapt by leaving out the odd anchovy or bit of ham that it's easy to eat well here.

The roasted pepper starter (stuffed with mozzarella, garlic, onions and olives with a neapolitan sauce) or garlic mushrooms are both rather special. There's also good old mozzarella and tomato salad.

Don't go mad on the main course, so you can try the 'dolce vita' – a sweet pizza with peaches, sugar, peach schnapps and Italian vanilla ice cream. Oral heaven. Children welcome at any time, starter size portions provided.

Bedfordshire

- 4 Kimbolton Rd
  Bedford MK40 2NR
- 01234 353470
- Serving times:
  Mon 6-11pm
  Tues-Sat 11-2pm
  & 6-11pm
- Major credit cards
- Small non-smoking
  area
- Licensed
- Children welcome
- 90 seats

Bruno's Mama Mia

Just a few minutes from Bedford's town centre is this long-established and family-run traditional trattoria, and it's where a lot of the local veggies head for their regular pasta and pizza fix.

Food is freshly prepared, so you could always ask them to assemble your own favourite combinations, but with dozens of dishes on the menu which are already meat-free, it's not essential to do your own editing to come up with some good veggie options. As you'd expect there are lots of starters including breads, mushrooms in a variety of sauces, deep fried mozzarella, salads and gnocchi, and many main course pastas and pizza. Opposite the St Peters St car park, with free parking after 6pm.

Golden Dragon

You'll look at the menu and think 'I can't have that', but then find you can eat the lot. Masters of the art of deception, there's gluten and soya protein masquerading as chicken, duck or sizzling beef, with vegan and hot and spicy dishes clearly indicated.

'Chicken' with cashew nuts in yellow bean sauce leaps off the menu, as does smoked spicy tofu with plum sauce. Kung Po 'duck' with water chestnuts, crushed garlic and sweet and sour chilli sauce is a mouth-watering must-have dish. There are hot pots, sizzling dishes, rice and noodle meals and a couple of excellent set menus.

Organic wine is served, and locals can get home deliveries for a minimum order, or have a discounted takeaway.

- 1 Tring Rd
  Dunstable LU6 2PX
- 01582 661485
- Serving times:
  7 days 12-1.45pm
  & 6-10.45pm
- Booking advisable
  Saturdays
- Major credit cards
- Non-smoking area
- Licensed
- Children welcome
- 80 seats
- Starters from £3,
  mains from £5.00

Bedfordshire

Hobbs Pavilion

There's a special vegetarian menu at this mainly omnivorous Mediterranean café named after the revered cricketer Sir Jack Hobbs, pleasantly situated opposite Parker's Piece in Cambridge.

They have the advantage of being open all day in summer for food and drink, and there's a children's menu of vegetable pasta, veggieburger or macaroni cheese. The place seats 100 (quite a lot, but no match for the 5000 who reputedly banqueted on The Piece itself to celebrate the end of the Napoleonic Wars) and there's no need to book; things move along efficiently enough to look after new customers arriving.

You'll want to try the roasted vegetarian lasagne or Bombay spicy vegetables and follow it with one of their refreshing sorbets or freshly pressed fruit juices.

- Park Terrace
  Cambridge CB1 1JH
- 01223 367480
- Serving times:
  April-August
  11am-10pm
  September-March
  12noon-3pm & 6-9pm
- Major credit cards
- Non-smoking area
- Licensed
- Children welcome
- 100 seats
- Lunch specials from £5,
  evening mains from £8

Cambridgeshire

- 9a Kings Parade
  Cambridge CB2 1SJ
- Opposite King's
  College gates
- 01223 321551
- Serving times:
- Tues-Sat
  10am-9.30pm
- Major credit cards
- Non-smoking
- Licensed
- Children welcome
- 50 seats
- Starters from £3

Rainbow Restaurant

If you want to impress someone, bring them here – it's opposite King's College and is itself in an historic building. Rainbow has been a finalist in the Vegetarian Society's 'Vegetarian Restaurant of the Year' award for the last three years, and they've a well-deserved reputation for good, freshly prepared food.

There's a daily homemade soup of vegetables and pulses that doesn't need added stock to impress, and various garlic breads with herbs or cheese. A giant chef's salad (or smaller salad plates with pasta or feta) compete for your attention with hot favourites like spinach lasagne or a Latvian potato bake. You can also enjoy a Peshwari curry, fava bean tagine, tagliatelle, risotto, or even an adaptation of the South African bobotie, with quorn in a sweet and spicy sauce.

The Tex-Mex section offers you chilli, enchiladas, and fajitas, and the daily specials can include a Roquefort plait or mushrooms en croûte

Their carrot cake is endorsed by none other than Nigel Slater, and there are some gorgeous desserts and gluten-free options like apricot and almond slice or a fresh cream roulade with ground almonds. Ice cream is the vegan Swedish Glace, and they keep almost half a dozen flavours.

The menu is very clearly marked for vegan and gluten-free options (you'll be spoilt for choice), and they're justly proud of their all-vegan and organic wine and beer list, and range of teas and juices. Children and babies are made welcome with high chairs, and smaller portions on request.

One of the very best.

Trattoria Pasta Fresca

A local trat but with homemade pasta and a helpfully labelled menu, and they recently picked up a national award for pasta restaurant of the year. Alongside some kitchen standards like pesto spaghetti and tortelloni with mushrooms, which are in a different league to the lazy supermarket version you do yourself, there's splendid goat's cheese or pumpkin ravioli. Delicious, substantial salads come with hunks of ciabatta and there are some very tasty vegetarian pizzas. The weekly specials always have at least one extra vegetarian dish per course.

Unsurprisingly, booking is always recommended. You can have an intimate dinner for two, or there's a separate party room if you're planning a big event.

- 66 Mill Rd
  Cambridge CB1 2AS
- 01223 352836
- Serving times:
  Mon-Fri 12-2.30pm
  & 6-10.30pm
  Sat 12-3.30pm
  & 6-10.30pm
  Sun 1-3.30pm
  & 6-10pm
  Closed bank holidays
- Booking essential
  Fri & Sat evenings
- Major credit cards
- Non-smoking area
- Licensed
- Children welcome
- 60 seats
- Pizzas from £4.95

Cambridgeshire

The Brewery Tap

The Brewery Tap is a free house, with award-winning beers from its own brewery and authentic Thai food.

Negotiate your way through the menu of snacks, noodles, stir fries and curries, with good vegetarian options in every section. Lunchtimes also offer Thai-style sandwiches and soups, and there are special vegetarian set meals at Christmas.

An extensive, 200+ seat venue with a large dance floor and a late licence on Fridays and Saturdays, it's popular with party bookings. If you're in the mood for decent Thai food, with good beer and the opportunity to boogie until the early hours, it's pretty much unbeatable.

- 80 Westgate
  Peterborough PE1 2AA
- 01733 358500
- Serving times:
  Mon-Thurs 12-2.30pm
  & 6-9.30pm
  Fri-Sat 12-late
  Sun 12-2.30pm
  & 6-9pm
- Booking recommended
  Thurs-Sat evenings
- Major credit cards
- Non-smoking area
- Licensed
- 200 seats
- Starters from £3

Cambridgeshire

Cambridgeshire

- Abbotsley
  St Neots PE19 6UL
- 01767 677765
- Serving times:
  Tues-Sun 12-2.30pm
  & 7-9.30pm
  Open, but no food
  served Mondays
- Booking advisable
- Major credit cards
- Non-smoking area
- Licensed
- Children welcome
- 38 seats

Jolly Abbot

Vegans may stampede for the palm heart and courgette risotto with pine nuts and toasted peppers at this organic restaurant on the village green – we wouldn't blame them – and the separate vegetarian menu is bursting with attractive choices like bubble and squeak with sundried tomatoes and mozzarella, and a frittata with guacamole and a red onion salad.

Recognised by the Vegetarian Society, there's a completely organic and vegetarian wine list as well as organic fruit juices for the day's driver.

If you're in town on the first Wednesday of the month (and we think you should make the effort), dive into their all-you-can-eat buffet featuring a different cuisine each month. Booking is essential for these high quality and remarkably good value monthly feasts.

Hertfordshire

- 7 East Barnet Rd
  Barnet EN4 8RR
- 200 yards from
  Sainsbury's
- 020 8364 8220
- Serving times:
  Mon-Sat 5-11.30pm
  Sun 1-11.30pm
- Major credit cards
- Non-smoking area
- Licensed
- Children welcome
- 50 seats
- Starters from £1.95,
  mains from £5.50

Blue Ginger

All Indian vegetarian menus are not the same and we were happily surprised to see vegetable koftas (made from specially selected grated vegetables cooked in a spiced sauce) available. There's also pani poori – wonderfully described as hollow wheat balls like egg shells with a spicy water sauce and chickpeas – for any weight-watching fusspots.

Blue Ginger offers lots of hot and cold starters, fabulous dosas (Indian pancakes made from rice and lentil flour), while children can have a very mildly spiced dosa, which may well start them on a lifetime's addiction. There are also some excellent thalis for the pathologically greedy. The menu is extensive, and Sunday offers a bargain vegetarian buffet for £6.95.

Viva Café

Viva is an internet café with good coffee, veggie breakfasts, baked potatoes, wraps, omelettes, salads and lots of snacks – bagels, baguettes, croissants, crumpets, sandwiches and panini, together with some imaginative vegetarian ways of filling them.

There's also a range of homemade cakes, biscotti, chocolate brownies and other sweet treats, and the café is completely non-smoking over the busy lunchtime period. Their freshly pressed fruit juices are popular in the summer.

If you're in this part of Hertfordshire, Viva café is the ideal place to go for a soya latte whilst checking your emails.

- 16 Bridge St
  Bishops Stortford
  CM23 2JY
- 01279 655531
- Serving times:
  Mon-Sat 8.30-6pm
  Late night Thurs 8pm
  Closed bank holidays
- No credit cards
- Non-smoking 12-2pm
- Not licensed
- Children welcome
- 40 seats
- Sandwiches from £1.40

King William IV

Enjoy the relaxed and intimate atmosphere in this traditional English pub, where you're not going to have to put up with a token selection of meat-free food tacked onto the end of a predominately carnivorous menu. Kick off with one of half a dozen starters, then get another beer in while you try to decide between an asparagus, shallot and broccoli-stuffed puff pastry or the aubergine, pine nut and feta bake. There's up to ten choices, and not a veggie lasagne in sight!

The 'lighter lunch' menu has fewer options (and we're sure they'll correct the typo that lists one of the fish starters as vegetarian) but, with this choice of mains, and food of this quality, we're prepared to forgive.

- 01763 838773
- Serving times:
  Mon-Sat 12-2pm
  & 6.30-9.30pm
  Sun 12-2pm
  & 7-9.30pm
- Booking recommended
  weekend evenings
- Major credit cards
- Non-smoking area
- Licensed
- Children welcome
- 80 seats
- Mains from £9

Hertfordshire

- 1 The Arcade
  Letchworth SG6 3ET
- Serving times:
  Thurs-Sat 10am-3pm
- No credit cards
- Non-smoking
- Licensed
- Children welcome
- 40 seats
- Snacks from £2

Bistro at The Place

This lunchtime bistro in The Place, an arts centre attached to a theatre, is ideal if you fancy a bit of culture with your grub.

Completely vegetarian, they're currently only open Thursday to Saturday, but you will find locally produced ingredients – often from smaller growers – gracing a menu choice which includes eggy brunch items, soup, and more substantial meals such as vegetable and bean casserole (served with home-baked bread) or broccoli, cauliflower and cashew nut curry. Daily specials can feature couscous, falafel, or lentil cake with creamed spinach and rice.

It's a quiet, relaxed space – ideal if you're not keen on rushed, elbow-battering dining – and there's a small wine and beer list to help it all along.

Hertfordshire

- 37 Station Rd
  Letchworth SG6 3BQ
- 01462 680893
- Serving times:
  Mon-Fri 8am-8pm
  Sat 8.30am-10.45pm
  Sun 10am-6pm
- No credit cards
- Non-smoking area
- Licensed
- Children welcome
- 40 seats
- Snacks from £2

Caffeines Bistro

Caffeines is a contemporary café-bar, with soft furnishings and a relaxed atmosphere. They check the meat-free credentials of all their ingredients, so you'll not find yourself wondering if the cheese in that panini really is made with vegetarian rennet.

The menu is American-Mediterranean influenced, with lots of bready options such as bagels and club sandwiches together with a freshly-prepared daily soup, which is usually vegan. Have a glass of wine from their good list to go with it, or select from a range of beers, lagers or freshly-pressed juices.

Caffeines holds monthly South American nights, and the veggie options can include avocado with green chilli and pine nuts, wild mushrooms, spinach enchiladas or baked squash served with refried beans and salad.

Waffle House Restaurant

Close to the Verulamium Museum, Waffle House is at Kingsbury Watermill, which has its own historic charm.

As well as specials like vegetable curries and stroganoffs, not surprisingly there's a good range of waffle-related fare, around half of which is vegetarian. Choose from toppings including garlic mushrooms, hummus and avocado or feta and mozzarella, or resign yourself to a trip to the gym and wallow in sweet selections like pecan nut with butterscotch sauce or the banoffee version with bananas, toffee sauce and flaked chocolate.

Outside heaters make year-round al-fresco dining a distinct possibility, and you'll be glad of their large parking area if you've recently tried to find somewhere to leave the car in St Albans.

- Kingsbury Watermill
  St Michael's St
  St Albans AL3 4SG
- 01727 853502
- Serving times:
  7 days 10am-5.45pm
  Closes 1 hour earlier in winter
- Major credit cards
- Non-smoking
- Not licensed
- Children welcome
- 50 seats and garden area
- Mains from £5

Hertfordshire

Down To Earth Wholefoods

This 100% vegetarian café can get so busy at lunchtimes that it's often a good idea to book if you're planning to visit between midday and 2pm. It's family-run, with the emphasis on good home cooking, and they cater well for vegans.

Choices can include falafel, vegetable curries and chillis, bakes and moussaka. The menu changes regularly and is chalked daily on the blackboard. Children are welcome, and are treated to inexpensive smaller portions, including starters from just £1.50.

Although the café isn't licensed, customers are welcome to bring their own (no corkage charge), and soya milk is available for tea and coffee.

Down to Earth is in a listed building at the opposite end of the road to the level crossing.

- 7 Amwell End
  Ware SG12 9HP
- 01920 463358
- Serving times:
  Mon-Fri 8.30am-5pm
  Sat 9.30am-5pm
- Booking recommended lunchtimes
- No credit cards
- Non-smoking
- Not licensed, but BYO with no corkage
- Children welcome
- 26 seats
- Soup from £1.95

Hertfordshire

137

leicestershire
northamptonshire

Leicestershire

Northamptonshire

City of LEICESTER

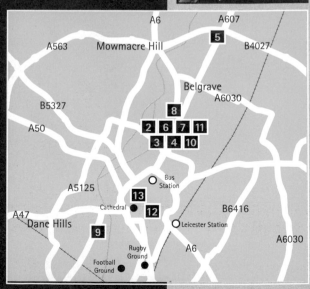

Loughborough □
□ Ashby-de-la-Zouch

□ Melton Mowbray

14 Somerby

■ Leicester

□ Hinckley

1 Church Langton

□ Corby

Market Harborough □

Rothwell **16**

15 Kettering

17 Wellingborough

□ Daventry   □ Northampton

NORTHAMPTONSHIRE

leicestershire • northamptonshire

Leicestershire

- Main St
  Church Langton
  LE16 7SY
- 01858 545181
- Serving times:
  Mon-Fri 12-2pm
  & 6-9.30pm
  Sat-Sun 12-10pm
- Major credit cards
- Non-smoking area
- Licensed
- Children welcome
- 40 seats

The Langton Arms

There's always a decent vegetarian choice at this pub a few miles north of Market Harborough, but we recommend you visit on a Tuesday and take advantage of their vegetarian night.

In addition to the all-week options such as roast butternut squash stuffed with vegetables and mozzarella, you'll be choosing from dishes far removed from the token animal-free fare so often offered in British pubs. There can be braised root veg and beans in tomato and basil sauce, toad in the hole, Lincolnshire bean bake or artichoke and brie tart, as well as a good range of starters and desserts.

The Langton Arms has a snug with an open fire for winter evenings, and a garden for summer dining.

Leicester

Vegetarian Indian Restaurant

Leicestershire

- 147 Belgrave Rd
  Leicester LE4 6AS
- 0116 266 2451
- Serving times:
  Mon 12.30-7.30pm
  Wed-Sat
  12.30-7.30pm
  Sun 1.30-7.30pm
- Major credit cards
- Non-smoking area
- Licensed
- Children welcome
- 40 seats
- Starters from £2.50

Ambica Sweetmart

Ambica is open from lunch until early evening and will satisfy a snack appetite or provide a full-blown feast. Dishes are individually prepared, so don't expect to be in and out in seconds flat.

Delicious snacks, samosas and puris can be followed up with flame-roasted aubergine cooked with tomatoes and spring onions, or old favourites such as pea or spinach paneers. Specials include spiced corn on the cob cooked with cashews, or a vegetarian slant on the very English tikka masala.

There are a couple of thalis, as well as a substantial Sunday special set meal. Sides of naan, parathas, poppadoms and rice are very reasonably priced, and there's a good choice of Indian desserts.

Bobby's

Only a year or two away from celebrating their 30th birthday, Bobby's is a favourite amongst many of Leicester's lovers of Indian food with its warm and friendly atmosphere. It also does a thriving takeaway trade from their shop next door.

Keen not to overwhelm the natural flavour of the ingredients by over-spicing, you won't find fiercely hot vindaloo-style curries; Bobby's favours delicate, subtle flavouring that could make you think you've discovered a whole new cuisine.

If it's a first visit you might want to try one of their thalis (including a smaller, especially mild one for children), but if you decide to plunge in à la carte you're unlikely to go far wrong with any of the choices.

- 154-6 Belgrave Rd
  Leicester LE4 5AT
- 0116 266 0106
- Serving times:
  Tues-Fri 11am-9.45pm
  Sat 11am-10pm
  Sun 11am-9.45pm
- Booking recommended
  weekends
- Major credit cards
- Non-smoking
- Licensed
- Children welcome
- 80 seats

Chaat House

The Chaat House is a long-established (28 years) Indian vegetarian restaurant on Leicester's Golden Mile. Renowned for their masala dosas, this is reputedly a favourite venue of Kapil Dev and his team.

Start with one of the chaats (or, if you're not going for this house speciality, choose from a dozen or more other options) before ordering that rice and lentil pancake stuffed with spicy potatoes and onions served with coconut chutney.

If you're in a group and want to try a larger range of what's on offer, there are also a dozen or so curries and bhajis. Not licensed, and BYO isn't encouraged.

- 108 Belgrave Rd
  Leicester LE4 5AT
- 0116 266 0513
- Serving times:
  Mon & Wed-Sun
  12-8.30pm
  Closed Tues
- Major credit cards
- Non-smoking
- Not licensed
- Children welcome
- 30 seats

- 432 Melton Rd
  Leicester LE4 7SN
- 0116 261 1000
- Serving times:
  Mon-Sat 12-2.30pm
  & 6-10.30pm
  Sun 12-9pm
- Major credit cards
- Non-smoking
- Licensed
- Children welcome
- 170 seats
- Starters from £2.50

Indigo

Open for lunch and dinner all week, with all-day opening on Sundays, Indigo serves Indo-Chinese and south Indian fare. They also have fresh juices (including passion fruit) and an extensive takeaway menu.

There are the trusty Indian dosas, and snack foods of pakoras, samosas, bhajis and the like, plus children's favourites such as potato wedges and chips with cheese and beans.

The main courses generally lean towards the Indo-Chinese, and there's lots of interesting noodly things with Chinese cabbage or various mixed veg together with hot (and not-so-hot) sauces.

The all-you-can-eat lunchtime buffet for around a fiver is particularly good value but, whenever you visit, you'll get a decent meal without breaking the bank.

- 87a Belgrave Rd
  Leicester LE4 6AS
- 0116 266 6186
- Serving times:
  Mon 6-10pm
  Wed-Fri 6-10pm
  Sat-Sun 2-10.30pm
- Booking recommended
  weekends
- Major credit cards
- Non-smoking
- Licensed
- Children welcome
- 70 seats
- Mains from £5

Jalsa Restaurant

On Leicester's 'golden mile' of Indian restaurants and shops, Jalsa offers good snacky food – sev poori and, unusually, a paneer samosa. Meals without onion and garlic are available.

The mains include a baingan barta – grilled aubergine Gujarati style – or maybe you'd prefer a dhal fry (mixed lentils with fresh tomatoes, onion, garlic and coriander) served with parathas, green salad and jeera rice. The dishes – already reasonably priced – include a side salad plus bread or rice.

Interesting sides include Jalsa pilau – steamed rice with spiced vegetables and cubes of paneer – which sounds like a meal in itself. If you must, order a dish of fried chillies – now there's a lager-inspired choice.

Mirch Masala

You know the dilemma: two of you fancy a curry, another refuses to eat anything but pizza and the fourth has a jalapeño habit. Solve the problem by making tracks for Mirch Masala, a highly regarded multi-cuisine eaterie.

Start with samosas or bhel and a main of paneer dosa or mixed veg curry whilst your chums tuck into garlic bread and table-sized pizza, or nachos followed by burrito and fajita. There are lots of favourites on the children's menu, plus a comprehensive snacks selection if you fancy some fries with your tarka dhal.

There are lunchtime specials Monday to Friday together with a good fresh juice bar, and they're planning another branch in the City Centre.

- Unit 19-20 Belgrave Commercial Centre McDonald Rd Leicester LE4 5AU
- 0116 261 0888
- Serving times: 7 days 11-10pm
- Major credit cards
- Non-smoking
- Licensed
- Children welcome
- 65 seats
- Mains from £5

Sakonis

A relative newcomer to the Leicester Indian restaurant scene, but a newcomer that's already sufficiently popular enough to warrant booking on weekends to avoid a possible two hour wait for a table.

Modelled on the successful London Sakoni's branches, the main draw is the all-you-can-eat buffet (£5.99 before 6pm, £7.99 evenings) where you can choose from around 30 Indian and Indo-Chinese dishes including curries, dhals, breads, chilli and mogo chips and more.

If you still fancy a pudding after all that, load up with ice cream or order from the separately-charged dessert menu. Not licensed, but there's a good range of juices and yoghurt drinks.

- 2 Loughborough Rd Leicester LE4 5LD
- 0116 261 3113
- Serving times: Mon 6-9.30pm Tues-Fri 12-9.30pm Sat-Sun 9am-10pm
- Booking essential weekends
- Major credit cards
- Non-smoking
- Not licensed
- Children welcome
- 180 seats
- Lunch buffet £5.99

- 30 Narborough Rd
  Leicester LE3 0BQ
- 0116 299 3300
- Serving times:
  7 days 10am-9.30pm
- No credit cards
- Non-smoking
- Not licensed
- Children welcome
- 50 seats
- Mains from £2.30

Sardaar

Friendly café-style Indian restaurant that's ideal if you're on a budget, and is popular with families and groups for an inexpensive evening out.

Like other pure Indian vegetarian restaurants they use no eggs, which obviously means one less question for the visiting vegan – and they're happy to point out those dishes which might have a drop of milk in. So if you've gone a stage further than just avoiding meat and fish, eat here with confidence.

There's also a counter where you can stock up on Indian savouries and snacks – perfect for that midnight feast you've been promising yourself.

Open 7 days from 10am. Unlicensed.

- 49 Belgrave Rd
  Leicester LE3 0BT
- 0116 266 5888
- Serving times:
  7 days 12-9.30pm
- Major credit cards
- Smoking throughout
- Licensed
- Children welcome
- 70 seats
- Full thali from £6.50

Sayonara Thali Restaurant

As the name implies, Sayonara specialises in thalis – complete meals where you sample a selection of different vegetables, curries, rice and parathas – and they've had more awards and honourable mentions than you can shake a samosa at.

The second string to their bow is a list of dosas – tasty rice pancakes wrapped around a spicy filling. If you aren't feeling as hungry as all that, they offer savoury snacks – patties, mogo chips, bhajias or a single spicy vegetable curry. Parathas come plain or stuffed, and you can slake your thirst with a mango lassi or falooda for around £2.50.

On Leicester's 'golden mile' – work your way along and discover which veggie restaurant is your favourite!

Sharmilee

In the heart of the Belgrave shopping area, this modern restaurant has won several awards since opening in the late 1980s.

With the usual selection of palate-tingling snack foods for starters, there are also south Indian specialities like dosas plus a selection of Chinese dishes prepared in an Indian style. There are plenty of vegetable curries to choose from; okra and tomato, spinach and baby corn, or white chickpeas with chilli and ginger are some of the more unusual choices, or try sweet peppers cooked with a hot and sour mustard curry sauce. There are a couple of thalis, always good value, including the special thali with three curries, two savouries, chutney, poppadoms , salad, rice, bread and dessert. Fully licensed, with a range of Indian beers.

- 71-73 Belgrave Rd
  Leicester LE4 6AS
- 0116 261 0503
- Serving times:
  Tues-Fri 12-2.30pm
  & 6-9pm
  Sat 12-9.30pm
  Sun 12-9pm
- Booking recommended
  Sat evenings
- Major credit cards
- Smoking throughout
- Licensed
- Children welcome
- 60 seats
- Mains from £4.25

tuckinn

Not a completely vegetarian takeaway, but very conscious of and committed to providing good vegetarian food. Staff are trained to have more than a passing knowledge of how to look after vegan and vegetarian customers, and the founders of the group are both non-meat eaters.

Open early for their bargain mix-and-match breakfast baguettes and rolls (including veggie sausage options), you can enjoy a substantial start to the day for little more than a couple of quid.

Lunchtimes are busy with trade from shoppers and workers, and you can choose sandwiches, jackets, salads and other café favourites, confident that they take great care to prepare and cook the meat-free choices separately. Let's hope the influence spreads.

- 40 Church Gate
  Leicester LE1 4AJ
- 0116 251 7077
- Serving times:
  Mon-Fri 7.30am-3pm
  Sat 8am-3pm
- No credit cards
- Not licensed
- Sandwiches from £1.10

- 19 Free Lane
  Leicester LE1 1JX
- 0116 262 6260
- Serving times:
  Mon-Fri 12-3pm
  Sat 12-4pm
  Closed bank holidays
- No credit cards
- Non-smoking area
- Licensed
- Children welcome
- 100 seats

The Good Earth

Opened in 1965 by local jazz musician Sonny Monk, The Good Earth is a landmark centrally located Leicester restaurant now run by his daughter Caroline van Dijk.

Using ingredients sourced daily from Leicester's famous market, and with a cosy farmhouse style, The Good Earth offers a great range of freshly prepared classic English – as well as Mediterranean influenced – dishes. Your choice of soups can include roasted tomato, rocket and mascarpone, red pepper and butternut squash or carrot, parsnip and apple. Mains may include a West Country cider bake with a cheddar pastry crust, or roasted leek with goat's cheese. Vegans are also well looked after: as well as a soup, some of the bakes – including the Mediterranean potato – are free of eggs and dairy produce. There's also a self-serve buffet section featuring up to five interesting and freshly prepared salads.

The dessert section normally runs to seven or eight choices: pecan pie, or blueberry and raspberry syllabub often feature, as do vegan date or apricot slices. Licensed, they offer a range of beers and wine – but if you don't fancy alcohol with your meal, why not try the homemade lemonade or freshly pressed apple juice.

Downstairs from the restaurant there's a shop selling frozen ready meals prepared in The Good Earth kitchens, and Caroline organises three or four gourmet evenings a year. These are very popular with local vegetarians and, even with the relatively large 100 seater dining room, can get fully booked well in advance. Call early if you want to join in.

Old Brewery Inn

The Old Brewery Inn is a pub with its own courtyard brewery, which you can book up to take a trip around and enjoy samples of their prize-winning beers (some of which are mind-blowingly strong) before settling down for dinner.

Soak it all up with specials such as mozzarella and leek macaroni cheese, wild mushroom tagliatelle, hazelnut and vegetable cranberry crumble or a mushroom stir fry, or choose from the regular menu between dishes like homemade vegetable curry or spinach and mascarpone lasagne.

There's a more limited range on the snacks menu (a couple of jackets, baguettes or ploughmans) but at least there's a children's option in the veggie grills with chips.

- High St
  Somerby LE14 2PZ
- 01664 454777
- Serving times:
  Tues-Thurs 12-2pm
  & 7-9pm
  Fri-Sat 12-2pm
  & 7-9.30pm
  Sun 12-2.30pm
  Open bank holiday
  Mondays
- Booking recommended
  weekends
- Major credit cards
- Non-smoking
  restaurant
- Licensed
- Children welcome
- 38 seats
- Mains from £5

Lee Garden

Lee Garden is the place our Northamptonshire veggie friends travel to when the need for a Chinese becomes overwhelming. Although by no means totally vegetarian, it still offers some good choices including the Vegetarian Feast set meal of mixed hors d'oeuvres, spicy chopped mixed vegetables in a golden basket, mangetouts in garlic sauce, bean curd prepared in both sweet and sour and Szechaun sauces, Singapore-style fried rice and The Three Mushrooms (not singing, unfortunately!).

You can also construct your own feast, à la carte, but it'll take a bit of rummaging around the menu. You could always enjoy one of their Chinese beers while you do, though.

- 2 Horsemarket
  Kettering NN16 0DJ
- 01536 483188
- Serving times:
  7 days 12-1.45pm
  & 6-11pm
- Booking recommended
  Sat evenings
- Major credit cards
- Smoking throughout
- Licensed
- Children welcome
- 100 seats

Northamptonshire

- 3 Market Hill
  Rothwell
  Kettering NN14 6EP
- 01536 712345
- Serving times:
  Mon-Sat 12-1.45pm
  & 6-10.45pm
  Sun 1-10.45pm
- Major credit cards
- Non-smoking area
- Licensed
- Children welcome
- 50 seats
- Starters from £4

Thai Garden Cuisine

Fancy a Thai meal in Northamptonshire, but at a restaurant where you're not going to have to bend the waiter's ear with endless questions on ingredients?

Make tracks for Thai Garden. This town centre Thai clearly lists the meat-free options and you can choose from half a dozen starters (including deep-fried aubergine, crisp bean curd simply prepared with salt and pepper, and lettuce-wrapped veg with a plum sauce), grab a mid-course vegetarian soup, and then dive into one of their dozen or so mains, including more Chinese-style dishes such as tofu with Szechaun sauce.

Arranged over three floors of a listed building, with just a handful of tables on each, this can feel like a very private dining experience.

Northamptonshire

- 33 Alma St
  Wellingborough
  NN8 4DH
- 01933 278800
- Serving times:
  Tues-Sun 6-11pm
- Major credit cards
- Non-smoking
- Licensed
- Children welcome
- 30 seats
- Starters from £1.75

Pooja

This simply decorated Indian restaurant is largely vegan, with a vast array of starters including bhel poori – Bombay mix with potato, onion, chana and tamarind sauce, and cocktail dhal wada – spicy fried pulse balls stuffed with onion.

The main course choice is equally daunting, featuring many regional Indian cuisines – from the baby corn chilli paneer in the China Gate section to the paper dosas (crispy thin pancake served with lentil soup and coconut chutney) from southern India. You can also enjoy thicker stuffed savoury uthappam pancakes and an excellent selection of paneer and curry dishes.

A bonus is being able to stock up on Indian sweets and savouries from the counter section.

derbyshire
lincolnshire
nottinghamshire

derbyshire • lincolnshire • nottinghamshire

Derbyshire

Lincolnshire

Nottinghamshire

- derbyshire
- lincolnshire
- nottinghamshire

□ Scunthorpe   □ Grimsby

NOTTINGHAMSHIRE

LINCOLNSHIRE

5 Glossop

Hathersage
6

□ Gainsborough   □ Louth

xton
□

nford-in **1 8** Rowsley   **3** Chesterfield
e-Water
Birchover **2 7** Matlock   **13** Wellow
4 Cromford
9

□ Worksop

11 Lincoln

Skegness **12**

□ Newark-on-Trent

10 Boston

Wirksworth
□ Derby   ■ Nottingham   □ Grantham

DERBYSHIRE

□ Spalding

City of NOTTINGHAM   □ Stamford

A611 A60
19   B684
B682

A610
A6130

20
A6130   A610   Bus Station ○

Leisure Centre ●   Victoria Centre ●

Theatre Royal ● **15**

A609   **14**   **18**

21 **17**   Ice Stadium ●

Broadmarsh Centre ●   ● Lace Hall
Castle ●

A6200   A6005   ○ Nottingham Station

A6005   A453   A60

16 (2 miles)   0   0.25   0.5

Miles

153

Derbyshire

- 3 Fennel St
  Ashford In The Water
  DE45 1QF
- By Sheepwash Bridge
- 01629 812488
- Serving times:
  Mon Wed Thurs Sat
  Sun 2.30-4.30pm
  Closed Tues and Fri
- No credit cards
- Non-smoking
- Not licensed
- Children welcome
- 20 seats
- Light afternoon tea
  from £3.00

Cottage Tearoom

The location has it all. A delightful stone cottage on an old drovers' road by a ford close to Sheepwash Bridge. Open afternoons only and offering a range of set teas, the Cottage Tearoom offers good company and conversation. The teas have a Famous Five quality, where every loaf and scone is freshly hand kneaded, home baked, and served with a pot of Cottage Blend tea.

Travel back to a gentler age with a full afternoon tea – the herb scone variety (cheese-topped scones with a slice of date and walnut loaf) is particularly appealing – and the wide range of teas and coffees will delight a connoisseur's heart. Hats off to Mr William Watkins for this quintessentially English establishment.

Birchover

Derbyshire

- Main St
  Birchover DE4 2BL
- 01629 650302
- Serving times:
  Tues-Sun 12-1.45pm
  & 7-9pm
  Evening last orders
  slightly earlier in
  Jan & Feb
- Booking advisable
- Major credit cards
- Non-smoking except
  terrace and foyer
- Licensed
- 90 seats & terrace
- Starters from £3.40,
  mains from £8.50

Druid Inn

Just outside the village in some wonderful walking country, the Druid Inn is a beautiful stone building, recently restored after a fire in 2002.

The menu has some substantial vegetarian mains: a puff pastry vegetable Wellington with stilton and two sauces, a vegetable hot pot with red cabbage, chilli and rice, plus deep fried brie with redcurrant and orange jelly, garlic bread and potted cheddar with walnuts, apple and celery. Also on offer are tempting desserts like raspberry crème brulée or apple and marzipan tart.

Even more tempting is the wine list, which also has a good range of half- and quarter-bottles if you were hoping to do something useful with the rest of the day.

Natural Choice Café

Winners of a coveted BBC Vegetarian Green Gourmet award, Paul and Dorothy Pennington's Natural Choice Café is in the heart of Chesterfield's historic Shambles, just off Market Place. Everything is made on the premises, and the menu varies with the season. Opening for breakfast at 9am, options later in the day include an eclectic range of sandwiches – savoury vegetarian sausage with chilli and onion or hot cheese with pineapple chutney for example – together with pizza, pasties and jackets. You can even ask for soya cheese with your ploughmans.

The specials board can feature savoury roasts, mushroom creole, goulash, leeks in white wine, and a range of curries. As you would hope, all eggs are free range and only organic flour is used; there's also an impressive range of vegan and gluten-free options.

If you're just dropping in for rapid refreshment during a day scouring the market for bargains, or having visited Chesterfield's answer to the Tower at Pisa (does it seem to straighten up after a night on the tiles we wonder?), try the homemade lemonade, a wonderful yoghurt and blackcurrant cocktail, or their own mulled apple juice, the perfect warming pick-me-up. Caffeine addicts are also well catered for with a range of coffees including soya cappuccino. Takeaway snacks and coffees are available all day.

If you're in the area during December, Natural Choice's Christmas lunch menu is extremely popular with locals, and they're very happy to cater for larger festive lunch parties with a little advance notice.

- 5 Long Shambles Chesterfield S40 1PX
- 01246 558550
- Serving times: Mon–Fri 9am–4.30pm Sat 9am–4pm Closed bank holidays
- Major credit cards
- Non-smoking
- Not licensed
- Children welcome
- 42 seats
- Snacks from £2.50

Derbyshire

155

Derbyshire

- The Promenade
  Scarthin
  Cromford DE4 3QF
- 01629 823272
- Serving times:
  Mon-Sat
  10am-5.30pm
  Sun 12-5.30pm
- No credit cards
- Non-smoking
- Not licensed
- Children welcome
- 20 seats

Scarthin Books Café

Tucked away from the marketplace, seek out this café in a superb bookshop by the village pond. Inhabiting a one-time domestic kitchen, there are only 20 seats, but you do get to look out onto the comings and goings in the shop itself.

There's normally some vegan goodies available, and gluten-free cake, and they try to use locally grown (occasionally from their own garden) organic produce where possible. Choose from dishes such as soup, homity pie, pizza, nut loaf, and mushroom pâté, all with salad or bread. They support an Apple Day celebration each October, with fruit crushing outside on the prom – worth a trip in itself.

In an attractive village, they're open every day except Christmas and Boxing Day.

Glossop

Vegan Restaurant

Derbyshire

- High St West
  Glossop SK13 8HJ
- 01457 852417
- Serving times:
  Mon & Wed bar
  hotpot available
  Thurs-Sat 5.30-9pm
  Sun 1-9pm
  Closed Tues
- Booking advisable
- No credit cards
- Non-smoking
- Licensed
- Children welcome
- 20 seats

The Globe

Right on the edge of Derbyshire's spectacular Peak District is The Globe – an unusual but welcome combination of real ale free house, live music venue and 100% vegan restaurant.

The cosy 20-seat restaurant is open evenings Thursday-Sunday, as well as for Sunday lunch, with bar snacks and hot pot available on Monday and Wednesday evenings. All mains (choose from the ever-changing menu on the blackboard) come with a salad selection, veg and potatoes, and a complete three course meal will set you back less than £10. Naturally, you'll find a great choice of vegan wines and beers. But it's not only vegans who'll enjoy eating here – Paula's cooking earned them a finalist place in 'The Publican' food awards.

Longlands Eating House

Open for lunch and snacks, Longlands is a proper caff with some good vegetarian options: quornburgers and salad, chickpea casserole with naan, filled jacket potatoes and a good selection of very reasonably priced cakes. There's also a children's menu featuring veggie sausages and chips, which reverses the trend and offers adult portions, a neat idea.

Alcohol can be served as part of meal, so you can have beans on toast and a glass of chardonnay if you feel so inclined. Breakfasts are available on Saturday and Sunday mornings, and they'll do you a fruit smoothie in the summer.

It's right next door to the petrol station, so your car can refuel at the same time.

- Main Rd
  Hathersage S32 1BB
- Above outdoor
  equipment shop
- 01433 651978
- Serving times:
  Mon 11am-4.45pm
  Tues-Fri 10am-4.45pm
  Sat-Sun 9am-5.30pm
- Major credit cards
- Non-smoking room
- Licensed
- Children welcome
- 55 seats
- Light meals from £2.50,
  mains from £5

Good For You World Food

This friendly co-op run café has a wholefood shop and also functions as a community centre. It goes without saying they are child friendly, with a play area. You can also book your private party here.

The soup and at least two daily specials are vegan, and there are plenty of gluten-free options from a mainly organic menu with specials that change every few days. There are light soups in summer, chunky ones for winter, gluten-free pasta salads, potato and vegetable bakes, different curries and red onion tarts. Look out for the mixed vegan fry-up, and the half price children's specials. Also on offer: takeaway sandwiches, no-bacon butties, cakes, crumbles and flapjacks – some vegan – and fair trade tea and coffee.

- 23 Firs Parade
  Matlock DE4 3AS
- 01629 584304
- Serving times:
  Mon-Sat 10am-4.30pm
  Cakes & drinks only
  after 3.30pm
- Major credit cards
- Non-smoking
- BYO with no corkage
- Children welcome
- 35 seats
- Snacks from £2.50

Derbyshire

- Caudwell's Mill
  Craft Centre
  Rowsley DE4 2EB
- 01629 733185
- Serving times:
  7 days 10am-5.30pm
  Last orders 4.30pm
  Nov-Mar
- No credit cards
- Non-smoking
- Not licensed
- Children welcome
- 54 seats
- Lunch specials
  from £5.85

Caudwell's Country Parlour

Caudwell's Mill Craft Centre, home to a variety of craft shops and glass, ceramic and woodturning workshops, also houses this completely vegetarian restaurant and tearoom.

The menu features a good selection of soups and pâtés, and the bakes – which can include pear and stilton quiche, homity pie, and leek and pepper croustade – are all made from flour produced at the on-site watermill. If it's on the board when you visit, try the apricot and cashew nut patties served with a hot salsa. There's also a great range of cakes, cholesterol-free fruit slices, puddings and teas as well as soya milk for the visiting vegan. During the winter – November through March – please note that last orders are a little earlier.

Derbyshire

- Crown Yard
  Wirksworth DE4 4ET
- 01629 822020
- Serving times:
  Tues-Sat 9am-3pm
  Sun 10am-2.30pm
- No credit cards
- Non-smoking
- Licensed
- Children welcome
- 30 seats
- Starters from £2.50,
  mains from £5.50

Crown Yard Kitchen

Special diets can be catered for at this café in a heritage centre which is also home to a pottery and silversmith. The café has a patio and is completely non-smoking.

No two menus are the same as they are updated each day, and everything is freshly prepared – no frozen food here. You may find grilled goat's cheese with sundried tomatoes, peppered parsnip soup or garlic mushrooms with pistachio and ginger, spinach and ricotta croquettes, spiced vegetable fajitas and lots of varieties of fruit pies and flans for dessert.

Enjoy summer cocktails and sangria, with mulled wine for the winter – perfect fortification after a hike through the Derbyshire countryside.

Maud's Tearoom

Adjoining a working windmill which grinds the flour for their scones, this simply-styled tearoom provides hot lunch specials as well as teas, and there's normally a vegan option as well as good vegetarian choices (the owners previously ran a completely vegetarian kitchen). The weekend brunch has a veggie option, and the miller's lunch features handmade vegetarian cheese.

You can also indulge in some fine old-fashioned puddings of the spotted dick, chocolate or jam sponge variety, or sample a wide variety of cakes – all of which are vegetarian. Choose your drink from a good selection of speciality teas and coffee.

Seasonal opening hours apply – do check if you're making a special journey.

- The Maud Foster Mill
  Willoughby Rd
  Boston PE21 9EG
- 01205 352188
- Serving times:
  Wed 10am-4pm
  Sat 11am-4pm
  Sun 12-4pm
  July-August also open
  Thurs-Fri 11am-4pm
  Open many bank holidays
- Major credit cards
- Non-smoking
- Not licensed
- Children welcome
- 40 seats
- Mains from £6

Pimento Tearooms

We could give you directions to find this small café and tearoom in Steep Hill, but we suggest it's simpler just to follow the aroma of roasting coffee... Sharing part of their space with the local speciality tea and coffee merchants, expect a decent brew as well as a great range of home-produced cakes – courtesy of members of the local Women's Institute.

There's always snacks, soup and jackets – with interesting fillings such as courgette and red onion or garlic mushrooms and white stilton – and daily specials which can include the vegan butter bean and tomato bake, vegetable and bean goulash or spicy casserole.

There's a small courtyard area if you're visiting in the summer, and locally produced Belvoir pressés.

- 26 Steep Hill
  Lincoln LN2 1LU
- 200 yards from Cathedral
- 01522 544880
- Serving times:
  Mon-Sat 10am-4.45pm
  Sun 10.30am-4.45pm
- Major credit cards
- Non-smoking
- Not licensed, BYO with no corkage
- Children welcome
- 35 seats

Lincolnshire

Lincolnshire

Skegness

Lincolnshire

Omnivorous Restaurant

- 29 Lumley Rd
  Skegness PE25 3LL
- 01754 767298
- Serving times:
  7 days 9am-9.30pm
  Last orders earlier
  in winter
- Major credit cards
- Non-smoking area
- Licensed
- Children welcome
- 65 seats

Copper Kettle Restaurant

Brace yourself, this is one of the only restaurants in Skegness to do a decent range of meat-free food, so if you know you'll be holidaying in this vegetarian desert, take their number with you.

The Copper Kettle is a charming oak-beamed traditional restaurant. Visit in the morning for their full veggie breakfast (including a smaller version for the kiddies), or pop in for a lunch of mushroom stroganoff, curry, chilli, salads, soups and a range of cruelty-free sides. The evening choices are similar, but with the addition of a chilli Grapler – a plate of chips smothered in vegetable chilli served with salad.

Give them a bell if you're planning an evening visit out of season – they sometimes close a little earlier.

Newark

Nottinghamshire

Omnivorous Pub

- Newark Rd
  Wellow
  Newark NG22 0EA
- 01623 861026
- Serving times:
  Mon-Sat
  11.30am-9.30pm
  Sun 12-9pm
- Booking recommended
  weekends
- Major credit cards
- Non-smoking
  except bar
- Licensed
- Children welcome
- 70 seats and garden
- Mains from £4.95

Durham Ox

The Durham Ox is a popular community pub in a 17th century coaching inn with a big garden. You can order food all day and the vegetarian selection can be prepared in smaller portions if you only fancy a light bite.

The main courses are pub standards, but there are lots to choose from: broccoli and hazelnut bake, leek and pasta mornay, leek and mushroom crumble, moussaka, two lasagnes and Thai noodles among other choices. Everything comes with salad, peas and chips, roast, boiled or jacket potatoes. There are cheap deals early in the evening or if you are a senior citizen. Good range of wine and beers, as you might expect. Book your table at weekends.

Alley Café Bar

With a modern, funky look, regular exhibitions of local artists' work, and guest dj's supplying the sounds, this is a place to chill out and eat well.

Snack on sandwiches – with fillings like smoked tofu and roast pepper with coriander mayo – grab some sides like sweetcorn fritters with a chilli dip or the vegan potato and parsnip cakes with bacon-style bits, or go the whole hog and choose a tempeh burger with fries, blackbean burrito, or a pizza with pretend ham and salami. Local organic growers supply a good deal of their ingredients.

You can enjoy a vegan milkshake or a fresh fruit cocktail, and there's a good range of wine and beer.

- Cannon Court
  Long Row West
  Nottingham NG1 6JE
- 0115 955 1013
- Serving times:
- Mon-Tues 11am-6pm
  Wed-Sat 11am-9.30pm
- Major credit cards
- Smoking throughout
- Licensed
- 30 seats
- Mains from £4.25

Antalya Restaurant

There's plenty of choice from the cold meze, hummus, tarator, stuffed vine leaves plus a few goodies on the hot starters – garlic mushrooms, or fried filo parcels with cheese and grilled halloumi.

There's also a separate selection of vegetarian mains including a moussaka and rice and guvec (a sort of Turkish ratatouille but much more savoury), or you could have a large selection of the cold hors d'oeuvres. Side orders include canteen favourites: chips and peas, or a feta salad. Finish with wonderful strong and sweet Turkish coffee or refreshing apple tea.

This would be a good place for a group outing; they also have a function room for special events. Book the outdoor seating in summer.

- 34 Forman St
  Nottingham NG1 4AA
- 0115 953 7788
- Serving times:
- 7 days midday-midnight
- Major credit cards
- Smoking throughout
- Licensed
- Children welcome
- 140 seats
- Starters from £2.50, mains from £8

- 14-16 Wollaton Rd
  Beeston
  Nottingham NG9 2NR
- 5 mins from
  Beeston bus station
- 0115 943 1000
- Serving times:
  Tues-Thurs 6-9pm
  Fri 6-10pm
  Sat 12-2.30pm
  & 6-10pm
- Booking recommended
  Fri & Sat evenings
- Major credit cards
- Non-smoking
- Licensed
- Children welcome
- 32 seats
- Starters from £3.25,
  mains from £7.50

Food Mountains

This restaurant succeeds in providing a global range of vegetarian and vegan food. Often 'global' is a euphemism for 'dog's breakfast' but here the menu is planned with love, expertise and interest. The starters and mains selection changes every couple of months but, if it's on, you might fancy the Indian 'bouncing' potatoes, if only for the daft name. These spicy balls of potato are flavoured with chilli and ginger, battered, fried and served with a coconut and coriander chutney. Half of the starters are vegan and, like the wheat-free options, are clearly marked. Salads come as side dishes or main portions.

The main courses range from tarts, pasta bakes and moussakas to curries (potato or coriander and coconut), enchiladas and a tower of blinis – tender yeast pancakes with mushroom and fennel sauce and salad.

Desserts, including vegan options, are on the blackboard, but you should consider the homemade ice cream sundaes; vanilla, honey and lemon ice cream with banana, fruit syrup and whipped cream is just one combination that seems likely to hit the spot.

On Sundays and Mondays you can hire the restaurant for private parties, when they can do you a very fine all-you-can-eat buffet, and recently Food Mountains started opening on Saturday lunchtimes: select two courses for just £9.50, or a starter and salad for under a fiver.

The quality and ambition of this restaurant puts it amongst the very best. Definitely worth a visit if you're in the area.

Pretty Orchid

Good enough for the Sultan of Brunei, so good enough for us! His former chef is the owner and head chef here, and there's a vegetarian set menu for two or more, with tom yum soup, monk's choice platter – lots of different goodies like spring rolls, vegetable satay, tempura and sushi – yellow curry and stir fried bean sprouts. If there are four of you, they'll add ginger mock duck and Singapore noodles sans the fishy bits.

If you're the only vegetarian, the choices are still good, so don't feel as though you have to hug the vegetable satay with peanut sauce all to yourself. All noodle and rice dishes can be made vegetarian. There's an extensive wine list featuring some organic choice.

- 12 Pepper St
  Bridlesmith Gate
  Nottingham NG1 2GH
- Behind M&S
- 0115 958 8344
- Serving times:
  Mon-Fri 12-3pm
  & 6.30-10.45pm
  Sat 12-10.45pm
  Sun 12-3pm
  & 6.30-10.15pm
- Booking recommended
  Sat evenings
- Major credit cards
- Non-smoking area
- Licensed
- Children welcome
- 80 seats
- Set meal from £15

Squeek

Reservations are essential most nights, but especially at weekends – which is not surprising when you read the glowing reviews from local and national press.

Start off with olives and focaccia and then glide into the realm of parsnip and rosemary fritters with chilli apple chutney, maybe followed by fresh fig and ricotta blinis with leaf salad and red onion marmalade. No? Try the warm muffins with 'bacon' and french bean chardonnay cream sauce, and then the roast shallot, tofu and organic ale casserole with spring onion mash and roast carrots. The menu changes monthly, and vegan options are marked.

Desserts are less baroque – white chocolate and blueberry cheesecake, sticky toffee pudding or cheese and oatcakes with homemade beetroot chutney.

- 23-25 Heathcoat St
  Nottingham NG1 3AG
- 0115 955 5560
- Serving times:
  Mon-Sat 6-10pm
- Booking recommended
- Major credit cards
- Non-smoking except
  for very small area
- Licensed
- Children welcome
- 45 seats
- 2 courses from £13.95

163

- 245 Gladstone St
  Nottingham NG7 6HX
- 0845 458 9595
- Serving times:
- Café Fri-Sun
  10am-6pm
- Bar Thurs-Sat
  6.30-11pm
  & Sun 12-5pm
- Bar for members and
  guests only
- No credit cards
- Non-smoking area
- Licensed for
  members only
- Children welcome
- Snacks from £1.50

Sumac Centre

Situated in a centre that is home to environmental, animal rights, peace and social change organisations – and sharing a room with a private members' bar – this café is completely vegan. They serve largely organic, fair trade food, and you can choose from snacks, a full breakfast, main courses such as mushroom au gratin with green and couscous salads or chestnut and aubergine bourguignon, or simply enjoy their selection of cakes. There is a separate children's menu offering, for example, vegan sausage sandwiches and BLTs. Among the drinks are soya shakes, smoothies and a hot mocha with ice cream float (mmm!), but you need to be a member or guest to indulge in anything alcoholic.

In fine weather, you can sit outside by the developing organic garden.

- 375 Alfreton Rd
  Nottingham NG7 5LT
- 0115 970 3333
- Serving times:
- Mon-Sat
  11am-2pm & 5-9pm
- Booking
  recommended
- No credit cards
- Non-smoking
- Not licensed, BYO
  with no corkage
- Children welcome
- 14 seats
- Starters from £2.50

The Vegetarian Pot

The Vegetarian Pot has a 20-year reputation for serving high-quality food, and the short menu is composed of Indian favourites in addition to rarer dishes such as slow-cooked stuffed marrow and steamed baby cucumber. The majority is vegan, including one of the thalis, and dishes which do contain dairy produce are clearly marked. Whatever you choose, expect to enjoy food which has been prepared with care, using the freshest ingredients.

It's a small restaurant with very limited seating so, unless you're prepared to be disappointed, do book rather than turn up on spec, and bring your own bottle – there's no charge for corkage.

V1

- 7 Hounds Gate
  Nottingham NG1 7AA
- 0115 941 5121
- Serving times:
  Mon-Sat 8am-6pm
  Sun 12-4pm
- Major credit cards
  over £5
- Non-smoking
- Not licensed
- Children welcome
- 70 seats
- Burgers from £2.50

Just around the corner from Marks & Spencer in the centre of Nottingham, V1 was set up by Tamsin Evans, a vegan, who in her words was "fed up with not being able to find fast food I could eat in the city centre". Subsequently nominated many times, V1 is a previous winner of a Vegetarian Society award.

Not surprisingly, the menu is completely vegetarian, and the café is also very aware of gluten-free and vegan diets. Pick up one of their information sheets for the lowdown on exactly which dishes and sauces are wheat- or dairy-free, or ask for the complete ingredients list. These people take what does (and doesn't) go into their food very seriously.

Available throughout the day is a huge range of burgers (all of them vegan) including spicy – potato and mixed spice with a hot salsa sauce, nut – with veg and rice or the beany, with rice, tofu and vegetables. If you prefer a more 'meaty' texture there's the ranch and the VLT. And if you visit in the morning try one of the breakfast baps – sausage, rasher and beans in a bun, served until 11am.

Don't fancy a burger? Try the soup, ratatouille or chilli, or choose from a wide selection of sides. There's also a children's 'jungle box', and they're very happy to help you organise and hold children's parties with them. V1 can also supply your corporate vegetarian cold buffet for a meeting or conference. Now, just where did we leave that Nottingham commercial estate agency info?

essex • norfolk • suffolk

Essex

Norfolk

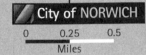

City of NORWICH

0   0.25   0.5

Miles

Suffolk

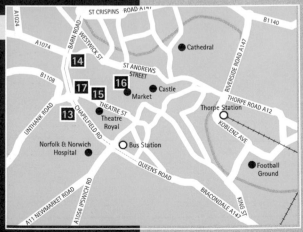

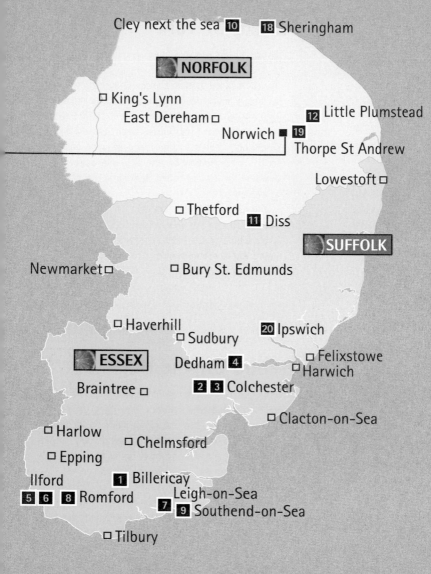

Cley next the sea **10**   **18** Sheringham

NORFOLK

King's Lynn

East Dereham

12 Little Plumstead

Norwich **19**

Thorpe St Andrew

Lowestoft

Thetford

11 Diss

SUFFOLK

Newmarket

Bury St. Edmunds

Haverhill

20 Ipswich

Sudbury

ESSEX

Felixstowe

Dedham **4**

Harwich

Braintree

2 3 Colchester

Clacton-on-Sea

Harlow

Chelmsford

Epping

Ilford

1 Billericay

5 6 8 Romford

Leigh-on-Sea

7

9 Southend-on-Sea

Tilbury

essex • norfolk • suffolk

Billericay

Omnivorous pub

- Southend Rd
  South Green
  Billericay CM11 2PR
- 01277 651403
- Serving times:
  7 days 12-2pm
  & 7-10pm
  Closed on bank
  holidays
- Booking recommended
  weekends
- Major credit cards
- Non-smoking
  restaurant
- Licensed
- 50 seats
- Mains from £7.95

Duke Of York

A classic English pub and restaurant, but with a decidedly un-oldeworlde menu of more than 30 vegetarian and vegan choices. Choose from starters such as vegetable dim sum or grilled banana and orange with sherry, and then fortify yourself further with a crispy tofu bake or mixed bean casserole. Not surprisingly there's a wide range of wine and beer, including a selection of real ales, and soya milk is available for tea and coffee. Booking is recommended at weekends.

There are also rumours that The Duke of York, existing on this site since before 1837, has a resident ghost who is in the habit of moving things around if upset. You have been warned.

Colchester

Omnivorous Restaurant

- 28 East Hill
  Colchester CO1 2QX
- 01206 791393
- Serving times:
  Tues 6-9.30pm
  Wed-Sat 12-2.30pm
  & 5.30-9.30pm
  Later servings by
  arrangement
- Booking essential
  weekends
- No credit cards
- Considerate smoking
- Licensed
- Children welcome
- 40 seats
- Mains from £8

Food On The Hill

Food On The Hill deserves inclusion for its imaginative vegetarian and vegan choices. Describing the food as European fusion, the fortnightly-changing menu may find you choosing between a red pepper and cashew loaf, lentil and cider cobbler or a chickpea stew flavoured with coriander, apricots and chilli.

Bread is baked daily, and they produce their own ice cream. Organic produce is often used, and you'll find the staff knowledgeable about the ingredients in any dish. There's also an excellent range of wines, spirits, beers – and great cocktails.

Booking essential at weekends. Ask for one of the tables in the beautiful south facing garden for the perfect summer lunch party.

Garden Café

Next door to the Essex Minories art gallery, this café has a large garden which can quickly fill up in the summer with people picnicking on the wide range of vegetarian food and drink. Choose from freshly prepared vegan soups with home baked organic bread, or try one of their vegetarian cakes with soya cream, which is often available. The lunch menu, served between 12 and 3pm, can include chickpea casserole, cashew nut curry, stuffed peppers, or their very own melenzana parmageni – an aubergine and tomato bake.

Open occasionally in the evenings; themes for these popular events have included Scottish, tapas and curry nights. Booking essential if you want to join in.

- 74 High St
  Colchester CO1 1UE
- 01206 500169
- Serving times:
  Mon-Sat 10am-4.30pm
  Lunch menu served
  12-3pm
  Occasional evening
  opening
- Book for evenings
- No credit cards
- Non-smoking
- Licensed
- Children welcome
- 40 seats and garden
- Mains from £4.90

Essex

Dedham Centre Tearooms

You can't argue (so don't try) with a 'Best Cuppa' recommended, virtually vegetarian tearoom in a listed church building that's also home to a thriving art and craft centre.

For lunch, served between 12 and 2pm, choose from a range of soups – celery and cashew or carrot, courgette and ginger often feature – or one of the regularly changing main course specials. Look out for the leek croustade or a tagliatelle bake, a nut roast or a selection of chillis. There are also always two quiches; try the brie and cranberry if it's on.

Outside of lunchtime there's a good range of interesting cakes and teas, and the café has a small courtyard area, ideal for sunnier days. Can get busy for Saturday and Sunday lunch – book to be sure.

- Dedham Art
  & Craft Centre
  Brook St
  Dedham CO7 6AD
- 01206 322677
- Serving times:
  Full lunch menu
  served 12-2pm
- Booking recommended
  weekend lunchtimes
- Major credit cards
  over £10
- Non-smoking
- Children welcome
- 31 seats
- Mains from £4

Essex

Essex

- 251 Cranbrook Rd
  Ilford IG1 4TG
- 020 8518 4477
- Serving times:
  Mon 6.30-10.30pm
  Tues-Thurs 12-2.15pm
  & 6.30-10.45pm
  Fri 12-2.15pm &
  6.30-11.15pm
  Sat 6.30-11.15pm
  Sun 6.30-10.45pm
- Booking essential
  weekends
- Major credit cards
- Non-smoking area
- Licensed
- Children welcome
- 150 seats
- Mains from £4.25

Masti

A short, clear menu separates the vegetarian goodies from the non-veg. Starters are substantial: tandoori paneer tikka – slow-cooked marinated homemade cottage cheese with tomatoes, onions and pepper – samosas and pakoras with dips or – the chef's own invention – crisp, battered chillies stuffed with yoghurt, cheese and spices.

The main dishes also feature some rarely-found items such as tomatoes stuffed with paneer and vegetables in a sweet and sour sauce.

Another unusual option is the dinner and dance and karaoke on Friday and Saturday evenings, which may well be a decider one way or the other for many potential customers. Book for the first floor if you want to exercise the vocal chords.

Essex

- 506 High Rd
  Ilford IG1 1UE
- 020 8598 2020
- Serving times:
  Mon-Thurs 6-10pm
  Fri 6-11pm
  Sat 12.30-3pm
  & 6-11pm
  Sun 12.30-3pm
  & 6-10pm
- Major credit cards
  over £10
- Non-smoking
- Licensed
- Children welcome
- 52 seats
- Starters from £2.50

Suruchi

About half a mile from the centre of Ilford, Suruchi is undergoing a major refurbishment and promises to reopen with an even more comprehensive menu of south Indian and indo-Chinese cuisine. We hope they retain their Indian food glossary – useful if you've ever confused your bhajis with your bhajias, or ordered what you thought was a main course and ended up with a plate of ice cream. There's currently a lunchtime three course special for around a fiver, and a good range of vegan options which are clearly marked.

They take plastic, but if you're planning to pay this way make sure you go with a friend or two – it's so reasonably priced that you might struggle to spend the £10 minimum credit card bill on your own.

Café Pulse

A small, friendly place, Café Pulse is Essex's only completely vegetarian restaurant. They do breakfasty stuff until noon – including a daunting power breakfast of thick toast, raw garlic, soy sauce, organic sprouting beans, poached egg and parsley.

The quick bites are marinated olives and herb bread, soup and a roll, minty broad bean pâté or warm carrot and tofu cakes with salsa and salad. There are tasty salads, mainly using interesting cheeses like Llangloffan organic garlic and chive, halloumi or feta. Dinner on Friday and Saturday can include pastas, chilli wraps, Glamorgan-style vegetarian sausage and mash or a tofu, red onion and thyme tart with rice salad, broccoli and lemon coconut sauce. More than half the menu is vegan, and there's a good wheat-free choice.

- 80 Leigh Rd
  Leigh on Sea SS9 1BZ
- 01702 719222
- Serving times:
  Mon-Thurs
  9.30am-4pm
  Fri-Sat 9.30am-9.30pm
- Booking recommended evenings
- No credit cards
- Non-smoking
- Not licensed, BYO with no corkage
- Children welcome
- 22 seats

Tropical Emas

Come straight out of the station and through the door of this wide ranging all-purpose oriental restaurant with dishes from Singapore, Indonesia and China. There's always a vegan option, and if you're on a gluten-free diet they're happy to give advice.

Select from around a dozen appetisers including vegetarian crispy duck with pancakes, spring onions and hoi-sin sauce, and 30 mains like vegetarian pad Thai, tofu (in a dozen or more incarnations), noodles, vegetables and cashew nuts in yellow bean sauce, or sweet and sour dishes with soya masquerading as various meats. A couple of set vegetarian meals for two or more people give you a guided tour of the menu without the pain of choosing, and there are lunch buffet deals Monday to Saturday.

- 6 Station Parade
  Victoria Rd
  Romford RM1 2JA
- 01708 752218
- Serving times:
  Mon 6-11pm
  Tues-Thurs
  11.45am-2.15pm
  & 5.30-11pm
  Fri-Sat 12-2pm
  & 5.30-11.30pm
  Sun 3-10pm
- Booking recommended Fri & Sat
- Major credit cards
- Non-smoking area
- Licensed
- Children welcome
- 55 seats

Essex

- 12 Clifftown Parade
  Southend SS1 1DP
- 01702 431313
- Serving times:
  Tues-Sat 12-2.45pm
  & 6-11pm
  Sun 12.30-3.15pm
  & 6.30-10.30pm
- Booking recommended
  weekends
- Major credit cards
- Non-smoking area
- Licensed
- Children welcome
- 50 seats and outside
  area
- Mains from £5

Singapore Sling

There's a dedicated vegetarian section on the menu at this oriental restaurant, with influences drawn from Thailand, Singapore, China and Japan. A generous portion of six spring rolls, crispy seaweed and aromatic or satay quorn make up the appetisers. There are three soups, while main courses include French beans, braised mushrooms and vegetarian spare ribs (honest). Select your own favourite main course sauce from blackbean, ginger and spring onion, sweet and sour, szechuan or salt and chilli.

If you can't decide, there's the option of a vegetarian gourmet set meal which offers mixed hors d'oeuvres, vegetable wrap and four main dishes.

Opposite the bandstand on the front, there's also a patio area overlooking the sea.

Norfolk

- High St
  Cley next the Sea
  NR25 7RN
- 01263 740336
- Serving times:
  Mid-Feb to mid-Nov
  Tues-Sat: dinner
  at 7.30pm
  Sun lunch 12.30-2pm
  (& dinner at 7.30pm
  in high summer)
- Bookings only
- No credit cards
- Non-smoking
- Licensed
- 12 seats

thecafé at Whalebone House

In summer months this restaurant is booked weeks ahead, and for the rest of their year (Feb-Nov) you're still going to have to plan in advance. They use fresh, seasonal produce – often from their own kitchen garden – and with just 12 covers they need to know how much to pull out of the ground, or buy from local – often organic – growers. Deciding what's going to be served at the single-sitting four-course dinner evolves during the day, but expect to find inventive but not over-fussily-presented dishes like saffron and butter bean couscous with watercress, parsley and pink grapefruit salad, celeriac and thyme cakes with puy lentil, white wine and saffron broth and cavalo nero, or coconut and cumin pancakes with spiced aubergine and cabbage and coriander lime oil.

Proper, grown-up dining. Get your booking in now.

Les Amandines

This respected French style café-restaurant is tucked away in the courtyard of a coaching inn which houses speciality retailers: deli, florist and antiques. Very busy at the weekends, they have tables outside in good weather.

There's always something for the vegan – most soups are suitable, as are the stir fries and salads. The influences are mainly British and European, and they cope happily with coeliac and other food intolerances. The menu can include guacamole and hummus dips with olives, salad and bread, chestnut and bean pie with sweet potato chips, pan-fried mushrooms or baked courgettes and cherry tomatoes on root vegetable mash. They're also open on occasional evenings; call for details of the next event.

- Norfolk House
  Courtyard
  St Nicholas St
  Diss IP22 4LB
- 01379 640449
- Serving times:
  Tues-Sat 10am-3.30pm
- No credit cards
- Non-smoking
- Licensed
- Children welcome
- 40 seats
- Specials from £4.50

Omnivorous pub

Little Plumstead

Brick Kilns

This is conscientiously prepared vegetarian pub grub – their specialist cook prepares this menu out of hours, to avoid any possibility of cross contamination.

There's a good vegetarian selection of casseroles, bakes and savoury crumbles, plus some vegan options such as red dragon pie – aduki beans, rice or wholewheat grain, carrots, soya sauce, herbs, onion and tomatoes. The helpful menu lists all ingredients in a dish, in case you're marmite-sensitive or the like. The main courses come with fresh vegetables, homemade chips, or rice and salad. Extra gold star for having vegetarian gravy available on request

It's best to book, especially weekend evenings or Sunday. Children's portions possible.

- Norwich Rd
  Little Plumstead
  NR13 5JH
- 01603 720043
- Serving times:
  7 days 12-2.15pm
  & 7-10pm
- Booking recommended weekends
- Major credit cards
- Non-smoking area
- Licensed
- Children welcome
- 75 seats
- Mains from £6

- 98 Vauxhall St
  Norwich NR2 2SD
- 01603 665066
- Serving times:
  Mon-Fri 7am-5.30pm
  Sat 7am-4pm
- No credit cards
- Hot lunch and salad
  from £1.75

Butlers Vegetarian Takeaway

Using organic and free range products where possible, Butler's inventive cooks offer oven-ready or fully cooked meals. You can't eat in but you can buy a foil-tray bake or take in your own ovenproof dish and they'll let you take the credit for a cashew nut roast or lentil and aubergine bake (among others).

Of interest to the vegetarian who isn't stocking up for home or looking for the perfect vegetarian caterer is the option of picking up a ready-to-eat lunch or picnic.

They make the distinction between flans and quiches, and there are also pies, savoury pancakes, pastas and lasagnes as well as good solid meal salads and cakes to choose from.

- St Benedicts St
  Norwich NR2 4PG
- 01603 660387
- Serving times:
  Mon-Sat 10am-3pm
- No credit cards
- Non-smoking
  downstairs
- Licensed
- Children welcome
- 44 seats

Norwich Arts Centre Café

The Arts Centre café is set in a converted church, next door to a specialist Thai shop which may explain the Thai influence to several of the dishes! About half the menu is vegetarian, with food prepared from organic ingredients wherever possible. Open for coffee and pastries from 10am, meals are served at lunchtime (last orders 3pm) when you can choose from starters such as vegan spinach soup or spring rolls with hot mango pickle, followed by the day's specials which could be winter vegetable crumble or Thai veg noodles. Or go for a veggieburger, a filled baguette, or the £4 veggie breakfast.

The Arts Centre stages music and exhibitions, and runs courses on photography-related new media.

The Greenhouse

This café is in the landmark Norwich Environment Centre, a Grade II* listed building that is a showcase for energy efficient and environmentally benevolent building techniques. With that kind of background, you rightly anticipate a good vegetarian café with fair trade ethics using local organic produce where possible. There are vegan options and they will recommend something appropriate for most special diets. Takeaways also available.

Sandwiches are made on organic bread from a local bakery, there's rye bread for your soup of the day, salad bowls and daily specials and ploughmans with rice cakes if you prefer. Good selection of cordials and extra points scored for pots of organic tea with loose leaves.

- Norwich
  Environment Centre
  42-46 Bethel St
  Norwich NR2 1NR
- 01603 631007
- Serving times:
  Tues-Sat 12-4pm
- Major credit cards
- Non-smoking
- Licensed
- Children welcome
- 40 seats and courtyard
- Daily special from
  £4.70

The Tree House

This cheery café co-op is hard by Norwich Market, with outdoor tables in summer to soak up the atmosphere. Many meals on the daily changing menu are gluten-free, there are sugar-free desserts and they'll work hard to accommodate any other special diets. The starter soups are generally vegan and served with bread for a substantial stopgap, and there's usually a choice of tasty main courses like cashew-topped lentil moussaka, black-eyed beans and courgettes in sweet and sour sauce or potato and butternut squash curry.

Good desserts can include mocha pecan pie, strawberry tofu cheesecake or chocolate banana cake – and there's hot and spicy apple juice, or homemade lemonade and vegan milkshakes in the summer.

- 14-16 Dove St
  Norwich NR2 1DE
- 01603 763258
- Serving times:
  Mon-Wed 10am-4pm
  Thurs-Sat 10am-9pm
  Lunch menu served
  from 11.30am
  Closed bank holidays
  Booking recommended
  for evenings
- No credit cards
- Non-smoking
- Licensed
- Children welcome
- 42 seats
- Starters from £2.95,
  mains from £6.80

Norfolk

- 39 St Giles St
  Norwich NR2 1JN
- 01603 612790
- Serving times:
  Mon-Sat 10am-10pm
  Sun 11am-10pm
- Major credit cards
- Non-smoking area
- Licensed
- Children welcome
- 80 seats
- Mains from £5

The Waffle House

Arrive in the morning for the Waffle House brunch of scrambled free range eggs on light, crisp Belgian waffles served with fried tomatoes and mushrooms, or later in the day for more waffle-related fare, around half of which is vegetarian. Choose from toppings like garlic mushrooms, hummus and avocado or feta and mozzarella, or resign yourself to a trip to the gym and wallow in sweet selections like pecan nut with butterscotch sauce or the banoffee version with bananas, toffee sauce and flaked chocolate. There are also daily specials including vegetarian soups, curries and stroganoffs.

Licensed, and with a good selection of proper milk shakes as well as freshly pressed orange juice, you're unlikely to go hungry or thirsty here.

Norfolk

- 32 High St
  Sheringham NR26 8DT
- 01263 822151
- Serving times:
  Tues-Sat 10am-2pm
  & 6-late
  Sun 11.30am-2pm
- Booking
  recommended
- No credit cards
- Non-smoking
- Licensed
- Children welcome
- 36 seats
- Mains from £8.50

Crofters

Looking more like a Scottish croft than anything traditional Norfolk architecture might have generated, the menu at this north Norfolk coast bistro is rich, the desserts phenomenal and you can choose from more than 60 liqueurs.

There's a bit of vegan choice – for example chargrilled tomato kebab with braised lettuce – but the slant is toward rich and creamy. Mushrooms are stuffed with herbs, chestnuts, cashew and cranberry with a herb crust and served with chive cream sauce, or try the chargrilled vegetarian brie with saffron rice and asparagus cream sauce or strudel milanaise with fresh tomato and oregano sauce.

Throw caution to the wind with alcoholic, creamy pancakes, ice creams or mousses. Way to go.

Norfolk

The Terrace Restaurant

This lunchtime bistro is not completely vegetarian, but still offers a good range of meat-free food.

Vegans can choose from such dishes as potato and butter bean korma, vegetable tempura, Hereford pie, or roasted flat mushrooms with spring onions and pine nuts. Alternatively, start with hummus and olives followed by mushroom stroganoff, or go with a friend and dive into the veggie combo for two featuring falafel, onion bhaji, samosas, pakoras and Cajun-style potato wedges with salsa and a salad.

There is a wide range of coffees, regular and herb teas, as well as lemon and gingergrass pressés, cordials, wine and beer. In fine weather you can sit outside on the terrace by the water feature.

- St Andrews Park
  Thorpe St Andrew
  Norwich NR7 0HS
- 01603 700719
- Serving times:
  Mon-Thurs
  11.30am-3.30pm
  Fri 11.30am-3pm
- Major credit cards
- Non-smoking area
- Licensed
- Children welcome
- 100 seats & terrace
- Starters from £2.50

Suffolk

Kwan Thai

OK, we know many Thai restaurants cater well for vegetarians, but at Kwan Thai you're going to find yourself having to choose between six soups, five starters and a dozen main courses. If can't-decide-itis sets in, there are four set vegetarian menus, for two, three or four sharing. Ease the angst that way.

As you would expect, bean curd features heavily: in the dow hoo phad het horm it is prepared simply with Chinese black mushrooms, while in the more exotic larp het and dow hoo, expect to find flavours of lemon, chilli and red onion.

A small selection of vegan items on the menu includes asparagus salad, sweet and sour vegetables, and at least one of the soups.

- 14 St Nicholas St
  Ipswich IP1 1TJ
- 01473 253106
- Serving times:
  Mon 6-11pm
  Tues-Fri 12-2pm
  & 6-11pm
  Sat 12-2pm
  & 6-11.30pm
- Booking recommended
  on Sat
- Major credit cards
- Non-smoking area
- Licensed
- Children welcome
- 70 seats
- Mains from £4.70

shropshire
staffordshire
west midlands

shropshire • staffordshire • west midlands

Shropshire

Staffordshire

West Midlands

Oswestry □

SHROPSHIRE

□ Leek

Newcastle-under-Lyme□ **6** Stoke-on-Trent

□ Stone □ Uttoxeter

Stafford□ Burton upon Trent□
5
Gnosall

3 Shrewsbury
□ Telford Cannock□ **4** Lichfield

2 Ironbridge □ Tamworth
Wolverhampton □ **14** Walsall

1 Church Stretton

Dudley□ **7** **8**
9 **10** Birmingham
Stourbridge □

Coventry **11** **12** **13**

WEST MIDLANDS

shropshire • staffordshire • west midlands

Virtually Vegetarian Café

Shropshire

- 26 Sandford Avenue
  Church Stretton
  SY6 6BW
- Opposite Barclays
- 01694 722495
- Serving times:
  Mon-Tues & Fri-Sun
  10am-5pm
  Thurs (in school hols)
  10am-5pm
- No credit cards
- Non-smoking
- Not licensed
- 40 seats & garden
- Light meals from
  £3.00

Acorn Wholefood Restaurant

Chris Bland has owned and cooked for the Acorn for more than two decades, which is a tribute to the quality of the goods this café provides.

Approached through an ivy arch, the café is on the first floor and also has its own garden. The Acorn's commitment is to provide quality wholefoods and to cater for people on special diets, so there's often a vegan option and Chris bakes inventive wheat-, sugar- and dairy-free cakes.

Decent lunches, soup and garlic bread, nut roast, ploughman's and baked potatoes are on offer, or you can enjoy a real afternoon tea with homemade cakes, wholemeal scones and plenty of refreshing alternatives to the extensive range of speciality teas and real coffee.

Vegetarian Restaurant

Shropshire

- 16 Barracks Passage
  Shrewsbury SY1 1XA
- 01743 350455
- Serving times:
  Mon-Fri
  9.30am-3.30pm
  Sat 9.30am-4.30pm
  Lunch served from
  11.30am
  Closed bank holidays
- No credit cards
- Non-smoking
- Licensed
- Children welcome
- 60 seats
- Mains from £3

Goodlife Wholefood

In a 14th century building down a passageway near the Lion Hotel, and owned by an experienced dietician, this restaurant is full of yummy, healthy options. There's a choice of around nine freshly prepared salads, or you might go for a lentil and vegetable or parsnip and apple soup served with organic bread, or a main course of spinach moussaka or chilli beanpot. There are quiches of goat's cheese and red pepper, or broccoli and stilton, and desserts like lemon cream flan or fruit crumble.

Vegans are well catered for with, for example, goulash, and there's soya marg, milk and tempting dairy-free puddings. Children are so welcome that you can book their birthday party here (so long as the parents are well-behaved...).

Olivers Vegetarian Bistro

Established in 1987, Olivers was Shropshire's first 100% vegetarian restaurant and offers a unique opportunity to eat in a listed building at a World Heritage Site. With the famous Iron Bridge just 50 yards away, this bistro is a room with a view, and offers tables on the pavement in summer. Ask about their gourmet nights (aren't they all?) and wine tasting evenings.

The daytime menu includes filled baguettes, toasties, baked potatoes, salad and pasta. The blackboard specials are interesting – leek, stilton and potato bake, cashew nut and carrot roast, red bean chilli. There are also afternoon tea goodies like scones and cakes, giant muffins or fruit salad.

The evening menu is more unusual with light starters like couscous with beetroot, mandarins and mixed leaves, or grilled avocado and mozzarella. Main courses can include a vegetable cobbler, a coconut, cauliflower and cashew korma or a delicious stack of wholewheat pancakes with spinach and potato and a smoked cheese sauce. You can order garlic bread with various extras as a side order, and all mains come with Cajun style potatoes and a mixed salad. There's always a vegan choice such as summer veg and hazelnut pie or Thai green curry with wild rice.

Excellent desserts include a black cherry and chocolate cheesecake – fashionably retro – a whole pear in mulled wine and spices, a cheeseboard or a tropical fruit salad glazed with toffee and lime.

Oliver's can cater for most dietary requirements and offers half-size portions for children.

Booking essential most evenings.

- 33 High St
  Ironbridge TF8 7AG
- 50 yards from the
  iron bridge
- 01952 433086
- Serving times:
  Tues-Thurs 7-9pm
  Fri 7-9.30pm
  Sat 12-3pm
  & 7-9.30pm
  Sun 12-5pm
- Booking recommended
  evenings
- Major credit cards
  with 5% surcharge
- Non-smoking
- Licensed
- Children welcome
- 45 seats

Shropshire

Vegetarian Café

- Unit 1&2
  Blewitt Court Bore St
  Lichfield WS13 6LL
- 01543 255879
- Serving times:
  Tues-Sat 10am-4pm
- Major credit cards
- Non-smoking
- Not licensed
- Children welcome
- 22 seats

Romain's Natural Living Café

Access this very English café via the health food shop next door and, on your way out, stock up on some of the goodies that your lunch was prepared with.

The all-day menu of veggieburgers, jackets, sandwiches and falafel-stuffed pitta is bolstered at lunchtime with daily specials such as stroganoff, pasta or a vegan chilli. Brunchy items include a vegetarian sausage-and-egg muffin or a very fine BLT sandwich, and children can be tempted with familiar spaghetti hoops, marmite on toast or veggie nuggets and chips.

Drinks include flavoured soya milk, organic and fair trade teas and coffee (freshly ground on the premises) and, in the summer, fresh fruit smoothies can be enjoyed in the small courtyard area.

Stafford

Vegetarian Tearooms

- The Horn Inn
  23 High St
  Gnosall
  Stafford ST20 0EX
- 01785 822255
- Serving times:
  Mon-Fri 12-3pm
  Sat 10am-5pm
  In summer, open from
  10am on Thurs & Fri
- No credit cards
- Non-smoking
- Licensed
- Children welcome
- 28 seats
- Sandwiches from £2

The Hayloft

This country kitchen style tearoom is attached to a public house, so serves delicious comfort food alongside organic vegetarian wines. You can also just have a cup of tea, but why do that when there are some heavenly homemade vegetarian pâtés on toast, the 'Dad's delight' (toast topped with onion, apple, mushrooms and covered in melted cheese) and that near-legendary savoury, Staffordshire oatcakes – a cross between a scotch pancake and a crumpet, but better and served with garlic mushrooms. Homemade cakes, some vegan, scones and bread pudding topped, if you like, with custard, cream or Swedish Glace induce a childlike sense of wellbeing just thinking about them. Even those on a wheat-free diet can tuck into a chocolate mocha slice.

Zest Bistro

Zest is a small intimate wine bar offering a lunch and early evening bar menu, with a full restaurant menu from 7pm several evenings a week. The vegetarian options change regularly and, as it's run by the people who previously owned Dylan's vegetarian restaurant, there's a good choice of interesting dishes, often featuring home-grown produce. Tasty-sounding ideas such as pine nut, fennel and leek tart, wild mushroom and tarragon risotto, and avocado stuffed with smoked and cream cheese abound, but do remember to book if you're hoping to sample the full evening menu – the restaurant does occasionally close early in the winter.

If you're in a large party they may even open specially, and can produce a completely vegan evening if requested in advance.

- 79 Broad St
  Stoke On Trent ST1 4JQ
- 01782 285111
- Serving times:
  Mon-Tues 12-2.30pm
  Wed-Thurs
  12-2.30pm & 6-9pm
  Fri-Sat 12-2.30pm
  & 6-10pm
  Check for evening
  opening after 7pm
  Bar menu served
  6-7pm Wed-Sat
- Booking advisable
- No credit cards
- Non-smoking
- Licensed
- Children welcome
- 30 seats

Staffordshire

Natural Choice

One of the food franchises operating in the 600 seat food gallery of Birmingham's Pavilion Central shopping centre, Natural Choice is the aptly named café for vegetarians visiting this part of the Bullring's redevelopment. 100% vegetarian – but with a limited vegan selection – the food court is open until 6.30pm Mon-Sat (4.30pm on Sundays).

Choose from freshly prepared soups and salads, or bakes, bhajis or samosas. With coffee, freshly pressed orange juice and a selection of vegetarian cakes and pastries available all day, we're accepting no excuses for an early finish to shopping due to insufficient caffeine or carbohydrate intake. Children's portions, for example cheese pie and beans, served all day.

- Pavilion Central
  High St
  Birmingham B4 7SL
- Next to M&S
- 0121 643 6096
- Serving times:
  Mon-Sat
  9.30am-6.30pm
  Sun 11am-4.30pm
- No credit cards
- Non-smoking
- Not licensed
- Children welcome
- 600 seats in food court

West Midlands

West Midlands

- 569-571 Stratford Rd
  Sparkhill
  Birmingham B11 4LS
- Opposite Lloyds TSB
- 0121 766 7199
- Serving times:
  Tues-Thurs 6-9.15pm
  Fri 12-1.30pm
  & 6-9.15pm
  Sat 1.30-9.15pm
  Sun 1.30-8.30pm
- Booking
  recommended
- Major credit cards
- Non-smoking
- Not licensed, BYO
  with no corkage
- Children welcome
- 56 seats
- Mains from £5

Jyoti

This predominately vegan Indian restaurant has won awards for the quality of its Gujarati and Punjabi cuisine under the experienced and watchful eye of director Mukesh Joshi. The comprehensive menu is inspiring; we'd make sure we went with friends to share, but if you're struggling to cope with this degree of choice, you could always opt for one of three Jyoti thalis.

Starters include black-eyed bean bhajia, cassava chips with a tamarind sauce or the spicy hot masala stuffed whole peppers. The extensive curry section (over 30 choices) includes aubergine and fenugreek, mixed vegetable and spinach, and cauliflower, tomato and pea. There's also one of the greatest ranges of paneer dishes we've seen: no less than eight variations, including this Indian cheese cooked with chilli and spices, wrapped inside aubergine with ginger and garlic, or with the more usual spinach or pea accompaniment.

Dosas – including the special masala dosa filled with potato, onions, pineapple and mild peppers served with a mixed vegetable sauce and coconut chutney – are a meal in themselves, and you'll definitely have to plan a return visit to savour even a fraction of what's on offer.

Not licensed, although there's no corkage charge if you bring your own. Soya milk is also available.

And, if you're planning to slum it at home, grab a copy of the takeaway menu and enjoy the same high quality dishes at a slightly lower price.

Rogans

At Rogans everything is homemade, with mainly organic ingredients, no GM products and a large vegan selection. Lunches are simple – filled baked potatoes, soup of the day, falafel in pitta, Mexican chilli or bhajis, all served with three salads. Try a vegan crumble, apple and raisin tart or flapjack for dessert.

The evening menu is longer and a little more adventurous with dishes like cashew nut pâté, garlic mushrooms, baba ghanoush, lentil lasagne or tomato and olive flan on wholemeal pastry.

Rogans is popular enough for us to recommend booking on Friday and Saturday evenings. Not licensed, but if you bring your own wine they generously don't charge corkage.

- 12 College Rd
  Handsworth Wood
  Birmingham B20 2HX
- 0121 515 3906
- Serving times:
  Tues-Sat 12-2pm
  & 5.30-8pm
- Booking recommended
  Fri & Sat evenings
- No credit cards
- Non-smoking
- Not licensed, BYO
  with no corkage
- Children welcome
- 22 seats
- Snacks from £1.20,
  lunch from £2.90

The Warehouse Café

Not far from the new Bullring, you might be grateful of a break from the shops in this spacious and airy restaurant above Friends of the Earth.

80% of the world-food menu is vegan, they aim to provide locally-sourced organic fare as far as possible, and everything is available in smaller portions for children. Open on Friday and Saturday evenings, look out for special events, like Greek, Mexican or jazz nights, which sell out quickly.

You'll find daily specials on the blackboard, as well as lighter bites including falafel, hummus, black olive pâté with garlic bread, and salads. There's also the tasty Warehouse burgers: peanuts, organic bulgar wheat and vegetables, or tofu, breadcrumbs and sesame.

- 54-57 Allison St
  Digbeth
  Birmingham B5 5TH
- Above Friends
  of the Earth
- 0121 633 0261
- Serving times:
  Mon-Thurs 12-2.30pm
  Fri-Sat 12-3pm
  & 6-9pm
  Closed bank holidays
- No credit cards
- Non-smoking
- Not licensed, BYO
  with no corkage
- Children welcome
- 50 seats
- Snacks from £2

- Earl St
  Coventry CV1 5RU
- 024 7622 1100
- Serving times:
  Mon-Sat 9am-11pm
  Sun 12-6pm
- Major credit cards
- Non-smoking area
- Licensed
- Over 18's only
- 400 seats
- Mains at £5.50

Browns

Almost impossible to describe adequately – Browns is a huge modern café/bar that manages an intimate atmosphere while seating 400 people. It's very popular with the adjacent university crowd, and also right next to the Cathedral and Art Gallery, so handy for visitors.

You'll be spoiled for choice with 16 different vegetarian options (vegan dishes clearly marked with a star) and lots of tempting gateaux to enjoy with a mind-boggling selection of speciality teas and coffees (caramel nut crunch cappuccino, anyone?). Mains range from spinach roulade with tomato and sweet pepper sauce to oriental stir fry, and everything (except desserts) is homemade – so the staff are happy to help if you want to know about ingredients.

- 18 Gosford St
  Coventry CV1 5DL
- 024 7633 5333
- Serving times:
  Tues-Sat 6-11pm
- Major credit cards
- Smoking throughout
- Licensed
- 50 seats
- Starters from £4

Caramba Café-Bar

Popular city centre café-bar with a good vegetarian choice. Start with nachos or their veg 'humdinger' – fiery baby corn, cheese jalapeños, mozzarella melts and mushroom-filled potato skins – then tackle the mains: vegetarian variations on the expected fajitas, enchiladas, burritos and chilli.

This branch in Gosford Street is the one you'll probably find yourself at if you've been visiting the cathedral, but travel a few miles north to Keresley if you fancy joining in one of Caramba's regular salsa nights. This much larger venue (300+ seats) has a more extensive menu with some additional tapas-style sides, as well as a children's play area, lots of parking, and opens from midday til late seven days.

Kakooti Restaurant

In a medieval part of town, in a 16th century building, who'd have thought you'd find a good selection of award-winning organic and vegan wines and a restaurant that tries hard to source organic and fair trade ingredients?

Food is cooked to order in this Italian-influenced restaurant, so catering for special diets isn't going to be a problem. Some interesting starters are on the menu: an arrosto of roasted vegetables and mixed leaves or the insalata dela casa – aubergine with capers, lemon and olives or, less solidly, a dish of marinated olives with a herb and walnut dressing.

Enjoy mains along the lines of pasta with mushrooms or olives, aubergine melanzane, or a very herby kidney bean dish with a fragrant lime sauce.

- 16 Spon St
  Coventry CV1 3BA
- 024 7622 1392
- Serving times:
  Mon-Thurs
  6.30-8.45pm
  Fri-Sat 6.30-9.45pm
- Booking recommended
  Fri & Sat
- Major credit cards
- Non-smoking area
- Licensed
- 98 seats
- Mains from £7.85

Cat's Tales

Based just 100 yards from the award winning art gallery on Walsall's regenerated canal wharf, Cat's Tales is run by Cat Desmenez, who moved to the UK from her native France in the early eighties. Open as a tearoom from 11am, lunch is served between 12-2.30pm and includes soup, lasagne, risottos and side orders.

Stepping up a gear for Friday and Saturday evenings, the menu features half a dozen starters, mains and desserts: kick off with dishes like a fruity nut pâté or garlic and herb cheese profiteroles, and move onto a selection of mains including spicy Mexican fajitas or red onion steamed savoury pudding. Vegans are well looked after, including Cat's dairy- and egg-free pancakes with pecan and maple syrup.

- Walsall Town Wharf
  Walsall WS2 8HE
- 01922 611622
- Serving times:
  Mon-Thurs
  11am-4pm
  Fri-Sat 11am-4pm
  & 6.30-9.30pm
  Lunch menu served
  12-2.30pm
- Booking preferred
- Major credit cards
- Non-smoking
- Not licensed, BYO
  with no corkage
- Children welcome
- 36 seats
- Starters from £2.75

cheshire
greater
manchester

cheshire • greater manchester

Cheshire

Greater Manchester

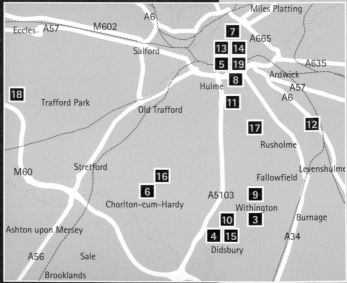

City of MANCHESTER

0   0.5   1

Miles

194

cheshire • greater manchester

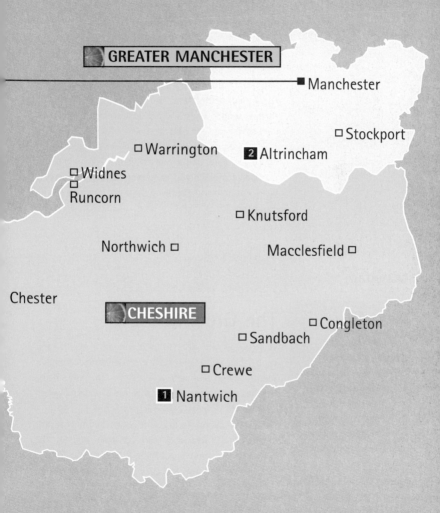

GREATER MANCHESTER

■ Manchester

□ Stockport

□ Warrington

2 Altrincham

□ Widnes
□ Runcorn

□ Knutsford

Northwich □

Macclesfield □

Chester

CHESHIRE

□ Congleton

□ Sandbach

□ Crewe

1 Nantwich

- 97 Welsh Row
  Nantwich CW5 5ET
- 01270 624758
- Serving times:
  Tues-Sun 12-2.15pm
  & 7-8.15pm
- Booking
  recommended
  Sundays
- No credit cards
- Smoking throughout
- Licensed
- Mains from £5.20

Oddfellows Arms

This small local pub is attractively decorated and also has tables in the garden. There's a vegetable balti for vegans and, if you're not on a dairy-free regime, a mild vegetable chilli, vegetable or mushroom lasagne, vegetable stilton crumble, or broccoli in a rich brie sauce with rosti – grated potatoes made into cakes which are then fried gently (and usually weighted) to give a melting tender inside and a deliciously browned crust.

Desserts are the best memories of school dinners – blackcurrant and apple crumble, chocolate pudding in chocolate sauce, and lemon or sticky toffee puddings.

Open for lunch and early evening meals six days a week, eat here without being disturbed by a juke box or big screen TV.

- 41-43 Oxford Rd
  Altrincham WA14 2ED
- 0161 929 4141
- Serving times:
  Mon-Sat 9am-5.15pm
- Major credit cards
- Non-smoking
- Children welcome
- 40 seats

The Greenhouse

This café is next door to (and part of) a health food centre. The impression is of a conservatory or garden room – large and airy with Classic FM, pine chairs, benches and tables, with plants and wonderful green chandeliers. Very National Trust tearooms.

You can choose from a wide range of yummy salads, quiches and cakes, and there are main courses like spaghetti and (non-)meat balls. A large range of teas such as Lapsang and Earl Grey are on offer, as well as Aqua Libra, decent coffee and hot chocolate.

In the summer you can sit at one of the pavement tables. A leafy place for a leafy town.

Aladdin

There's a great selection of hot and cold hors d'oeuvres on the authentic Arabic and middle eastern menu from which to construct a substantial dinner if the few vegetarian and vegan main courses don't appeal.

There's a choice of delicate deep-fried cheese pastries, falafel or green beans with olive oil and pitta (which is a lot more exciting than it sounds). Try vegetable kibbeh – a crushed wheat pastry with grenadine paste, stuffed with parsley mushrooms and pine kernels – an interesting item too rarely seen, or Mujaddara – a rice and lentil combination with fried onions. Take your own alcohol if you want, and try the intensely sweet pastry desserts accompanied by a strong coffee.

- 529 Wilmslow Rd
  Withington
  Manchester M20 9BA
- 0161 434 8588
- Serving times:
  Tues-Fri 5-10.30pm
  Sat 3-11pm
  Sun 2-10pm
- Booking advisable weekends
- Major credit cards
- Non-smoking area
- Not licensed
- Children welcome
- 60 seats
- Starters from £2.50

Cachumba Café

Seema Gupta's Cachumba Café is popular with local vegetarians, and can get extremely busy on Friday and Saturday evenings.

The short but interesting menu is around half vegetarian, including three vegan-friendly options, and you can savour choices including spiced okra and onions, mung bean dhal with spinach, or mtoki – green Ugandan bananas cooked with various spices. Order two or three dishes each (pretend you're in a tapas bar, the portions aren't huge), add in a pitta and pilau rice, and enjoy an authentic and satisfying meal for around a tenner. Not licensed, but corkage for wine and beer is only 50p per person for parties of four or more. Cachumba is bookable for private parties, and Seema can also cater your own event in the area.

- 220 Burton Rd
  West Didsbury
  Manchester M20 2LW
- 0161 445 2479
- Serving times:
  Mon-Sat 6-9.30pm
- Booking recommended weekends
- No credit cards
- Non-smoking
- Not licensed, but BYO 50p per person
- Children welcome
- 40 seats
- Dishes from £3.50

- 70 Oxford St
  Manchester M1 5NH
- Next to station
- 0161 200 1508
- Serving times:
  Mon-Sat
  11.30am-10pm
  Sun 11.30am-9.30pm
  Opens at 5pm some
  bank holidays
- Major credit cards
- Non-smoking area
- Licensed
- Children welcome
- 70 seats
- Starters from £3.25,
  mains from £4.95

Cornerhouse Arts Centre

Feeding the customers for three indie cinemas and art galleries, the Cornerhouse offers a full menu at both the bar and the upstairs café/restaurant.

Snack on sweet potato wedges, garlic bread, soup or garlic mushrooms, or for something more substantial there are some well-flavoured pizzas, including a vegan version without cheese, and interesting pastas.

You can have a sociable meze platter for two, either Middle Eastern, completely vegetarian, or Mediterranean (which needs some editing when ordering to lose the fish). With a glass of wine or a cocktail from the bar, you can while away the time until the need for some cultural activity strikes. On Sunday mornings there's a vegetarian full breakfast if you fancy it.

- 16-20 Turner St
  Manchester M4 1BZ
- 0161 834 9232
- Serving times:
  Tues-Sat 10am-5pm
- No credit cards
- Non-smoking
- Not licensed
- Children welcome
- 55 seats
- Mains from £2.45

Earth Café

Here in Manchester's Buddhist Centre, you can eat ethically, healthily, very reasonably and mainly organically. The only non-vegan aspect is the option to have dairy milk in your tea or coffee. They also do fabulous juices to order – with carrot, celery, beetroot and ginger or grape, lemon and apple among the combinations. They'll manage a wheat-free or garlic-free diet if you require it, and give demonstrations of vegan cooking on the occasional evening.

The main courses are pies, stews, stir fries and bakes, while the chef's special gives you a main dish, two salads and a side dish for a perfectly balanced meal. Soups are either hearty or refreshing, there's homemade cake and crammed salad sandwiches.

Diamond Dogs

This is a cool, friendly, café set in a cute little backwater known as Chorlton Village, in a street lined with wine bars and interesting shops. Inside, the walls are shocking pink, with red bench seating along one side, and fairy lanterns behind the counter, together with a diamond dog or two. Look up and you'll see an amazing mobile of tiny origami birds made from dollar bills. There is art on the walls and, best of all, extraordinary collages of writing, drawings and photographs beneath the glass table tops. Even the loo has an eye-catching collage.

The café's sub-title is 'Out of Harm's Way' and, true to their word, they offer a delicious range of organic, fair traded and microwave-free food, with loads of vegan options. The menu offers everything from an all-day breakfast, (vegan version with tofu in soya sauce and garlic, beans, mushrooms, tomatoes and sausage) through paninis, to snacks, salads, soups and sandwiches. You can choose a main course such as roast pepper lasagne, green Thai curry (vegan), enchiladas or gumbo, or enjoy a wide selection of puddings including Caribbean bread and butter pudding, mango crème brulée and vegan mocha cheesecake.

To drink, choose from teas, coffees or chocolate, or find yourself tempted by the smoothies (all with a choice of two soya milks or dairy milk) or freshly squeezed juices, as well as a large range of bottled drinks. And don't forget – except for the sausages, it's all organic.

- 52 Beech Rd Chorlton Manchester M21 9EG
- 0161 882 0101
- Serving times:
  Mon-Wed
  10am-6pm
  Thurs-Fri
  10am-9.30pm
  Sat 9am-9.30pm
  Sun 9am-6.30pm
  Thurs-Sat bar
  until 11pm
- No credit cards
- Non-smoking
- BYO, wine corkage £2
- Children welcome
- 20 seats
- Snacks from £2.50

Gtr Manchester

- 111 Oxford Rd
  Manchester M1 7DU
- 0161 273 1850
  (café)
- 0161 273 4859
  (restaurant)
- Serving times:
  Mon 9.30am-7pm
  Tues-Sat 9.30am-9pm
  Restaurant menu
  from 5.30pm
- Booking recommended
  Sat evenings
- Major credit cards
- Non-smoking
- Licensed
- Children welcome
- 70 seats
- Restaurant menu
  from £3.50

Eighth Day

This long-established workers' cooperative moved to a new building in late 2003 – after quite some time working out of temporary premises – and they are now softening their new home with plants, artwork and sympathetic lighting. Open café hours six days a week, the restaurant menu comes into play in the early evening. The cooking is innovative and completely vegetarian, and they'll happily cater for most dietary requirements.

The café kicks off the day with a full veggie breakfast (served until 11.30am – very civilised), and follows up with a comprehensive lunch menu of daily bakes like red dragon or homity pies, curries, casseroles, salads and jackets. Expect high standards of cooking with good vegan options using GM-free and organic ingredients.

The restaurant menu won't disappoint with starters like pressed terrine of ricotta, spinach and roasted vegetables, or a lentil and Doddington cheese croquette with beetroot ketchup and rocket. Main courses tickle the tastebuds with dishes such as a nut, seed and quinoa roast with a red wine jus, and spinach, red onion and feta strudel with roast peppers and tomato fondue.

There are delicious side salads and home baked flat bread, and an ambitious dessert menu which can see you making the difficult choice between a lime tart and chocolate sorbet or mango tarte tatin with butterscotch ice cream.

Enjoy seasonal menus – including some very special events at Christmas – and a good wine and beer list (all vegetarian, and all but one vegan).

Fuel

This café bar is a favourite student hangout with a latin feel. Lively as the evening moves on, there's Spanish beer on tap, Mexican and Italian food on the menu and a disco upstairs on Saturday nights. You can choose dishes ranging from breakfast to paninis to a huge plate of chilli fajitas with salad and wedges, while puddings include massive Belgian waffles with a choice of berries and cream, or chocolate and maple syrups with fried bananas. There is a wide choice of drinks, both alcoholic and non-alcoholic, and the menu warns you to be patient while they squeeze the juices.

The atmosphere is noisy and friendly – you don't have to be a student, but it helps!

- 448 Wilmslow Rd Withington Manchester M20 3BW
- 0161 448 9702
- Serving times: Mon-Sat 9am-11pm Sun 9.30am-10.30pm
- Major credit cards
- Smoking throughout
- Licensed
- Children welcome
- 32 seats
- Snacks from £2

Herbivores

In the basement of a listed building on the Manchester University campus, Herbivores is popular with overseas students – for its international feel as well as the good food; the staff will guide you towards appropriate options if you're on a wheat or sugar-free diet.

Typical dishes include spicy chickpea and potato soup, hummus and pitta, vegetable lasagne and salad, homity pie, and the well-loved fruit crumble and custard. If you're vegan, chow down on soup – which is always dairy-free – as well as some of the sandwich fillings, the occasional main course, and finish with one of their flapjacks. If you're there in December, they serve Christmas lunches from the first of the month and, during the summer, take advantage of the seating in the courtyard.

- The Burlington Rooms Burlington St Manchester M15 6HQ
- Next to John Rylands library
- 0161 275 2408
- Serving times: Mon-Fri 8am-6.45pm Sat-Sun 11am-5pm Closed bank holidays Closed weekends out of term time
- No credit cards
- Non-smoking
- Not licensed
- Children welcome
- 140 seats

Gtr Manchester

- 43 Lapwing Lane
  West Didsbury
  Manchester M20 2NT
- 0161 434 4259
- Serving times:
  Mon 5.30-10.30pm
  Tues-Fri 12-2pm
  & 5.30-10.30pm
  Sat 5.30-10.30pm
  Sun 12.30-3.30pm
  & 5.30-10.30pm
  Closed bank holidays
- Booking essential for
  evenings
- Major credit cards
- Smoking throughout
- Not licensed, BYO
  with no corkage
- Children welcome
- 34 seats
- Starters from £3,
  mains from £10.25

Greens

Open for both lunch and dinner, just scan the menu and you'll understand why it's essential to book for the evening. Partner Simon Connolly and TV chef Simon Rimmer have composed a menu full of variety and interest that doesn't try too hard to impress, so has you swearing allegiance as soon as you read it.

The set menu (Sunday and Monday night, Sunday lunch and early evening until 7pm the rest of the week) is a steal. Try Lebanese salad followed by pumpkin laksa and finish with a chocolate pudding and butterscotch sauce, or choose the grilled goat's cheese with pecan and rocket, a chestnut mushroom risotto, and rhubarb fool. If you want to be there longer and later, try the Thai spiced potato cake with wasabi and lime leave coleslaw, which will perk up the taste buds and leave them ready to be seduced by gnocchi with rich red wine, rosemary and woodland mushroom ragoût. If you fancy something lighter, there are dishes like baked goat's cheese cannelloni with thyme and olive oil roasted cherry tomatoes. Side dishes include garlic and rosemary ciabatta, creamy mash and a tangy sun-blush, plum and cherry tomato salad.

There are some nursery delights in the desserts: banana and vanilla fudge cheesecake, Bailey's and chocolate button trifle, or a more sophisticated lemon tart with raspberry sauce. (Note: not a coulis. They talk sensibly here.)

No corkage charge for your own wine or beer which makes this a very reasonably priced posh dinner out.

Misty's

Everything is made on the premises at this 50% organic, 80% vegan, locally owned and managed café.

Soup – for example spicy pumpkin – is around £1.50 including bread, while a main course like Moroccan vegetable tagine with apricots, citrus, vine fruits and couscous is only £3. There's a selection of vegan cakes, including a dairy- and egg-free cheesecake. It's not licensed, but there's no corkage as long as you are having a meal, or you can try the hot spiced apple juice or vegan shakes and smoothies. Great value for a café in a shopping centre, and not part of some global horror.

Misty's can also cater your party or corporate event – call Phil for full details.

- 531 Stockport Rd Manchester M12 4JH
- 0161 256 3355
- Serving times:
  Mon-Sat
  9.15am-5.45pm
- No credit cards
- Smoking throughout
- Not licensed, BYO with no corkage
- Children welcome
- 25 seats
- Mains from £3

Royal Orchid

In a centrally located Grade II listed building, The Royal Orchid has a devoted following amongst those who like their Eastern cuisine authentic. All the chefs hail from Thailand, and they claim accreditation from the Thai government in case you were in any doubt.

Choose from a good range of starters, three soups (rather than just a token vegetarian-friendly option), red or green curries, plenty of stir fries – including mock duck with chilli, aubergine and sweet basil, garlic fried mushrooms or sweet and sour vegetables – as well as a decent range of noodles and rice options.

At Christmas there's a set vegetarian feast – insist on going here to ensure you don't feel short-changed at the next office knees-up.

- 36 Charlotte St Manchester M1 4FD
- 0161 236 5183
- Serving times:
  Mon-Fri 12-2.30pm
  & 6-11pm
  Sat 1-11pm
  Sun 1-10.30pm
  Closed at lunch on bank holidays
- Booking essential Sat
- Major credit cards
- Non-smoking area
- Licensed
- Children welcome
- 90 seats
- Starters from £4

- 54 Portland St
  Manchester M1 4QU
- 0161 236 1388
- Serving times:
  Mon-Fri
  11.30am-2.30pm
  & 5.30-11.30pm
  Sat 5-11.30pm
  Sun 5-11pm
- Booking recommended
  Saturdays
- Major credit cards
- Smoking throughout
- Licensed
- Children welcome
- 55 seats
- Mains from £6.90

Siam Orchid

Siam Orchid was the first Thai restaurant in the north, and there's a sizeable vegetarian section to the menu of this friendly eaterie in Manchester's China Town. A close reading also reveals quite a few vegan choices.

Mushrooms in a spicy coconut cream soup, garlic fried mushrooms, aubergines with sweet basil and vegetable curry are deservedly popular. You have the option of adding vegetarian duck or meat (gluten and tofu substitutes) to any vegetarian main dish for just £1.

They are open all day from mid to late December if you need to have a Christmas shopping respite – or are planning an afternoon office do. Otherwise there are separate sittings for lunch and dinner, with booking strongly advised for Saturday night.

- 210 Burton Rd
  West Didsbury
  Manchester M20 2LW
- 0161 445 5200
- Serving times:
  Mon 6-11.30pm
  Tues-Fri 12-2.30pm
  & 6-11.30pm
  Sat-Sun 6-11.30pm
- Major credit cards
- Smoking throughout
- Licensed
- Children welcome
- 90 seats
- Starters from £4

Thai E-Sarn Classic

There's a good vegetarian choice, student discounts and entertainment at the weekends at this well-regarded Thai restaurant. You're invited to 'Enjoy Crazy Wendy as Elvis Presley, Tom Jones and Shirley Bassey' – which, magnet-like, will either attract or repel you.

Starters include a green papaya salad with chilli, herbs, tomatoes and lime juice – ideal to exhilarate your taste buds for mains including vegetarian mock duck, red and green curries, Thai noodles and a good selection of milder dishes.

There's also a set vegetarian menu with around seven dishes for two or more people, and desserts including fried ice cream and mango with sticky rice. Takeaways available, with discounts for larger orders.

The Bean Counter

An ethical café during the day, The Bean Counter also opens as a restaurant on Friday and Saturday evenings, when it's preferable to book. There are some splendid all-day full breakfasts – including a mighty vegan version with sausages, rashers and mushroom haggis – together with a choice of vegetarian sausages in a ciabatta sandwich. Stave off those lunchtime pangs with burritos, wraps, homity pie or a Greek meze, and quench your thirst with smoothies, Whole Earth organic fizzies or fair trade coffee.

The evening menu can include feta, pine nut and olive tartlets, stuffed mushrooms, puff pastry parcels, roasted red peppers or aubergine and feta fritters. Add some dauphinoise potatoes to really spoil yourself.

- 535 Wilbraham Rd Manchester M21 0UE
- 0161 882 0700
- Serving times:
  Wed-Thurs 10am-5.50pm
  Fri-Sat 10am-9.30pm
  Sun 11am-4.50pm
- Booking appreciated Fri & Sat evenings
- Major credit cards
- Non-smoking except evenings
- Not licensed, BYO in the evening with £2 corkage
- Children welcome
- 25 seats
- Evening starters from £3.50

The Greenhouse

There's a huge choice at this popular and much-loved vegan and vegetarian restaurant – which also clearly marks wheat-free choices – but regulars have been known to pre-order their favourite dishes in case they're not featured on that day's specials board.

Choose from tasty starters such as deep-fried cheese cubes – with English cheeses for once – falafel, stuffed vine leaves, Glamorgan- or Lincolnshire-style sausages (the latter vegan), and then revel in a choice of mains that may find you opting for the blindfolded-with-a-pin method. New dishes are added on a regular basis, and you could probably eat here every week for a year without trying the same dish twice.

Good range of organic and vegan beers and wine, and regular special dining and happy hour deals.

- 331 Great Western St Rusholme Manchester M14 4AN
- 0161 224 0730
- Serving times:
  Mon-Sat 6.30-9.30pm
  Sun 12-9pm
  Mon-Sat lunch opening by arrangement
- Booking essential Sat evening
- Major credit cards
- Non-smoking
- Licensed
- Children welcome
- 40 seats

- 11a The Orient
  The Trafford Centre
  Manchester M17 8EH
- 0161 747 2700
- Serving times:
  Mon-Fri 9am-10pm
  Sat 9am-9pm
  Sun 9am-7pm
- No credit cards
- Non-smoking area
- Not licensed
- Children welcome

V2Go

Fast food with a heart in the middle of The Trafford Centre, where you'll find welcome relief from the usual shopping mall fare in their selection of veggie and spicy Mexican burgers, hot dogs, falafel, chips and a decent salad selection. Expect vegan options and smaller children's portions, as well as the usual coffee, juices and soft drinks.

Members of The Vegetarian Society's Food and Drink Guild, you can be confident that eggs are free range, and that there's no GM produce on your plate.

Another branch has already opened at Manchester's Arndale Centre, and there are plans to expand to other cities. Visit www.grapevineguides.co.uk for details of the latest openings.

- 14 Oxford Rd
  Manchester M1 5QA
- Opposite BBC
- 0161 236 8438
- Serving times:
  Mon-Sat 12-11pm
  Sun 4-10pm
  Closed late July
  -late August
- Booking recommended
  Fri & Sat evenings
- Major credit cards
- Non-smoking area
- Licensed
- Children welcome
- 50 seats
- Mains from £4.70

Zumbar

Zumbar's owner Kevin Dunne enjoys claims to fame which include a 'Restaurateur of the Year award', being the purveyor of the UK's first all-vegan pizza, and a credit for being one of the first to bring Mexican food to the UK restaurant scene.

This modern, minimalist wine bar - opposite BBC Manchester - is still heavily Mexican-influenced, and has a wide range of vegan options.

Choose from a spinach and feta wrap, potato and carrot cake, fried potato skins with a selection of dips, or opt for the more substantial vegetarian enchilada or enchirito. Vegan cheese and bacon are available as pizza toppings, while other dairy- and egg-free choices include stir fries, falafel and burgers. Also look out the weekly specials and vegan ice cream.

isle of man
lancashire
merseyside

isle of man • lancashire • merseyside

Isle of Man

Greens Vegetarian Restaurant Douglas 210

Lancashire

2   Patagonia Café Bolton 210
3   Rice 'n' Three Bolton 211
4   Sokrates Horwich Bolton 211
5   Surya Bolton 212
6   Red Triangle Café Burnley 212
7   The Vegetarian Restaurant Colne 213
8   The Whale Tail Café Lancaster 213
9   North Star High Crompton Oldham 214
10 City Deli Preston 214

Merseyside

11 Blackburne House Café Bar Liverpool 215
12 Bluecoats Café Bar Liverpool 215
13 Everyman Bistro Liverpool 216
14 Green Fish Café Liverpool 216
15 The Egg Vegetarian Restaurant
    Liverpool 217
16 The Pod
    Liverpool 217
17 Yuet Ben
    Liverpool 218
18 Daydreams Café
    Wallasey 218

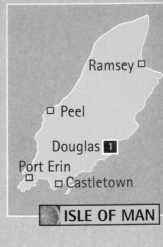

ISLE OF MAN

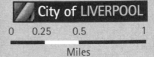

City of LIVERPOOL

0   0.25   0.5   1

Miles

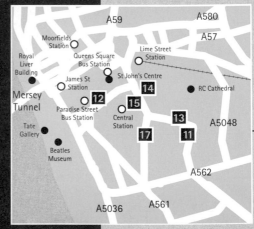

Morecambe □

8 Lancaster

□ Fleetwood

Clitheroe □

7 Colne

□ Blackpool

LANCASHIRE

6 Burnley

10 Preston □ Blackburn

□ Southport

Horwich

□ Rochdale

4

□ Bury **9** High

2 **3** **5** Bolton

Crompton

□ Formby

Oldham □

□ Bootle □ St Helens

Wallasey **18**

Liverpool

Birkenhead □

16

MERSEYSIDE

isle of man • lancashire • merseyside

Douglas

- North Quay
  Douglas Steam
  Railway Station
  Douglas IM1 4LL
- 01624 629129
- Serving times:
  Mon-Sat 9am-4.30pm
  Lunch menu served
  11.45am-2.30pm
- No credit cards
- Non-smoking area
- Licensed
- Children welcome
- 100 seats
- Mains from £4.95

Greens

The only completely vegetarian restaurant on the island, Greens is based in the Victorian railway station waiting room, and during the summer season you can enjoy the historic steam trains that still use the track.

The full lunch menu is served from 11.45am with a couple of soups for starters, followed by a range of bakes – broccoli and pasta, and spicy potato often feature – together with moussaka, pizza or quiche. Vegan choices can include a vegetable broth or Greens' Red Dragon pie – a mashed potato topped bake of aduki beans, brown rice, carrots and onions seasoned with herbs, soy sauce and chilli powder.

If you're in a large group, they appreciate advance notice. You can also book Greens for a private evening party, minimum 30 covers.

Bolton

- 116 Bradshawgate
  Bolton BL2 1AY
- 01204 528533
- Serving times:
  Mon-Fri 9.15am-4pm
  Sat 9am-5pm
- No credit cards
- Non-smoking
- Not licensed, BYO
  with no corkage
- Children welcome
- 66 seats
- Soups and snacks
  from £2.50

Patagonia Café

This American-style coffee house serves simple, freshly prepared scoff. Excellent value soup-and-sarnie, soup-and-quiche combinations or baked spuds, there's also a children's menu and homemade milkshakes with ice cream and fresh fruit. Limited vegan options, but if you visit on a weekend try the chilli.

A full range of good coffee is available and, if you can't get through the day without a glass of wine, bring your own and they won't charge corkage.

This totally non-smoking café also showcases work by local artists, with the exhibition changing every couple of months. Reasonably priced, nothing too outlandish, somewhere that provides the staples in life is my homage to Patagonia.

Rice 'n' Three

Does what it says on the tin. The menu changes by the weekday – rather like school dinners, if it's Wednesday if must be dhal, potatoes and spinach. A plate of rice and three vegetarian curries is just £2.20. Sundries are silly cheap, a samosa for fifty pence, poppadoms twenty pence, garlic naan fifty pence, and all the vegetable curries are vegan.

Situated on the High Street, Rice 'n' Three do fast food and takeaways and will cater for much bigger events by arrangement.

Ideal if you need a spice fix in the middle of the day and you've only got a pocket full of small change.

- 19 Great Moor St Bolton BL1 1NZ
- Opposite Boots
- 01204 365605
- Serving times: Mon-Sat 11am-5.30pm
- Closed during Ramadan and bank holidays
- No credit cards
- Non-smoking area
- Not licensed
- Children welcome
- 30 seats
- Lunch from £2.20

Sokrates

A popular local haunt for an informal night out, Sokrates offers a vegetarian meze banquet, and there's also a special double platter deal on Sundays.

The separate vegetarian sections on the menu will have you spoilt for choice, but careful analysis of the appetisers and salads will reveal even more goodies.

Try fried aubergine slices with garlic sauce, courgette fritters or coriander salad to start, with mains including those fab giant oven-baked beans with feta cheese and onions, vine leaves stuffed with lentils and rice or moussaka with potatoes, aubergine, courgettes and cheese and béchamel sauce.

Essential to book at the weekend, and with all this choice and a relaxed atmosphere, you can see why.

- Winter Hey Lane Horwich Bolton BL6 7NZ
- 01204 668033
- Serving times: Mon-Sat 6-10.30pm Sun 4-10pm
- Booking essential Fri-Sat
- Major credit cards
- Smoking throughout
- Licensed
- Children welcome
- 80 seats
- Starters from £4

Lancashire

Lancashire

- 98 Derby St
  Bolton BL3 6HG
- 01204 380679
- Serving times:
- Mon-Fri
  11.30am-2pm
  & 6-10.30pm
- Sat-Sun
  11.30am-10.30pm
- Major credit cards
- Non-smoking area
- Licensed
- Children welcome
- 35 seats
- Starters from £1.50

Surya

A vegetarian haven opposite KFC and McDonalds, this snack bar is the front window for a catering company – a neat idea if you are wanting to stage a big event and try out some new ideas.

The usual well-loved suspects of samosa, bhel, bhajia, puris (and more) appear in the starters section. Move on to south Indian delicacies like idlis, ragda pattice (potato cakes with spicy peas and yoghurt chutney) or the house curries such as mutter paneer, stuffed aubergine and potato, or the mixed vegetable curry of the day. Rice and breads are so cheap they're almost giving them away. Try the buffet, where the menu changes according to the day of the week, for just £6.99.

- 160 St James St
  Burnley BB11 1NR
- 01282 832319
- Serving times:
- Tues-Thurs
  11.30am-6.45pm
- Fri-Sat 11.30am-
  6.45pm & 7-9.30pm
- Sun open occasionally
  for music nights
- Booking advisable
  evenings
- No credit cards
- Non-smoking area
- Licensed
- Children welcome
- 22 seats
- Evening mains
  from £5.50

Red Triangle Café

Red Triangle is Burnley's only dedicated vegetarian eating place. Run as a co-operative, they are proud to host music and poetry events and art exhibitions. They can also cater your local buffet.

A community café by day and an informal bistro on Friday and Saturday evenings, the menu features good soups with homemade bread rolls, and a choice of main dishes like haricot bean and chilli pattie with Italian vegetables and tomato sauce, or a Tunisian brik, with egg garnish and leaf salad. Winter choices include comforting hot desserts such as sultana pancakes with syrup, and in the summer there's homemade ice cream.

Live music occasionally features on Sunday evenings – phone for details of the next event.

The Vegetarian Restaurant

Over 20 years in Colne, this restaurant has achieved landmark status in the vegetarian world. Well-known for its music, with monthly Tuesday night live performances and a music festival in August, if you're into a bit of rhythm and blues with your food, you've come to the right place.

Specials on the menu change weekly – you can choose between specials like linguine with vegetables and a gorgonzola and garlic sauce, or lemon marsool dhal with vegetables and a roast almond biryani. Standard dishes are omelettes, curries and garlic breads, with a choice of desserts – lemon cheesecake, caramel apple pie Mississippi mud pie as well as a vegan option. Fully licensed, settle down with a beer or two while you eat and listen to some real music.

- 19-21 New Market St Colne BB8 9BJ
- Opposite Hippodrome
- 01282 868828
- Serving times:
  Thurs-Sun 7pm-10pm
  Open occasional Tues for live music, and August bank holiday for R&B festival
- Booking recommended Fri & Sat
- No credit cards
- Non-smoking area
- Licensed
- Children welcome
- 45 seats
- Starters from £2

The Whale Tail Café

In a converted cheese warehouse with original features, the Whale Tail is the oldest café in town – with good organic and fair trade credentials.

The vegetarian or vegan full monty breakfast should have them queuing round the block, with vegetarian bacon, sausage, fried potatoes and the rest, and free refills of tea or coffee. Lunches include jacket potatoes, homity pie and salads, beanburgers and outstanding specials like sweet potato, smoked cheese, caramelised onion and spinach bake or a vegan hazelnut roast with an orange and tarragon stuffing.

Desserts are mainly vegan: chocolate fudge cake, banana loaf or carrot cake with some wheat- and sugar-free choices. The whole menu, apart from the big breakfast, can be done to take away.

- 78a Penny St Lancaster LA1 1XN
- 01524 845133
- Serving times:
  Mon-Fri 9am-4pm
  Sat 9am-5pm
  Sun 10.30am-3pm
- No credit cards
- Non-smoking
- Licensed
- Children welcome
- 65 seats
- Soup from £2.20, mains from £4.85

Lancashire

Lancashire

- Rushcroft Rd
  High Crompton
  Oldham OL2 7PR
- 01706 845214
- Serving times:
  Mon-Fri 5-9pm
  Sat-Sun 12-9pm
  Open all day
  bank holidays
- Booking recommended
  weekends
- Major credit cards
- Non-smoking
- Licensed
- Children welcome
  until 8.30pm
- 30 seats
- Starters from £2.50

North Star

This pub, close to High Crompton Park, is in an old farmhouse building with a separate dining room, and there are good, varied vegetarian options.

The starters cover pâté, garlic mushrooms, Greek salad, a selection of Indian morsels or stuffed potato skins, and main courses include vegetarian rag pudding – a vegetarian suet pud with quorn mince and vegetarian gravy, which must be worth a go. Otherwise, try the curry or pasta of the day, Louisiana vegetable roast with mango and lime sauce, quorn fillets, spinach and mushroom in a mascarpone and brie sauce or stuffed peppers. Everything comes with chips, rice or new potatoes and fresh vegetables.

If all this is too much, choose deli sandwiches or garlic bread side orders.

- 8b Winckley St
  Preston PR1 2AA
- 01772 204777
- Serving times:
  Mon-Wed 9am-6pm
  Thurs 9am-10.30pm
  Fri-Sat 9am-6pm
  Sun 11am-5pm
- Major credit cards
- Non-smoking
- Licensed
- Children welcome
- 24 seats
- Mains from £4.95

City Deli

Offering a welcome retreat from the hustle of Fishergate, the City Deli restaurant in Winckley Street is at the back of the eponymous delicatessen. With a predominately vegetarian menu – often Mediterranean or Mexican influenced – choose from an interesting range of salads or platters including the comprehensive choice of cheeses stocked by the deli itself.

Hot meals feature several calzone including spinach and chickpea with cinnamon, lemon and chillis, a bean and cheese quesadilla, corn and chilli burrito and sage and mushroom roll, all served with couscous, salad, coleslaw and high quality balsamic dressing.

Drinks include fruit smoothies, organic fruit juices, together with several wines. Open 7 days a week, including until 10.30pm on Thursdays.

Blackburne House Café Bar

This café and bar is inside Blackburne House – an organisation set up in the early eighties to provide vocational training – but you don't need to be a student to pop in and enjoy their food and drink, and it's popular with local theatre-goers for a pre-performance snack or jar.

Predominately vegetarian, expect a bistro-style menu of dishes such as black-eyed bean and vegetable chilli, mushroom and feta-stuffed peppers or roast veg, goat's cheese and pine nut strudel. You can also try their homemade soups, sandwiches (on freshly baked focaccia), paninis, and jackets, or visit the salad bar.

There's also a wide selection of cakes, and good coffees – including soya milk options.

- Blackburne Place
  Liverpool L8 7PE
- 0151 709 4356
- Serving times:
  Mon-Thurs
  10am-7.45pm
  Fri 10am-2.45pm
- No credit cards
- Non-smoking
- Licensed
- Children welcome
- 80 seats

Merseyside

Bluecoats Café Bar

In busy central Liverpool, in the heart of the thriving art and culture area, this café-bar is a handy stop for a bite and a coffee. There's a courtyard and a garden at the rear to enjoy some fresh air while you have a quick lunch as a break from work or shopping.

Local produce is used where possible, eggs are free range and cheese is vegetarian. There are vegan opportunities in soup, hummus, vegetable curry, baked potatoes and home-baked beans, with other mains including frittata, burritos, vegetarian chilli and a welcome selection of salads.

You can also enjoy a good selection of fruit and more traditional teas, and proper desserts such as rice pudding, lemon tart or an enticing burgundy cake.

- Bluecoat Chambers
  School Lane
  Liverpool L1 3BX
- 0151 709 2179
- Serving times:
  Mon-Sat 10am-5pm
- No credit cards
- Non-smoking area
- Licensed
- Children welcome
- 75 seats

Merseyside

Liverpool

Omnivorous Bistro & Café

Merseyside

- 9-11 Hope St
  Liverpool L1 9BH
- 0151 708 9545
- Serving times:
  Mon-Wed
  12-midnight
  Thurs 12-1am
  Fri-Sat 12-2am
- Closed bank holidays
- Major credit cards
- Non-smoking area
- Licensed
- Children welcome
  until 9pm
- 200 seats
- Starters from £2.20,
  mains from £4.90

Everyman Bistro

Well established and extremely popular among the arts and media crowd around the Everyman Theatre, the Everyman Bistro becomes more of a pub in the evening, but one that does food until closing time. There's also a foyer café on the ground floor serving light meals and sandwiches on weekday lunchtimes.

They use organic and quality local produce on the regularly changing menu, and there's always lots of vegetarian choice. Tagliatelle with roast vegetables, artichokes, sundried tomatoes and a lemon and olive dressing, potatoes sautéed with mushrooms, filo pie or dhal and bread. There are also pizzas, quiches, salads and homemade desserts.

The Bistro has been CAMRA recommended and there's an extensive wine list.

Liverpool

Vegetarian Café

Merseyside

- 11 Upper Newington
  Liverpool L1 2SR
- 0151 707 8592
- Serving times:
  Mon-Sat 12-4.30pm
  Closed bank holidays
- No credit cards
- Smoking throughout
- Not licensed
- Children welcome
- 40 seats
- From £1.50

Green Fish Café

Green Fish is cleanly furnished and inexpensive with the added bonus of the attached Domino art gallery. Pop in for a vegan soup and bread, or fortify yourself for a shopping marathon at the local Lewis's department store with one of up to eight vegetarian main dishes: risotto, roast veg and the like.

Pizza and quiche are under £2, with main meals from £2.50 – or just an extra quid if you want some mixed salad. Children can tuck in to smaller portions from the main menu.

This branch allows smoking throughout but has no wheelchair access, while a companion branch on Hanover Street (closed on Saturdays) is non-smoking with wheelchair access.

The Egg

The board in the street advertises vegetarian food but that's the only sign we could see – you could eat here without ever finding out what the place is called.

Climb the steep stairs to the top floor, open the door, and you're in a large loft with open plan storage to one side, and the café seating area with roof-top views on the other. Ah! the seating area – one of each sort of dining chair ever made around numerous tables. There is a large choice of food, much of it vegan, from leek and broccoli bake to tandoori mushrooms, via spaghetti bolognaise, nut roasts and salads. To drink you can pick anything from cappuccino (soya or not) to herb teas, juices and milk shakes. And don't miss their exceptional cakes.

- 16-18 Newington
  Liverpool L1 4ED
- 0151 707 2755
- Serving times:
  Mon-Sat
  8am-10.30pm
  Sun 8am-4.30pm
- No credit cards
- Non-smoking area
- Not licensed, BYO
  with £1 corkage
- Children welcome
- 60 seats
- Starters from £2

Merseyside

The Pod

There's a warm candelit table waiting for you in this converted bank. Pop in for lunch or go for tapas-style grazing in the evening, but do book for the weekend.

Among other choices that change frequently there's a chickpea burger with parsley, onion and cheddar on a ciabatta bun with fries, a vegetarian club sandwich with quorn fillets, avocado, roasted tomato and rocket, or a veggie burrito.

The evening tapas has over a dozen choices ranging from Spanish omelette, courgette fritters and patatas bravas to other less Hispanic items. Rest assured that any eggs are free range. Everything's cooked to order so there may be a short wait, but as you're sitting in a well-stocked bar we don't imagine you'll complain.

- 137-139 Allerton Rd
  Liverpool L18 2DD
- 0151 724 2255
- Serving times:
  Mon-Sat 12-3pm
  & 6-9.30pm
  Sun 6-9.30pm
- Booking recommended
  weekends
- Major credit cards
- Smoking throughout
- Licensed
- Children welcome
- 65 seats
- Lunch from £5.50

Merseyside

- 1 Upper Duke St
  Liverpool L1 9DU
- 0151 709 5772
- Serving times:
  Tues-Thurs 5-11pm
  Fri-Sat 5-midnight
  Sun 5-11pm
- Booking recommended
  weekends
- Major credit cards
- Smoking throughout
- Licensed
- Children welcome
- 40 seats
- Mains from £5

Yuet Ben

This restaurant has been run by the same family for more than 30 years and is a very popular destination for Peking food lovers. They have an excellent separate vegetarian section on the menu, and the vegetarian banquet at £12.50 per person is extremely good value.

There are some interesting-sounding tofu dishes – kwa tofu, in a reduced red wine and garlic sauce, tofu with broccoli and carrots, shredded tofu pancakes, and lots of steamed or stir fried and deep-fried fresh vegetables. The rice and noodles are well done, as you would hope. Fans of the Pete McCarthy Singapore Noodles Index will not be disappointed. Without doubt, several cuts above your average High Street Chinese.

- 78 Victoria Rd
  New Brighton
  Wallasey CH45 2JF
- 0151 630 0544
- Serving times:
  Summer 7 days
  9am-7pm
  Winter 7 days
  10am-5pm
- Major credit cards
- Non-smoking
- Not licensed
- Children welcome
- 22 seats
- Snacks from £2

Daydreams

Although no longer completely meat-free, this dolls' house shop is an oasis in the Wirral veggie desert, where you can eat a cooked vegetarian breakfast, or lunch on anything from a baked potato with decent fillings to a full meal of Thai schnitzel. Alternatively you could choose a vegetarian BLT or simply enjoy one of a choice of teas, coffee or juices.

You might opt for one of their homemade soups after a bracing walk down the promenade (as if...). Although the children's menu is basic, you can order small portions from the adult menu. Cosy in the winter, in good weather it is a pleasure to sit at one of the pavement tables and enjoy the (distant) sea views.

south yorkshire
west yorkshire

south yorkshire • west yorkshire

South Yorkshire

West Yorkshire

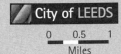

City of LEEDS

0   0.5   1

Miles

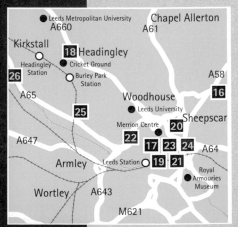

Leeds Metropolitan University   Chapel Allerton
A660   A61
Kirkstall
18 Headingley
Headingley   Cricket Ground
26 Station   A58
         Burley Park
         Station   16
A65   Woodhouse
                       Leeds University
25
                 Merrion Centre   Sheepscar
              22   20
A647   17 23 24   A64
A647
Armley   Leeds Station 19 21
                                    Royal
Wortley   A643   Armouries
                                    Museum
                       M621

south yorkshire • west yorkshire

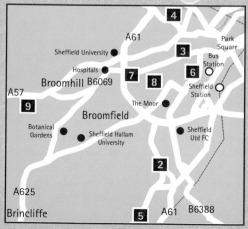

WEST YORKSHIRE

27 Otley
□ Keighley
□ Shipley
Bradford 12 11 10 28 ■ Leeds
Pudsey
13 14 Hebden Bridge
29 30
Todmorden Dewsbury □ 31 Wakefield
15 Huddersfield

□ Barnsley Doncaster
1

SOUTH YORKSHIRE

□ Rotherham

■ Sheffield

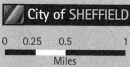

4
A61
Sheffield University ●   3   Park Square
Hospitals ● 7   6   Bus Station ○
Broomhill B6069 8   Sheffield Station ○
A57
9   ● The Moor
Broomfield
Botanical Gardens ● ● Sheffield Hallam University   ● Sheffield Utd FC
2
A625
5 A61 B6388
Brincliffe

City of SHEFFIELD

0   0.25   0.5   1
Miles

South Yorkshire

- 25 Copley Rd
  Doncaster DN1 2PE
- 01302 738730
- Serving times:
  Mon-Wed
  9am-3.30pm
  Thurs-Fri 9am-3.30pm
  & 7.30-10pm
  Sat 9-4pm
  & 7.30-10pm
  Closed most
  bank holidays
- No credit cards
- Non-smoking area
- Licensed
- Children welcome
- 24 seats
- Evening mains
  from £5.20

Eating Whole

Close to Doncaster's market area, Eating Whole draws its weekly-changing menu from a wide repertoire of cuisines, with everything freshly prepared on the premises. Join the regulars for a daytime menu heaving with vegan choice which can include bean and veg paella, mushroom and potato pie or a lentil and spinach casserole. Also a great range of dairy- and egg-free puds and, if you've had the foresight to arrange for someone else to drive, try one (or several) of the interesting range of organic beers and wines.

Open Thursday to Saturday evenings in addition to daytime Monday – Saturday, Eating Whole also open on Christmas Day. A very, very fine idea in our book. Reservations essential for this special vegetarian feast.

South Yorkshire

- 239 London Rd
  Sheffield S2 4NF
- Opposite NatWest
- 0114 249 2090
- Serving times:
  Mon-Fri
  11am-5.45pm
  Sat 11am-4.45pm
  Closed bank holidays
- Major credit cards
- Smoking throughout
- Not licensed, but
  BYO with no corkage
- Children welcome
- 24 seats including
  garden
- Light lunches from £2

Airy Fairy

Just off a busy main road, the Airy Fairy has a lovely secluded garden which seats as many as the café. They strive for 100% organic and fair trade standards with a high percentage of vegan items, and use local produce as often as possible.

The soups come with homemade (vegan) bread, and you can have hummus or cream cheese with olives and tomatoes. They also have an inspiring selection of cakes which can include include lime and coconut, bakewell tart, lemoncurd, or vegan specials like blackcurrant crumble cake or a wheat-free fruit variety.

Soya milk is available, excellent coffee and tea, organic chocolate from Green & Black's – or buck the trend and go for Coke!

Blue Moon

The café is open from 8am for breakfast, or drop in at lunchtime for an excellent choice of mains often including two hot vegan dishes, alongside pastries and vegan snacks. Boston beans (not vegan) are much more exciting than they sound, being a haricot bean and vegetable casserole with a yam, cheese and potato mash top – eat your heart out, 57 varieties. Main courses are modestly priced at a fiver, cakes an even more modest £1.50. Wine and beer, as well as soya milk for your tea or coffee are on offer and they'll do an evening buffet for pre-booked parties.

Eat at Blue Moon with confidence: the local vegetarian group (hi, guys) have been known to hold their Xmas do here.

- 2 St James St
  Sheffield S1 2EW
- Near the Cathedral
- 0114 276 3443
- Serving times:
  Mon-Sat 8am-8pm
  Lunch served from midday
  Closed bank holidays
- Major credit cards
- Non-smoking
- Licensed
- Children welcome
- 50 seats
- Main meals from £5

South Yorkshire

Fat Cat Pub

This highly regarded pub is next door to Kelham Island Industrial Museum, whose signposts will help you find it. Famous for real ales with its own brewery, there's a lovely atmosphere which isn't remotely suggestive of beards and damp wool.

Food is freshly prepared and there are always good vegetarian, vegan and wheat-free options. The menu changes weekly: leek and stilton potato bake, savoury aubergine pie, vegetable chilli casserole, various pastas and cheese and onion pie have all recently been eagerly ordered by the local and visiting vegetarian in the know.

No music or slot machines, a no-smoking room, open fires in the winter, great food and excellent beer. No wonder they keep getting awards here.

- 23 Alma St
  Sheffield S3 8SA
- Next to Industrial Museum
- 0114 249 4801
- Serving times:
  Mon-Fri 12-2.30pm
  & 6-7.30pm
  Sat-Sun 12-2.30pm
- No credit cards
- Non-smoking room
- Licensed
- Children welcome
- 80 seats
- Mains from £3

South Yorkshire

South Yorkshire

- 353 Abbeydale Rd
  Sheffield S7 1FS
- 0114 250 1076
- Serving times:
  Wed-Sat
  6-10.30pm
  Sun 1-3pm
- Booking essential
  Fri & Sat
- Major credit cards
- Non-smoking area
- Not licensed, BYO
  with no corkage
- Children welcome
- 30 seats
- Starters from £4.50

Kumquat Mae

Open most evenings and for Sunday lunch, you can also book Kumquat Mae early in the week for your own party. The restaurant, in Sheffield's antiques mile, also houses monthly-changing exhibitions for local artists.

The imaginative menu caters for vegans and wheat- and gluten-free diets. Anything else they'll tackle with notice. The Mediterranean-influenced menu can feature braised fennel and celeriac with lemon, capers and steamed lemon dumplings, Bloody Mary soup (roast tomatoes, basil, vodka) and roasted red pepper filled with refried beans, lime, chilli and fresh coriander. Desserts are wickedly attractive: toffee apple crumble or chocolate soufflé with a raspberry coulis and cream should demand your attention.

Bring your own booze, no corkage.

South Yorkshire

- 117 Norfolk St
  Sheffield S1 2JE
- 0114 272 8886
- Serving times:
  Mon-Sat 9am-4.30pm
- Major credit cards
- Non-smoking
- Licensed
- Children welcome
- 32 seats
- Mains from £4.60

Olive Garden

The Olive Garden is a friendly and informal café that's ambitious without over-reaching itself. Drawing menu influences from around the world, you can expect a diverse and weekly-changing range of starters, mains and yummy cakes. Olives, delicious bread and soups such as wild mushroom, asparagus, or red pepper and sweet potato spiced with wholegrain mustard make excellent snacks, or a prelude to a range of mains which include stir fries, curries, casseroles and bakes. With a selection of four salads as well as wheat-free and vegan choices, whatever your preference, you will eat well here.

You can choose wine or beer to accompany your meal, but we reckon it would be a shame to miss their freshly pressed fruit and vegetable juices.

Sheiks Restaurant

Opposite the Old Glossop Baths, this is a Lebanese and middle Eastern restaurant which caters well for the likes of you and us.

There are salady starters: tabouleh, fatoush, grilled aubergine purée with sesame paste and lemon juice, and green beans in olive oil, tomatoes and garlic. Also on offer is labneh – a mild homemade yoghurt cheese dressed with olive oil. Mains include moujaddara – a lentil, rice and fried onion mixture topped with yoghurt – as well as the more usual stuffed vine leaves, vegetable kebabs and an Arabic ratatouille or tabseh. For dessert try their semolina with pistachio nuts, cream and sugar.

Sheikh's can also host your party, and provide entertainment with music and belly dancing.

- 274 Glossop Rd
  Sheffield S10 2HS
- Opposite Old
  Glossop Baths
- 0114 275 0555
- Serving times:
  7 days 6-11pm
- Major credit cards
- Non-smoking area
- Licensed
- Children welcome
- 54 seats
- Starters from £2.95

South Yorkshire

The Forum

In the Devonshire Quarter, The Forum is the kind of place you'd be happy to have a coffee, a drink and a quick snack, or prime yourself for a night's drinking. It's open late, but food is only served until mid-evening. The choices are simple: a couple of sandwiches, a few salads, pasta, vegan sausage and mash, vegetarian burger and fries or a vegetable chilli.

They also do a vegetarian Sunday roast, a children's menu and some tasty sides, like bread and oil or olives – good to know about if you're with a bunch of people with varying levels of hunger pangs. You know you're among friends with the option of soya milk for your tea or coffee, and there's enough space not to have to worry about booking.

- 127-129 Devonshire St
  Sheffield S3 7SB
- 0114 272 0569
- Serving times:
  7 days 12-8pm
- Major credit cards
- Non-smoking area
- Licensed
- Children welcome
- 120 seats
- Mains from £5.50

South Yorkshire

Sheffield

South Yorkshire

- 257 Fulwood Rd Sheffield S10 3BD
- Opposite NatWest
- 0114 268 7807
- Serving times:
  Mon-Sat 12-3.30pm & 5-11pm
  Sun 2-4pm & 5-11pm
- Booking recommended
- Major credit cards
- Non-smoking area
- Licensed
- Children welcome
- 75 seats
- Mains from £3.50

UK Mama

Yorkshire boasts one of the UK's leading African restaurants in Sheffield's UK Mama, and we know of nowhere else that you'll find such an exotic choice of authentic African vegetarian food. Choose from dishes like the vegan stewed couscous with a black-eyed bean and plantain accompaniment, stewed mushrooms with yam or a peanut casserole. There are nine vegetarian main courses, and dozens of side dishes.

Prices are low, and there are also regular special offers – at the time of writing they included half price dishes on Mondays and Wednesdays, and two courses for under £6 if you're eating between 5 and 7pm. Featuring African and Caribbean beers and lagers, it's also worth trying the freshly prepared fruit punch.

Bradford

West Yorkshire

- 21-23 Albion St Bradford BD1 2LY
- 01274 734160
- Serving times:
  Fri 12-3pm & 7-9pm
  Sat 12-5.30pm
- No credit cards
- Non-smoking
- Licensed for members
- Children welcome
- 30 seats

1 in 12 Club

Operated by members of the local anarchist group, the 1 in 12 Club (the name is a reference to the infamous Raynor report of the early eighties) is a meeting place, bar, and live music venue – which includes a vegetarian café run by one of the collectives.

Recently refurbished, expect a predominately vegan snacky menu of veggieburgers, pizzas, salads, pretend-bacon and sausage butties, as well as occasional three course do's such as the peasant's collective harvest meal in October. Around half the food comes from their allotments, and a good deal of the rest has fair trade credentials or is from small local organic growers. Currently only open Fridays and Saturdays, visit www.1in12.com for updates on possible extended opening hours.

Fair Trade Café

Located in the basement of the University chaplaincy, this not-for-profit café uses fair trade, organic and locally-sourced produce wherever possible. Much of it is vegan – you could choose from lentil and tomato or spiced parsnip soups, nut and mushroom flan, or Moroccan rice and lentils to take just a few examples.

You might fancy a fruit crumble, or homemade cakes and biscuits, and there's a range of teas and coffees (with soya milk if you prefer) and organic soft drinks. Usually only open in the daytime, there are occasional themed evening events combining food and drink with music or story-telling. Bring your own wine to these without a corkage charge.

- 2 Ashgrove
  Bradford BD7 1BN
- Opposite sports centre
- 01274 727034
- Serving times:
  Mon-Fri 12-3pm
  Open only during
  university terms
- No credit cards
- Non-smoking
- Not licensed, BYO
  with no corkage
- Children welcome
- 60 seats
- Mains from £2

West Yorkshire

South Square Café

Nestled in a courtyard of Victorian cottages, with artists' workshops, a gallery and picture framers all about, this café opens at lunchtimes and on seasonal Friday evenings. There's a small choice of sandwiches on good bread, toasties, baked potatoes with mixed salad and veggieburgers, and you can make a side order of chips and dips. Don't miss the daily specials on the blackboard for a more comprehensive bill of fare like Italian fennel soup, courgette, tomato and basil crumble, spicy bean enchiladas or date and apple crumble cake.

There's always something vegan, besides the soup, and children are welcomed with highchairs, toys and smaller portions. Unfussy, and all the better for it.

- South Square
  Thornton Rd
  Thornton
  Bradford BD13 3LD
- 01274 834928
- Serving times:
  Tues-Sat 11.30am-
  2.30pm
  Sun 12-2.30pm
  Seasonal Fri evenings
  6-8pm
  Closed bank holidays
- No credit cards
- Non-smoking
- Not licensed, but BYO
  with no corkage
- Children welcome
- 32 seats
- Snacks from £2

West Yorkshire

- Hebden House
  The Birchcliffe Centre
  Birchcliffe Rd
  Hebden Bridge
  HX7 8DG
- 01422 844425
- Serving times:
  Thurs-Sat
  single sitting 8pm
  Sun single sitting 5pm
- Bookings only
- Major credit cards
- Non-smoking
- Licensed
- Children welcome
- 50 seats
- 3-courses £17.95

Laughing Gravy

Hebden Bridge – Totnes of the north, candles and sandals town – is also home to this very fine restaurant, open for single-sitting dining Thursday to Sunday. There's a new menu every week, and you don't have to worry about choosing, because you get to try all four starters, mains and desserts (quite definitely our sort of place...) Imagine sampling curried lentil pâté, courgette fritters, mushroom loaf with tarragon salsa, and tomatoes stuffed with Stilton – merely for starters – and progressing on to spinach and potato cake, vegetable frittata with creamy basil sauce, braised leeks in port and wild mushroom sauce, and chickpea, coconut and coriander casserole.

Come here to enjoy the occasional jazz sessions and other music events alongside first-class cooking.

- 2 Market St
  Hebden Bridge
  HX7 6AA
- 01422 843429
- Serving times:
  Tues-Wed 9am-5.30pm
  Thurs-Fri 9am-7.30pm
  Sat 9am-5.30pm
  Sun 10am-4.30pm
  Open some
  bank holidays
- Major credit cards
- Non-smoking
- Off-licence
- Children welcome
- 32 seats
- Starters from £2.50,
  mains from £3.95

organic house

The café here also sells organic produce and they use local and fair trade goods as far as is possible. The store has previously won 'Organic Specialist of the Year' at the Northern Natural Trade Fair. They serve fresh juices, wheatgrass, and a rather fab vanilla soya hot chocolate.

The menu changes daily. Soup of the day is always gluten-free and vegan and there are gluten- and wheat-free options throughout. There can be baked pâté with red chilli peppers and toast, feta and olive salad, spicy potato wraps and a good selection of homemade cakes.

You can't make bookings, but the upstairs room is available to hire if you're planning an organic, fair trade knees up.

The Blue Rooms

In a Victorian arcade, close to the railway station, this café serves breakfast until midday. Highlights include a full veggie breakfast (with free pot of tea) or, if the previous night hasn't been too heavy, mushrooms on toast, crumpets or toasted tea cakes.

There's a daily specials board, and starters can include soup, mushroom pâté, raw veg with a hummus dip, vegetable samosas and aioli with bread. Mains can feature vegetable chilli, two different raviolis, hot baguettes, toasted ciabattas or tofu burgers with enticing extra toppings. You can also choose from a salad and olive bar.

They serve good coffee and tea, fancy hot chocolate, milkshakes – with ice cream if you prefer – wine by the glass and bottled beer.

- 9 Byram Arcade
  Westgate
  Huddersfield HD1 1ND
- 01484 512373
- Serving times:
  Mon-Fri 10am-4.30pm
  Sat 9am-4.30pm
  Closed bank holidays
- No credit cards
- Non-smoking
- Licensed
- Children welcome
- 50 seats
- Mains from £3.60

Anand Sweets

Anand Sweets is a small, deli-style store where you can stock up on Indian sweets and snack food such as samosas, pakoras and spring rolls – individually or by the kilo. Popular with local vegetarians, it's also a good place to enjoy an inexpensive takeaway, or you could grab one of the handful of seats in the very small café area and eat in.

Well-flavoured curries – including a good selection of vegan options – rice and breads are freshly made each day, and the emphasis is on healthy cooking using a minimum of oil.

Simple – but authentic and tasty – Indian food at very reasonable prices.

- 109 Harehills Road
  Leeds LS8 5HS
- 0113 248 1234
- Serving times:
  Tues-Sun
  11am-7.30pm
- No credit cards
- Non-smoking
- Not licensed
- Children welcome
- Limited seating
- Curries from £2.20

Beano Wholefoods

- 36 New Briggate
  Leeds LS1 6NU
- Next to the
  Grand Theatre
- 0113 243 5737
- Opening times:
  Mon 9am-5pm
  Tues 9.30am-5pm
  Wed 9am-5pm
  Thurs-Fri 9am-5.30pm
  Sat 9am-5pm
- Major credit cards

OK, so it's not a restaurant or a traditional takeaway, but if you're in central Leeds and you want a great range of veggie and vegan sandwiches or snacks to go, this is somewhere well worth knowing about.

As well as the sarnies, this established (25th birthday) wholefood shop has loads of other vegan and vegetarian goodies to take home – burritos, calzones, pizza, pasties, flapjacks and scones. They don't have a hot food or alcohol licence yet, but are soon moving to bigger premises, so phone and find out if the situation's changed. In the meantime, support the only workers' co-operative in central Leeds and don't go hungry on your way to the Grand Theatre next door.

Citrus Café

- 13 North Lane
  Leeds LS6 3HG
- 0113 274 9002
- Serving times:
  Mon-Sat
  10am-3.45pm
  & 6-10pm
  Sun 11am-3.45pm
  & 6-10pm
- Major credit cards
- Non-smoking area
- Licensed
- Children welcome
- 80 seats
- Starters from £2.95,
  mains from £6.95

There's a nice mix of students and families at this child-friendly, simply decorated modern café restaurant.

The specials change fortnightly and the standard menu includes dishes like rocket and garden pea risotto, bruschetta, goat's cheese and roast veg tarts and stuffed peppers. The desserts include a luxury banoffee pie (how do you make it more luxurious?).

It's licensed and you can BYO with a corkage charge, although you need to be a member (a simple matter of a bit of form-filling, we're assured). There are also freshly made juices and smoothies, subject to availability. Sit outside in a heated area, weather permitting. Plenty of space, no booking needed apart from parties of six or more.

Dimitri's

Open all day, booking is recommended evenings and weekends in this very vegetarian-friendly wine bar. Until 5pm you can get snack food like pitta with falafel and hummus, or feta and aubergine, or eat from the wide ranging tapas and meze based menu. There are loads of individual cheese and vegetarian scoffs; have one as a starter or build a do-it-yourself plate.

If you're feeling more than a little peckish, try the kalamata platter or mega meze for two. Each comes bursting with selections from the tapas menu plus salad and pitta bread, with vegetable kebabs, couscous and pilaf putting in an appearance on the mega meze. Last orders can be put in reassuringly late at 11pm most nights.

- Simpsons Fold
  20 Dock St
  Leeds LS10 1JF
- 0113 246 0339
- Serving times:
  Mon-Sat 11am-11pm
  Sun 11am-10.30pm
- Booking recommended evenings and weekends
- Major credit cards
- Smoking throughout
- Licensed
- Children welcome
- 120 seats
- Tapas from £3.95, full meze from £10.95

West Yorkshire

Hansa's

This award-winning restaurant's menu is virtually vegan. The cuisine is from the north-western Indian state of Gujarat, where people share a dessert at the beginning of the meal. However, you might want to wait to see if you have room left...

There are four thalis or, if you want to eat à la carte, starters include patra – tropical colocasia leaves pasted with curry batter, steamed and stir fried with onions and mustard seeds, or Hansa's Spice Bomb – deep-fried potato with a spicy masala filling. Then there's a choice of dhals, main dishes, plus specialities such as masala dosa or Hansa's chaat – chickpeas, puffed rice and potato with onions, tamarind sauce and yoghurt – not forgetting the rice and bread selection. Drinks include a fully organic wine list.

- 72-74 North St
  Leeds LS2 7PN
- 0113 244 4408
- Serving times:
  Mon-Thurs 5-10pm
  Fri 5-10.30pm
  Sat 6-11pm
  Sun 12-1.45pm
- Booking recommended weekends
- Major credit cards
- Non-smoking area
- Licensed
- Children welcome before 9pm
- 60 seats
- Mains from £6

West Yorkshire

- 24 Central Rd
  Leeds LS1 6DE
- 0113 243 9090
- Serving times:
  Mon-Thurs
  11.30am-9.45pm
  Fri-Sat
  11.30am-10.45pm
  Closed bank holidays
- Major credit cards
- Non-smoking
- Licensed
- Children welcome
- 150 seats
- Starters from £3

Little Tokyo

As you might expect of a traditional Japanese restaurant, Little Tokyo is not completely vegetarian, but ...wow! You might be tempted to head for the door when presented with vegetarian choices including chicken legs and steak, but when they're 100% soya-based (and often vegan-friendly too), stay seated, and get ordering.

You can also try vegetarian ramen – a soup noodle dish made with mountain yam flakes, daikon, seaweed, lotus root, watercress and mange tout – plus a decent choice of shallow-fried noodle dishes. There's a wide range of Japanese beers, and interesting teas including chrysanthemum and Japanese green varieties, and soya milk is available if you fancy a more traditional English cuppa.

- 79 Great George St
  Leeds LS1 3BR
- 0113 234 7000
- Serving times:
  Mon-Wed
  10am-5.30pm
  Thurs-Sat 10am-6pm
- Major credit cards
- Non-smoking
- Not licensed
- Children welcome
- 6 seats
- Sandwiches from £3

Org

Stock up on environmentally-friendly products at this organic grocers before grabbing one of the handful of seats in their café for a well-earned break, a freshly-pressed juice and a spot of lunch.

Choose from some great sandwiches such as blue cheese or wensleydale with apple and salad, or roast tofu with apricot and ginger chutney or dairy-free mayo, all on homemade bread. All the soups are vegan, and you can also enjoy other hot dishes like veggieburgers, jackets or a vegan Thai-style tofu and peanut pizza, as well as some very fine salad selections.

Expect some punchy juices and creamy smoothies, soya milk shakes and dairy-free cappuccinos.

Roots & Fruits

Conveniently situated for the Grand Theatre, this serves a splendid all-day breakfast to line your stomach if you're heading for a four-hour epic next door. They do a nice, if familiar, line in wine bar snacks – deep fried brie, potato wedges with sour cream, spring rolls or baguettes and ciabatta filled with good cheese and something extra, or a vegetarian pâté.

Main courses give a vague nod in the direction of Europe: cannelloni, moussaka, Greek salad, or you can satisfy your veggieburger needs and choose from a range of appealing extra toppings. A good choice of juices, including mango, great selection of teas and coffees, and homemade desserts from the blackboard make this a reliable fuelling station.

- 10-11 Grand Arcade Leeds LS1 6PG
- Next to Grand Theatre
- 0113 242 8313
- Serving times:
  Mon-Fri 11am-6.45pm
  Sat 10am-6.45pm
  Closed bank holidays
- Major credit cards
- Non-smoking area
- Licensed
- Children welcome
- 46 seats
- Snacks from £2.95

Sahara Café

If you are looking to eat North African food at 3am, this is the place for you! Although not predominately vegetarian, there is still a wide range of interesting dishes to appeal. You can choose from a range of sandwiches and baguettes filled with falafel, Mediterranean vegetables and hummus, or potato and melted cheese or, for a larger meal, start with olives, garlic bread or Greek salad, and follow up with main courses including vegetarian couscous or tagine (both vegan), and stuffed peppers or aubergines. Desserts include chocolate cake, ice creams and sorbets.

Wash it all down with mint tea, a spicy coffee, a Sahara cocktail or freshly squeezed juice. And, if you pick the right night, enjoy the belly dancing!

- 23 Eastgate Leeds LS2 7LY
- 0113 243 6060
- Serving times:
  Mon-Thurs 10am-3am
  Fri-Sat 10am-4.30am
  Sun 1pm-2am
- No credit cards
- Smoking throughout
- Not licensed, BYO with no corkage
- Children welcome
- 150 seats
- Snacks from £2

- Burley Lodge Centre
  42-46 Burley
  Lodge Rd
  Leeds LS6 1QF
- 0113 275 4142
- Serving times:
  Mon-Tues & Fri
  12-2.15pm
- No credit cards
- Non-smoking
- Not licensed
- Children welcome
- 40 seats
- Mains from £2

The Green Room Café

This is a volunteer-run community café, committed to promoting healthy and affordable food. You can eat in or take away and they also run an outside catering service. Three quarters of the food is vegetarian, and there's normally a vegan option as well.

One of the most reasonably priced venues we know of: the dish of the day is just £2 and comes with a salad and homemade coleslaw. If you are on an even stricter budget, fill up on a lunchtime jacket potato for little more than £1.

Panini and toasted sandwiches are available, as are homemade cakes, puddings and smoothies. Children can enjoy smaller main meal portions.

- 2-4 Commercial Rd
  Kirkstall
  Leeds LS5 3AQ
- 0113 275 7555
- Serving times:
  Mon-Sat 5-10pm
  Sun 12-10pm
- Booking
  recommended
- Major credit cards
- Non-smoking apart
  from lounge and bar
- Licensed
- Children welcome
- 54 seats
- Mains from £10.75

The Millrace

It's best to book at this recent winner of North East Restaurant of the Year. The bar and restaurant are in a lovingly restored stone building with specially commissioned furniture.

There's a Mediterranean-Asian fusion feel to the menu. The steamed savoury pudding of summer vegetables and smoked tofu, with saffron potatoes and sherry sauce is a bit of a winner, and likewise the warm terrine of Mediterranean vegetables with an artichoke and feta salad. Interesting side-dishes – sundried tomato fritters and polenta bubble and squeak with relish, plus salads and mash.

The imaginative desserts can include a dairy-free crème caramel and a triple chocolate ice cream dessert. Good British cheeseboard to choose from.

The Cheerful Chilli

You can bring your own wine (£1 corkage per table of four) to this small evening-only café-style restaurant housed in an old farm building. Be sure to book at the weekend, or hire it for your own bash on a Thursday.

Start off with the chargrilled vegetable salad or soup, or choose from the usual Mexican standards of nachos, potato skins and quesadillas. Move on to spinach enchilada, chimichanga, tacos or a build-it-yourself pizza.

The desserts add a bit of class to the menu: rich chocolate cake with homemade lemon ice cream or baked lemon cheesecake. They take pains to use GM-free ingredients and have vegan substitutes for cheese, soured cream, milk and garlic bread.

- Ramblers Tearooms
  East Chevin Rd
  Otley LS21 3DD
- 01943 466567
- Serving times:
  Tues-Wed
  6.30-9.30pm
  Fri-Sat 6.30-9.30pm
  Open Thursdays for
  large bookings
- Booking advisable
- No credit cards
- Non-smoking
- BYO £1 corkage
- Children welcome
- 26 seats
- Mains from £5

Aagrah

There's no shortage of Indian restaurants in this part of the world, but this is one that values its vegetarian customers, and doesn't just offer a few morsels from the nether reaches of the menu or expect them to be happy with a couple of meat-free side dishes.

Start with pakoras, bhajis or samosas (or have a bit of everything in their special starter for two), and move on to some well-spiced mains including kormas, madras and vindaloo-strength curries or house specialities such as chana achar or the mixed veg hyderabadi. Good balti-style selection, including half a dozen paneer dishes cooked with chickpeas and potatoes, okra, peas or mixed veg.

There's also a comprehensive selection of sides together with good rice and breads.

- 438 Bradford Rd
  Pudsey LS28 8EA
- 01274 668818
- Serving times:
  Mon-Thurs 6-11pm
  Fri-Sat 6-11.30pm
  Sun 12.30-11pm
- Booking advisable
  weekends
- Major credit cards
- Smoking throughout
- Licensed
- Children welcome
- 80 seats
- Mains from £4.50

West Yorkshire

West Yorkshire

235

- 29 Rochdale Rd
  Todmorden OL14 7LA
- Opposite the library
- 01706 813737
- Serving times:
  Mon-Thurs 9am-5pm
  Fri-Sat 9.30am-11pm
- Booking recommended
  Fri & Sat evenings
- No credit cards
- Non-smoking
  restaurant area
- Not licensed, BYO
  with no corkage
- Children welcome
- 40 seats
- Lunchtime mains
  from £3

Bear Café

Worth a visit for the architecture alone, this café is in a lovely 19th century co-operative building with original features and a light and airy feel.

The Bearistas cover the globe, cooking-wise, with lunchtime wraps, pies, Greek salads and well-stuffed ciabattas. Do let yourself go on the vegan hot chocolate cake. They open on Friday and Saturday evenings for dinner, book a table for their excellent tapas menu, more Mediterranean than Spanish, and none the worse for that. Middle-eastern dishes, like apricot and pecan pilaf or a Tunisian brik line up with mushrooms a la grecque, marinated olives and green salad.

You can buy a bottle of organic wine from the shop downstairs or bring your own without corkage charges.

- 15 Water St
  Todmorden OL14 5AB
- 01706 810030
- Serving times:
  Wed 11am-4pm
  Thurs 11am-9pm
  Fri-Sat 11am-9.30pm
  Sun 11am-4pm
  Closed bank holidays
- Booking recommended
  at weekends
- Major credit cards
- Non-smoking area
- Licensed
- 90 seats
- Starters from £2,
  mains from £5.95

Tenth Muse

This laid back and, in the evening, candlelit café bar will serve you food from breakfast until mid-evening, with the bar going on until 11pm.

Veggie and vegan cooked breakfasts give way to a lunch menu of baked potatoes, sandwiches, omelettes and salad, with tasty sides like fried halloumi or Greek haricot beans and garlic mushrooms. In the evening you can also have nut roast, halloumi kebabs, penne pasta, burritos, chilli, a dedicated and comprehensive vegetarian meze or burger and chips. There are also some good substantial vegetable salads in starter and mains portions.

Everything is freshly made on the premises and they keep soya milk. Open for Sunday lunch.

Thai Kitchen

Centrally located very close to the Cathedral, this popular Thai restaurant stays open late when it's busy. Thai Kitchen is a popular Valentine's night destination and they will also cater weddings and banquets.

There's a very reasonable vegetarian menu that includes sweetcorn cakes, deep fried tofu, and spicy sweet and sour mushroom soup with coconut milk. The main courses feature inventive ways with tofu – for example curried with peanuts, potatoes, red and green peppers – plus plenty of stir fries featuring Thai basil, chillies, ginger or blackbean sauce. Noodles or Thai rice provide the comforting plain backdrop for the spicy food to perform against. There's a late licence if you're there for the duration.

- 3 Cross Square Wakefield WF1 1PQ
- Close to the Cathedral
- 01924 298555
- Serving times:
  Mon-Thurs 5-10pm
  Fri-Sat 5-11pm
- Booking recommended Sat evenings
- Major credit cards
- Non-smoking area
- Licensed
- Children welcome
- 60 seats

West Yorkshire

east riding
north yorkshire

east riding • north yorkshire

East Riding

North Yorkshire

Skipton

11 Whitby

7 Robin Hood's Bay

□ Northallerton

8 Scarborough

10 Thirsk

□ Ripon

NORTH YORKSHIRE

1 Bridlington

4 Brearton

5 **6** Knaresborough

Harrogate **12** **13** York

EAST RIDING

□ Beverley

□ Selby

2 **3** Hull

□ Goole

east riding • north yorkshire

- 10 Wellington Rd
  Bridlington YO15 2BG
- Opposite cenotaph
- 01262 679800
- Serving times:
  Tues-Fri 11am-2.30pm
  Sat 11am-2.30pm
  & 6.30-8.30pm
- Booking recommended
  for Sat evenings
- No credit cards
- Non-smoking
- Not licensed, BYO
  with £1 corkage
- Children welcome
- 60 seats
- Evening starters
  from £3.50

Bean There

As good as it gets in the vegetarian café world. Everything homemade, including the bread, using mainly organic and locally-grown seasonal produce. Open for lunch in the week and for gourmet evenings on Saturday – when you can bring your own booze – this is like going to a superbly competent friend's house for a good meal.

The lunchtime menu is a complete bargain – main meal, pudding and a drink, all for around a fiver. There are soups, flans, bean burgers and sausages, as well as a good range of cakes and puddings.

The gourmet dinners have plenty of vegan choice and mains such as spinach, roast potato and mushroom bake with seasonal veg, or a feta and vegetable pie.

- 80b Newland Avenue
  Hull HU5 3AB
- 01482 494352
- Serving times:
  Mon-Sat 9am-5.30pm
  Open Sundays
  in summer
- No credit cards
- Smoking throughout
- BYO with minimal
  corkage
- Children welcome
- 50 seats

The Zoo

Down a small path off Newland Avenue, this friendly, relaxed café offers a range of homemade healthy food, using organic produce where possible.

There is a different soup each day, and you can choose from main courses ranging from vegan bean burritos to stuffed peppers via stilton mushrooms and cheesy garlic ciabatta. There are also yummy cakes such as chocolate nut brownies, carrot cake and vegan lemon sponge. Children can enjoy a smaller portions from the main menu. In addition to the more usual drinks, you can try a non-dairy smoothie, or a fruit-of-the-day milkshake. In good weather enjoy your meal outside in a veritable sun trap.

Call for details of The Zoo's next vegan nights, which they hold a few times a year.

Hitchcock's

Where to start with this one? In Hull's old town, in a marvellous listed building with too many stairs, you – the diner – can dictate the menu. The first person to book for a given night chooses the menu style for the evening: Italian, Indian, Chinese, Thai, Cajun – you name it, Bruce Hitchcock and Jane Inckle have tried it, won, and are still prepared to accept new challenges.

There's one sitting per night, buffet style. The choice of a couple of starters and around a dozen mains allow your taste buds to run riot in the style of the evening and then return to base with a standard range of desserts (crumble, pecan pie, chocolate cake, fruit salad etc). The Cajun menu (okra gumbo, fried plantain, Jamaican curry, red beans and rice, black-eyed bean fritters, hot tomato salsa, griddle cake) would excite anyone's interest, but given their reputation you can be pretty sure they're all amazing. They have house wine for just £7 a bottle, or you can bring your own and pay a pound corkage.

At £12 for three courses or £10 for concessions (£15 and £12 on Fri and Sat), Hitchcock's deserves to be popular. You may find yourself queuing for the buffet, but with such a high standard of cooking and an unusual approach to restaurant dining, you wouldn't think of noticing. Even the most anti-vegetarian bigot would be beguiled by the exciting food and relaxed atmosphere. Book well ahead and decide the menu, or go with the flow. It would be hard to imagine a more enjoyable way of eating out.

- 1 Bishops Lane Hull HU1 1PA
- 01482 320233
- Serving times: Tues-Sat single sitting at 8pm
- Booking essential Fri, Sat, and during December – recommended on other nights
- No credit cards
- Generally non-smoking
- Licensed
- Children welcome
- 100 seats
- Three courses £12 (£15 on Fri & Sat)

East Riding

North Yorkshire

- Brearton, near Harrogate HG3 3BX
- 01423 862929
- Serving times:
  Tues-Sat 12-2pm
  & 7-9pm
  Sun 12-2pm
- No credit cards
- Non-smoking area
- Licensed
- Children welcome
- 40 seats
- Mains from £5.50

Malt Shovel Inn

This respected real ale pub is willing to cater for special diets and do smaller portions for children, and there's a small outside seating area.

The vegetarian selection of around ten choices embraces potato and tomato curry, pasta with mushrooms and garlic, spinach lasagne, nut roast as well as a couple of tasty sounding salads. The dessert menu can include rum and raisin bread pudding, treacle tart and apple and bramble (blackberry) crumble.

In addition to a good selection of proper beer, there's a comprehensive and keenly priced wine list.

Everything on the menu is homemade, and it's only Sunday night and Monday that you can't get food; presumably the chef's out cold with a beer in his hand.

North Yorkshire

- Jockey Lane Knaresborough HG5 0HF
- 01423 869208
- Serving times:
  Mon-Wed &
  Fri-Sat 10am-4pm
  Sun 12-4pm
  Closed Thurs
- No credit cards
- Non-smoking
- Licensed
- Children welcome
- 26 seats

Pollyanna's Tearoom

Pollyanna's is a traditional English tearoom, which is also licensed and serves some substantial lunches. Most food is made from local, organic produce and some special diets can be catered for, although there's not automatically a vegan choice.

Choose from two starters and a good selection of main courses. Soups are freshly made – leek and potato, tomato and basil or carrot and coriander – then move on to dishes such as a fresh spinach lasagne, broccoli and cashew nut quiche, sesame seed pancakes with mushroom filling, or omelettes and jacket potatoes.

Most desserts are vegetarian and all are homemade. Children are welcome, and can enjoy smaller portions of almost anything on the menu.

Wild Ginger

All the food here is vegan (with the exception of the option of dairy cheeses or non-soya milk), so when you see a ham and cheese toastie on the menu, don't panic – it's definitely soya based and safe to eat!

Expect a brunch and lunch menu of both full and lighter breakfasts, speciality salads, toasties, sandwiches and both hearty and lighter daily specials, and enjoy food that's been prepared with ingredients that indicate a distinct – rather than passing – commitment to organic and local produce.

The bright and lively décor works well with the more traditional pine furnishings, and it's candlelit in the evenings – when you can take advantage of the early bird menu between 5-7pm. Evening starters feature traditional favourites like garlic breads, soup, mushrooms, olives or dips and chips, and there's mains such as haggis (yep, you read that right) with carrot and swede, potato wedges and gravy.

There are occasional themed evenings – last year's Halloween bash at the end of October had its own (rather fun) menu of around half a dozen specially prepared dishes. These events are advertised in the restaurant and, if you want to join in, do book your place early.

As well as serving organic and vegetarian/vegan wine and beer, there's also an appealing range of smoothies and juices.

Winners of the Vegan Society's best restaurant award three years running, and known to customers as far afield as Chile, this venue is very definitely worth a detour.

- 5 Station Parade
  Harrogate HG1 1UF
- 01423 566122
- Serving times:
  Tues-Thurs 10am-3pm
  Fri-Sat 11am-7pm
- Booking recommended
- Major credit cards
- Non-smoking
- Licensed
- Children welcome
- 40 seats
- Lunch mains
  from £4.95

North Yorkshire

- Chapel St
  Robin Hood's Bay
  YO22 4SQ
- 01947 881174
- Serving times:
  7 days 10am-5.15pm
  Summer serving
  until 7.15pm
- Major credit cards
- Non-smoking inside
- Not licensed, BYO
  with no corkage
- Children welcome
- 44 seats including
  terrace
- Mains from £5.50

North Yorkshire

Old Chapel Café

Overlooking the famous bay, this café in a converted Wesleyan chapel is open until 6pm – later in summer or by arrangement.

There's a couple of specials each day, which are always vegan: for example carrot and walnut pie with five veg mish-mash, mushroom and dhal korma or an almond and lemon roast. The snacks menu offers noodles, couscous or baked potatoes with a huge range of toppings including scrambled egg and chilli, garlic spread, hummus and carrot or mushroom pâté with pickle. There's also main course salads, and sandwiches on organic bread with vegan-friendly spread.

Look up the monthly themed weekends – Caribbean, Mexican, Thai, Victorian (where dressing up is, we're relieved to report, optional). BYO with no corkage charge.

Scarborough

- 70 North St
  Town Centre
  Scarborough
  YO11 1DE
- 01723 341361
- Serving times:
  Mon-Sat 11am-10pm
  Sun 5-10pm
- No credit cards
- Non-smoking area
- Licensed
- Children welcome
- 20 seats
- Pizzas from £4

North Yorkshire

Icon Pizzeria & Grill

Bright cheery café bar where vegan isn't a foreign language and vegetarians can enjoy a range of pizzas and pastas far greater than the usual couple of choices at some other pizzerias.

Choose from sandwiches including feta and olive and falafel with salad on freshly baked baguettes, stuffed pitta bread, salads which don't need editing to lose the odd fishy bit, and around a dozen pizza and pasta dishes.

All the veggie options are clearly marked, and you can also indulge in vegetarian desserts of fudge cake, passion cake and ice cream. There's a short wine list, and freshly squeezed juices including apple and carrot, and homemade lemonade.

Wild Oats Café

At this traditional café above the Healthy Life healthfood shop, everything is prepared daily in a reassuringly open kitchen. Vegan, wheat-free and gluten-free diets are cheerfully accommodated.

The freshly prepared soups are generally vegan and there are vegan bakes as well. Check the specials board, but don't arrive too late at lunchtime or you may find the last remaining portion of your first choice being happily consumed by an earlier arrival! Otherwise, chow down on hefty wholemeal sandwiches with hummus and roasted peppers, peanut butter and apple or choose one of the main course salads.

Good coffee comes by the cafetière and you can have scones, flapjacks or some lovely sweet nibbles including dairy-free orange cake.

- 10 High St
  Skipton BD23 1JZ
- 01756 790619
- Serving times:
  Mon-Sat
  9.30am-4.30pm
- Major credit cards
- Non-smoking
- Children welcome
- 32 seats
- Soups from £2.75

North Yorkshire

Charles Bistro

This modern bistro in a listed building just off Thirsk's Market Square opens for lunch and dinner and has a menu heaving with great vegetarian choices.

Choose one of their sandwiches – served with proper homemade chips and a small salad – from a range including vegetarian sausage and onion rings, or feta, sundried tomatoes and olive, or revel in something more substantial like a Mediterranean vegetable and cheese Wellington, the (vegan) capsicum pepper filled with Provençal vegetables, or a nut roast with all the trimmings. Children's portions of some dishes are available, and there's a serious dessert menu.

Currently offering two courses for under a tenner on Wednesday evenings. Booking essential if you plan to visit on Friday or Saturday.

- Bakers Alley
  Off Market Place
  Thirsk YO7 1HD
- Behind NatWest
- 01845 527444
- Serving times:
  Tues-Sat
  11.30am-2.30pm
  & 6.30-9.39pm
- Booking essential
  Fri & Sat
- Major credit cards
- Non-smoking
- Licensed
- Children welcome
- 32 seats
- Mains from £8

North Yorkshire

North Yorkshire

- 95 Church St
  Whitby YO22 4BH
- 01947 825010
- Serving times:
  7 days 9am-5pm
  Open seasonally
  Thurs-Sat evenings
- Booking essential
  Sat evenings
- Major credit cards
- Non-smoking
- Licensed
- Children welcome
- 90 seats including
  garden
- Snacks from £2.50

Sanders Yard

Open daily all year and seasonally for the evenings, the style here is broadly Mediterranean. There's a courtyard and garden for the summer and, if you stay in one of their cottages or B&B rooms, their full cooked vegetarian breakfast is included in the price.

Lunches include sandwiches, baked spuds and veggieburgers, or savouries such as mushrooms on toast as well as daily specials. Evenings have dishes like wild mushroom and leek risotto or leek and mushrooms in a spinach pancake, and there are occasional weekly themed menus including tapas with choices like garlic potatoes, marinated onions, whole roasted garlic with cream cheese or a toasted walnut and almond risotto. Stunning desserts – plum and Wensleydale crumble or strawberry chocolate tart.

North Yorkshire

- 15-17 Grape Lane
  The Quarter
  York YO1 7HU
- 01904 610676
- Serving times:
  Mon-Sat 10am-
  midnight
  Sun 12-midnight
- Booking recommended
  Fri & Sat evenings
- Major credit cards
- Smoking throughout
- Licensed
- Children welcome
- 50 seats
- Starters from £2

El Piano

Well, lots of marks for effort here, for this very vegan-aware Spanish/Hispanic influenced restaurant, the like of which you'd probably never get in Spain.

Open from 10am for a Spanish breakfast of bread, manchego cheese, tortilla, olives and salsa, which should stave off the pangs until evening. They do meal deals for two, big platters of mixed salad, pâtés, baskets of pakoras or falafel and a great choice of desserts, such as vegan and gluten-free chocolate pie or coconut and banana pie.

You can buy olives, olive oil, Spanish crisps and coffee from their bazaar and they duly credit their suppliers on the menu. Very central in busy York if you're up for the weekend.

The Blake Head Café

A lovely combination – bookshop and café – and this one has a part-beamed, part-glazed ceiling and solid, quality furniture. Food and wine are often organic, with good vegan choices.

The special changes daily, but there are always soups, quiches, savouries like mushroom and butter bean chasseur with lemon and thyme dumplings or homity pie with roasted red onions and pine nuts, vegan and wheat-free pâtés and some absolutely cracking cakes – chocolate, hazelnut and ricotta or Tunisian orange syrup.

Also available: tasty breakfasts, from veggie mixed grill to sautéed mushrooms and the divine sounding potato and parsnip rosti with a (free range, of course) poached egg, mushrooms and gremolata, or the batard aux raisins – toasted fruit bread to you.

- 104 Micklegate
  York YO1 6JX
- Behind Blake Head bookshop
- 01904 623767
- Serving times:
  Mon-Sat 9.30am-5pm
  Sun 10am-5pm
- Major credit cards
- Non-smoking
- Licensed
- Children welcome
- 40 seats and courtyard
- Light lunch from £3.50

North Yorkshire

cleveland
cumbria
durham
northumberland
tyne & wear

cleveland • cumbria • durham
northumberland • tyne & wear

Cleveland

Cumbria

Durham

Northumberland

Tyne & Wear

□ Berwick
-upon-Tweed

NORTHUMBERLAND

□ Morpeth

CUMBRIA

Newcastle upon Tyne

Hexham **18**   **19** **20**

□ Carlisle   Consett □   **TYNE & WEAR**

Caldbeck   **17** Durham

Cockermouth **4**   Hartlepool □

5 **6**   **14** Little Salkeld   Middlesbrough

3 **12** Keswick   □ Penrith

raithwaite   **DURHAM**   **1**

Grasmere **8** **9**   Darlington   Eaglescliffe

ether **13**   **2** Ambleside

Vasdale   **7**   **15** Staveley   **CLEVELAND**

Coniston **10** **11** Kendal

16 Ulverston

□ Barrow-in-Furness

cleveland • cumbria • durham
northumberland • tyne & wear

Cleveland

- 9 Station Rd
  Eaglescliffe
  Stockton On Tees
  TS16 0BU
- 01642 780465
- Serving times:
  Tues-Sun 9am-5pm
  & 6.30-10pm
  Limited menu 2-5pm
- Evening booking
  recommended
- Major credit cards
- Non-smoking area
- Licensed
- Children welcome
- 50 seats
- Starters from £3.50

The Waiting Room

The Waiting Room is an informal bistro-style restaurant, which also serves coffee, cakes and sandwiches until 5pm. Local organic producers supply a good proportion of the fruit and veg (and there's also a range of organic wines and beers) and you can enjoy live entertainment some Sunday evenings.

Evening starters can include a fried halloumi salad, roast aubergine, garlic and mushroom pâté, daily soups and baked mushrooms with blue cheese and pecans. Tasty main courses feature dishes such as spinach and feta cakes with chilli jam, and aubergine cannelloni accompanied by artichoke hearts, olives and pine nuts. Smaller portions for children can be made to order.

The restaurant includes a light conservatory area, and there are some good value set menus at Christmas.

Braithwaite | Omnivorous Café

Cumbria

- Whinlatter
  Visitors Centre
  Braithwaite
  CA12 5TW
- 017687 78410
- Serving times:
  7 days 10am-5pm
  Closes earlier
  in winter
- No credit cards
- Non-smoking
- Not licensed
- Children welcome
- 50 seats
- Mains from £4.75

Siskin Café

At the top of the Whinlatter Pass, Siskin is an omnivorous café – but one with good vegetarian choices and run by a proprietor with more than a passing knowledge of vegetarian and vegan ingredients and cooking.

The two or three daily soups are vegetarian, including a vegan option, and the daily specials can include nut roast or a creamy leek croustade. If you just want a sandwich you won't have to settle for cheddar of unknown origin – there's a design-your-own option with fillings ranging from hummus, feta or roast peppers through to three-nut butter and chocolate-hazelnut spread – and you could also enjoy a hot panini.

There's also a choice of yummy home-baked cakes.

Zeffirellis

You'll be begging for a wet week in the Lake District now you know about this. The daytime menu at Zeffirellis will cheer and sustain you with a variety of entirely vegetarian options. Hot ciabattas with roasted vegetables and feta or olive tapenade, goat's cheese and red pepper salsa, baguettes with cream cheese, stilton, pears and walnuts and bruschetta with pesto, cherry tomatoes and mozzarella. Or fancy a baked potato or pizza? You're in the right place for a good selection, confident that it'll be organic where possible as well as GM-free. You can also blow in for a quick cuppa and cake from the counter service.

The best is yet to come. This family-run business also owns a cinema (two screens here, two in the newly converted junior school 200 yards away) so you can book for a candlelit dinner and a movie. The more adventurous evening Italian vegetarian menu has succulent favourites like Piedmont peppers or griddled aubergine, stilton and mushroom tagliatelle, and there's sophisticated mushroom ravioli with a wild mushroom and black truffle sauce, plus a great choice of pizzas. Desserts include fresh lemon tart, soft frozen yoghurt with frangelico liqueur (think alcoholic Nutella), and summer pudding.

For £15.95 you get a two-course dinner and a reserved seat for a film, and there are some good art house bills going on here. It's a marvellous idea; they should start a chain. And if you're looking for the perfect private party venue for a milestone celebration, you can book the bar and restaurant area on the first floor. We'll be back.

Compston Rd
Ambleside LA22 6PR

015394 33845

Serving times:
Mon-Fri 10am-4pm & 6-9.45pm
Sat-Sun 10am-4pm & 5-9.45pm
During summer, Mon-Fri evening orders start from 5pm

Book for combined meal/cinema deals

Major credit cards

Non-smoking

Licensed

Children welcome

160 seats

Light meals from £2.50, evening mains from £6.50

Cumbria

Cumbria

- Priests Mill,
  Church Terrace
  Caldbeck CA7 8DR
- 016974 78267
- Serving times:
  Lunch 12-3pm, 7 days
  Open 10am-5pm
  (11am-4pm Mon)
  Open one evening a
  month, normally Fri
  Closed Jan to mid Feb
- Book for evenings
- No credit cards
- Non-smoking
- Not licensed, but BYO
  for evening openings
- Children welcome
- 50 seats
- 3-course evening
  meal £16.75

The Watermill

Find this café in an award-winning mill conversion on your travels through the Lake District National Park, and relax on the terrace overlooking the river and village cricket pitch.

Lots of local produce and organic ingredients make up the daytime menu. There are snacks like hummus, with dips and chips, vegan soups, or the more weighty aubergine and almond layer, smoked cheese and broccoli bake and Mediterranean lasagne. Finish with the crumbles of the day or locally made ice cream and sweet tarts. Children won't feel left out with favourites like spaghetti or beans on toast, and baked potatoes.

There's usually a special dinner evening each month, normally on a Friday, so book up if you've planned your holiday schedule.

Cumbria

- 7a Station St
  Cockermouth
  CA13 9QW
- 01900 822790
- Serving times:
  Tues-Thurs 10am-3pm
  Fri 10am-3pm
  & 6-9.30pm
  Sat 10am-3pm
- No credit cards
- Non-smoking
- Licensed
- Children welcome
- 25 seats
- Sandwiches from £2

Merienda

Kay Watson's Merienda is a modern, relaxed café-bar that also showcases work from students at the local art college. The short menu is at least half vegetarian, with a lot of care taken to source ingredients from Cumbrian suppliers – and all the better for it.

Arrive before midday if you fancy a light breakfast, confident that your eggs will be free range and locally sourced, and the stack of accompanying soldiers made with bread from a local bakery. There are daily specials like brie and tomato with a red onion marmalade on granary bread, and interesting pasta salads or sandwiches and soup, together with a good coffee selection including soya Tia Maria latte. There's also local beer and premium spirits. Open Friday evenings from 6pm with a separate tapas menu.

Quince and Medlar

Hitch up the wagon and head north for Cockermouth. Quince & Medlar has won the Vegetarian Society's 'Vegetarian Restaurant of the Year' three times (most recently at the 2003 awards – jointly with Manna in London) and been a runner up on many more occasions.

Settle into the lounge with its comfy settees for pre-dinner drinks and canapés and, when you're ready, head for one of the two small candlelit dining rooms.

The menu ranges from the deliciously simple (and therefore hardest to pull off): fresh asparagus with citrus roasted crumbs, roast red onions stuffed with couscous and feta on red chard, to the adventurous apple and parsnip timbale, wrapped in spinach on puff pastry with mushrooms and red wine, or a Wensleydale and French bean crown (where are you Grommit?), topped with nuts and a tomato and chilli salsa.

Desserts are rich and voluptuous, such as amaretto parfait, chocolate orange pie or white chocolate cheesecake with a dark chocolate sauce.

The wine list is mostly organic, but if you've drawn the short straw and been nominated as the day's driver, you can enjoy a selection of cordials including passion fruit or lime and lemongrass, or a peach, pear or apricot fruit nectar.

A high proportion of customers aren't vegetarian, but head here in their droves attracted, doubtless, by the numerous name-checks Q&M receives in national foodie magazines and the Sunday supplements.

This is destination dining, a really special treat.

- 13 Castlegate
  Cockermouth
  CA13 9EU
- 01900 823579
- Serving times:
  Tues-Sat 7-9.30pm
  Open Sundays on
  bank holiday
  weekends
- Booking advisable
- Major credit cards
- Non-smoking
- Licensed
- Children over
  5 years welcome
- 26 seats
- Starters from £4,
  mains from £12.50

Cumbria

- Torver
  Coniston LA21 8AZ
- 01539 441282
- Serving times:
  7 days 12-9pm
- Major credit cards
- Smoking throughout
- Licensed
- Children welcome
- 60 seats

The Church House Inn

Right next to the church, this 14th century pub is the oldest in the Lake District. Although not completely vegetarian, there is a wide range of veggie-friendly traditional pub food: you might decide to start with broccoli and stilton soup, then choose veggie-sausage casserole in Yorkshire pudding, or honey and nut roast, and finish off with sticky toffee pudding or homemade apple pie. Real ale drinkers will be delighted by the cask and guest ales.

Children can choose from vegetarian burgers, sausages, or small portions from the adult menu. With log fires in both bars in the winter and a beer garden to relax in for sunnier days, this is a great way to finish a day at the lakes.

Grasmere

Vegetarian Café & Restaurant

- Church Bridge
  Stock Lane
  Grasmere LA22 9SN
- By St Oswald's church
- 015394 35528
- Serving times:
  Easter-Oct 7 days
  10am-5pm & 6-9pm
  Winter: closed
  Mon-Tues & evenings
- Major credit cards
- Non-smoking
- Licensed
- Children welcome
- 40 seats & terrace
- Snacks from £4

The Rowan Tree

Café by day, and restaurant during the evening (although they only open for dinner between Easter and October), The Rowan Tree doesn't shout about its vegetarian credentials but rest assured, you will be able to enjoy absolutely anything they serve.

The daytime menu includes paninis, sandwiches and baguettes plus specials like a roasted vegetable and feta cheese tart, Wensleydale and potato pie, or the vegan chilli or fruit and vegetable curry. Evenings can find you choosing between a great selection including vegan soups, samosas, mushroom, hazelnut and red wine pâté, Thai green curry with Jasmine rice or smoked cheese and asparagus pancakes.

There's a Mediterranean feel to the restaurant, with a terrace overlooking the Rothay for summer dining.

Cumbria

Cumbria

Lancrigg

Consider coming here for a few days stay: a grand Georgian house in 30 acres of landscaped woodland and gardens – perfectly quiet and seemingly isolated, but only half a mile from Grasmere village. Breakfast, morning coffee, afternoon teas and dinner are served seven days a week in the candle and chandelier lit dining room, with exceptional views over the valley.

Completely vegetarian, with vegan choices, the dinner menu can feature starters such as cashew nut, coriander and sesame rice cakes with a pirri pirri dipping sauce, or you could find yourself choosing between a Middle Eastern meze or cream of cauliflower soup – unusually teamed with coconut and a poppy seed roll.

The main courses have included an aubergine and sundried tomato roulade with rosemary and sage roast potatoes and steamed vegetables, or the chef's salad with feta cheese or marinated tofu. The wine, beer and spirits all have organic accreditation, and there's a good cellar to select from.

Lancrigg are sensitive to the needs of those on special diets, and they'll also do children's meals of pizza, pasta or baked potatoes if the little ones are insisting on something familiar.

Desserts are rich – rum pudding with chocolate, walnuts and figs or an apple pear and caramel crumble, as well as lighter options including homemade ice creams and interesting fruit salads.

If you need time away, and want to be pampered and well fed in some of the Lake District's most beautiful scenery, this is the place to be.

- Easedale Grasmere LA22 9QN
- Half a mile from centre of Grasmere village
- 015394 35317
- Serving times: 7 days 8.30am-5.30pm & 6.30-8.30pm
- Booking essential for evenings
- Major credit cards
- Non-smoking
- Licensed
- Children welcome
- 30 seats
- Light lunches from £6

Cumbria

259

Cumbria

- Friends Meeting House
  Stramongate
  Kendal LA9 4BH
- 01539 722975
- Serving times:
  Mon-Sat
  10am-4.15pm
  Closed Sat Nov-Mar
- No credit cards
- Non-smoking
- Not licensed
- Children welcome
- 36 seats
- Daily special
  from £4.50

Tapestry Tearooms

Taking its name and style of décor from the Quaker Tapestry exhibition centre, this tearoom changes the menu daily – generally including a vegan choice as well as something tasty if you're on a gluten free-diet. A typical menu offers two soups and a couple of mains, together with freshly made sandwiches and cakes.

Specials are not without ambition – chestnut and mushroom Wellington with cranberry sauce, or tofu and vegetable satay sticks with rice, topped with peanut sauce, for example – while the soups can include cream of celeriac and parsnip, celery and cashew nut or the Tuscan-inspired butter bean and tomato.

Ideal if you're on a budget, but still want proper, freshly-prepared food, they also offer discounts if you're a pre-booked group visiting the exhibition.

Cumbria

- Kent View
  Waterside
  Kendal LA9 4DZ
- By Miller Bridge
- 01539 729743
- Serving times:
  Mon-Sat 8.30am-4pm
- Major credit cards
- Non-smoking
- Licensed
- Children welcome
- 36 seats
  & outside area

Waterside Wholefoods

In an attractive Georgian building, Waterside Wholefoods specialise in outside catering, and run a vegetarian hotel (www.lakelandnatural.co.uk) as well as this café overlooking the river.

Everything is prepared daily on the premises, and there's no fixed menu – just good food cooked according to season and availability. Soups, savouries like cheese, leek and mushroom pie, ratatouille lattice, casseroles, garlic mushroom quiche and pizza are staples, while lasagnes, salad boxes, tarts and cakes are all great takeouts. At Christmas you can enjoy special lunch menus, and if you get a large enough (12+) group together they'll open for you specially in the evenings.

Licensed, with a vegan wine and beer list that's mainly organic.

The Lakeland Pedlar

Popular with cyclists and walkers, this place has great views of the fells. Get there early for breakfast and good coffee by the cafetière or from the espresso machine. A soft ciabatta roll with pretend streaky bacon or a ribsticking full veggie breakfast of eggs, beans, grilled tomatoes, mushrooms, toast and hash browns will make your 5-3-1 tubing groan.

Lunch visitors can try Mexican style burritos, chilli and pitta bread, soup of the day with a salad, baked potatoes or pizzas. Afternoon tea fans can choose teacakes, scones, flapjacks, chocolate tiffin and homemade cakes. In either case, check out the specials board for hot dishes. Choose organic lemonade, orangeade or cranberry juice and other soft drinks. Licensed; all beer and wine is organic and vegan.

- Hendersons Yard
  Bell Close
  Keswick CA12 5JD
- Look for the Penny Farthing on the gable wall!
- 017687 74492
- Serving times:
  Mon-Sun 9am-5pm
  Also special evening openings
- Major credit cards
- Non-smoking
- Licensed
- Children welcome
- 60 seats, including 28 outside
- Soup from £2.95, mains from £5

Cumbria

The Screes Inn

You know it's a traditional pub with lunchtime sandwiches and scampi and chips on the menu but, deep joy, the vegetarian chefs make sure that you won't go bored or hungry.

The food is home cooked, with some organic choices and there's normally a vegetarian special as well as the regular menu of penne pasta with mushrooms, vegetarian chilli, sweet potato and chickpea curry or goat's cheese strudel with roasted parsnips, celeriac, leek and apple. Not much walking after that lot, but you could make dinner here instead.

They will cater for special diets and there's always soya milk for your tea and coffee. Children's menu isn't vegetarian but pick carefully from the main choice.

- Nether Wasdale
  CA20 1ET
- 019467 26262
- Serving times:
  Mon-Sun 12-2.30pm
  & 6-9pm
- Booking advisable for weekends
- Major credit cards
- Non-smoking area
- Licensed
- Children welcome
- 70 seats
- Starters from £2.75, mains from £6.25

Cumbria

Cumbria

- Little Salkeld
  Penrith CA10 1NN
- 01768 881523
- Serving times:
  7 days 10.30am-5pm
  Closed 23rd Dec
  -early Feb
- Major credit cards
- Non-smoking
- Not licensed
- Children welcome
- 25 seats

The Watermill

Restored by Ana and Nick Jones in 1975, the watermill provides organic flour for their café which overlooks the stream. The Jones' small but dedicated team produce a delicious range of breads, cakes and light lunches.

No ordinary ploughmans here: with the finest cheeses from the local Loch Arthur dairy in Dumfries, those marvellous home-baked breads, and fresh seasonal salads, the Watermill's Miller's lunch is tucker of the highest order.

Lunch is served all day, seven days a week (excepting annual hols 23rd December-early February). In good weather we'd arrive early, having had a morning traipse around the Long Meg stone circle just a mile away, and lay claim to the bench outside the mill itself.

Cumbria

- Mill Yard Back Lane
  Staveley LA8 9LR
- 01539 822329
- Serving times:
  Mon-Fri 10am-5pm
  Sat-Sun 9.30am-5pm
  Closes half hour earlier
  weekdays in winter
- Booking essential for
  evening openings
- Major credit cards
- Non-smoking
- Not licensed, BYO
  with no corkage
- Children welcome
- 90 seats
- Snacks from £2

Wilf's Café

Wilf's is a daytime café with fortnightly special evening openings, which are definitely worth booking for. Located in an old bobbin loft, there's a deck overlooking the river's weir and salmon jump, and a cosy sofa area downstairs.

Have yourself a great veggie breakfast if it's that time of day, or choose from big salads, burgers, jackets or Wilf's famous veggie chilli. Look out for the display of guest cakes, plus flapjacks, caramel shortbread, pineapple fruit cake and the like.

Bring your own beer and wine to the occasional evening openings which feature a lot more than just token veggie choices, or ask them to take the strain when organising your own party – outside catering is another string to their bow.

World Peace Café

Founded by Buddhists, the aim is to bring about world peace through first achieving inner peace oneself. Here's a good place to begin.

The café is thoroughly organic, but not at all spartan – offering iced latte alongside ayurvedic herbal teas. Check the board for the soup of the day and specials, or choose from the regular mains of falafel in pitta, stir fried noodles, or a vegetarian kebab in a tortilla wrap, together with well-stuffed sandwiches – cheese, walnuts and mayonnaise or fried tofu, lettuce and tomato (TLT?) and scrambled egg with crème fraiche and dill.

Friday nights offer a three course supper and a meditation class to end the week in a wonderfully calming way. Don't knock it until you've tried it.

- 5 Cavendish St
  Ulverston LA12 7AD
- 01229 587793
- Serving times:
  Tues 10am-4.30pm
  Wed 10am-3pm
  Thurs-Sat
  10am-4.30pm
  Lunch served until
  2.30pm (2pm Wed)
  Friday 7.30pm for
  meditation class and
  3 course meal
- No credit cards
- Non-smoking
- Not licensed
- Children welcome
- 40 seats
- Main meals from £4.20

Almshouses

It may be the requests from the local student population for decent meat-free options that brings us the inventive and freshly prepared veggie food at Almshouses – if so, thanks guys.

Expect a short daily specials menu that can include freshly prepared options such as tofu, aubergine and honey pâté served with bread from the local Dents bakery, or roast pepper stuffed with curried rice, apricots, dates and cashew nuts. Soups are homemade: for example turnip and ginger, cauliflower and cardamom or parsnip and apple, and you can also enjoy good filled rolls on high quality bread.

Right by the cathedral, Almshouses is open seven days a week – until 8pm in summer.

- Palace Green
  Durham DH1 3RL
- 0191 386 1054
- Serving times:
  7 days 9am-5pm
  Open until 8pm
  in summer
- Major credit cards
- Non-smoking
- Licensed
- Children welcome
- 65 seats
- Soups from £3

Cumbria

Durham

- 11 St Marys Chare
  Hexham NE46 1NQ
- 01434 656284
- Serving times:
  Tues-Sat
  8.30am-4pm
- Booking recommended
  lunchtime
- No credit cards
- Non-smoking
- Licensed
- Children welcome
- 35 seats
- Starters from £2.15,
  mains from £3.70

Hexham Tans

This is a friendly and relaxed community café involved with a local employment project. They open early for a coffee hit and a spot of breakfast, and then you can keep popping back for a refuel later in the day.

Lunch items include granary batons with vegetarian Northumberland sausage or vegetarian bacon and mushroom toastie, daily specials such as vegetable bakes and herb crêpes, or a large jacket potato stuffed with curried vegetables, cream cheese and chives or half a dozen other fillings.

Later, a traditional Northumberland afternoon tea will settle you with a fruit scone, butter, cream and jam as well as your choice of cake! Very competitive pricing and a comfortingly familiar menu will keep the customer sweet and loyal.

Newcastle Upon Tyne

Vegetarian Pub

- 32-40 Sandhill
  Newcastle Upon Tyne
  NE1 3JF
- 0191 261 1037
- Serving times:
  Mon-Sat 11am-7pm
  Sun 10am-7pm
- Major credit cards
- Smoking throughout
- Licensed
- Children welcome
- 30 seats
- Mains from £2.95

Bob Trollop

In Newcastle's quayside area, the Bob Trollop is one of the few vegetarian pubs in the UK, and also features a dedicated vegan menu.

Food is served until 7pm seven days a week, so if you've ever felt left out with the lean pickings at a lot of British hostelries, visit Bob Trollop and revel in a vegetarian mixed grill: sausage, burger, beanburger, tomato, garlic mushrooms, onion rings and jacket wedges – the perfect antidote for the morning after – or choose from a huge range of starters, pasta, brunches and specials.

The building is Grade I listed, there's a great range of beer, and if you arrive early enough you can grab a table with a view of the quayside. What more do you want?

The Sky Apple

This acclaimed eating-place is a café by day, but has a more restauranty feel on its evening openings Thursday-Saturday. Visit at lunchtime for a hummus burrito – roasted vegetables and homemade hummus wrapped in tortilla with a spicy salsa and salad – or a chilli non carne, or drop in earlier for a full veggie breakfast or a no-bacon sandwich. Toasted sandwiches with fillings like cheese, cheatin' pepperoni and jalapeño or pesto, mozzarella and tomato are available all day, and there's always a good vegan choice.

At night, try starters like sausage-less toad in the hole, and main courses such as aubergine schnitzel and Chinese-style noodles. Finish with one (or more) of their puddings which include a dairy- and egg-free spicy upside-down cake.

- 182 Heaton Rd
  Heaton
  Newcastle Upon Tyne
  NE6 5HP
- 0191 209 2571
- Serving times:
  Mon-Wed
  10am-5.30pm
  Thurs-Sat 10am-9pm
- Booking recommended for evenings
- No credit cards
- Non-smoking
- Not licensed, BYO £1pp
- Children welcome
- 34 seats
- Mains from £4

london • west end & city

West End & City of London

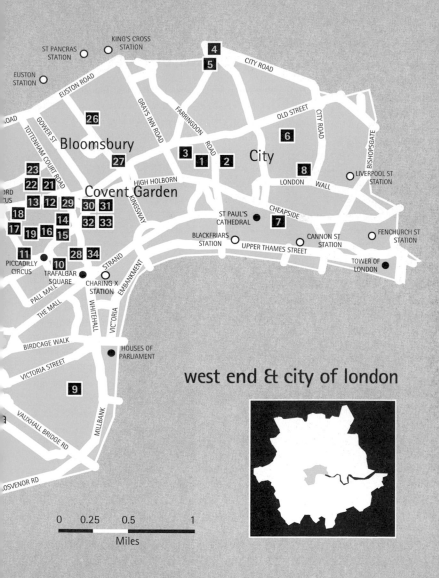

west end & city of london

0   0.25   0.5   1
Miles

269

West End & City

- **CTB**
- 88 Leather Lane
  London EC1N 7GG
- 020 7242 6128
  Mon-Sat 12-10pm
- Licensed

- **Tai**
- 10 Greek St
  London W1D 4DH
- 020 7287 3730
- 7 days 12-11pm
- Licensed

- **Joi Café**
- 14 Percy St
  London W1T 1DR
- 020 7323 0981
- Mon-Sat 12-10pm
  Sun 1-10pm
- Licensed

- **Wai Café**
- 32 Goodge St
  London W1T 2QJ
- 020 7637 4819
- Mon-Thurs 12-10pm
  Fri-Sat 12-11pm
  Sun 12.30-10pm
- Not licensed, BYO

- **Chi**
- 55 St Martins Lane
  London WC2N 4EA
- 020 7836 3434
- Serving times:
  Mon-Fri 11am-11pm
  Sat-Sun 1-10pm
- Licensed

London's Chinese & Thai vegetarian buffets

These wholly vegetarian Chinese and Thai all-you-can-eat buffets have opened all over north and central London in the last couple of years and, if you've not yet eaten at one, you're in for a bit of a treat. The format's fairly similar at all of them: find an empty table, grab a plate and help yourself from a huge range of Chinese and Thai dishes including many featuring soya protein prepared in a way to mimic the textures and flavours of traditional oriental meat dishes. So, when you see options such as sweet and sour 'chicken', 'beef' in blackbean sauce, Beijing 'duck' or 'prawn' crackers, don't worry, it's safe to tuck in.

If you prefer your soya and veg in a more natural state, you won't go hungry either; expect almost unlimited quantities of spring rolls, vegetable chow meins, Thai curries and more simply prepared veg and, for those with a sweet tooth, often a dessert selection as well. If you fancy a takeout, fill one of their lunchtime boxes with your choice from the buffet for just £3 (although we're told it's not polite if the only way you can close the lid is by sitting on it...).

A few aren't licensed (although you can BYO at a couple) – preferring to serve soft drinks, juices and teas – and all are non-smoking. None accepts credit cards – but as these all-you-can-eat feasts are usually priced between £5-6, you can see their point.

Tas Pide

This Farringdon Road venue is the fifth Tas Restaurant to open in London, and the second Tas Pide. Like all the Tas venues there's a really good vegetarian choice of cold and hot starters as well as interesting casseroles and, at this restaurant, the signature Pide. This traditional Anatolian dish is made from freshly made dough baked in a wood-fired oven and then stuffed with beautifully cooked fillings like artichoke, peas, carrots, tomato and spring onion, or leek, green lentils, potatoes and raisins. The crisp crust and boat shape of the cooked dough also makes it ideal to eat by hand. There's also a tremendously good value vegetarian meze.

Open seven days a week till late, there's the usual comprehensive and well-priced Tas wine list.

- 37 Farringdon Rd
  London EC1M 3JB
- 020 7430 9721
- Serving times:
  Mon-Sat 12-11.30pm
  Sun 12-10.30pm
- Booking recommended
- Major credit cards
- Non-smoking area
- Licensed
- Children welcome
- 100 seats
- Pide from £5.95

West End & City

The Greenery

Popular with the local office workers for takeaway breakfast and lunches, this busy café was a recent runner up in the 'Best Vegetarian Café/Restaurant' awards presented by the Vegetarian Society.

A large selection of pizzas, quiches, pasties, jacket potatoes and sandwiches are always available, along with homemade soups and a dish of the day such as aubergine and potato bake. The desserts are from a local small bakery, and everything is very reasonably priced. The juice bar offers a thirst-quenching selection of fruit and vegetable juice cocktails – try the beetroot blast, a mixture of carrot, beetroot, apple and ginger – or add some soya milk for a delicious shake.

- 5 Cowcross Street
  London EC1M 6DW
- 020 7490 4870
- Serving times:
  Mon-Fri 7-4pm
  (5pm in summer)
- No credit cards
- Non-smoking
- Not licensed
- Children welcome
- 15 seats inside &
  tables on pavement

West End & City

Omnivorous Café

- 3 Torrens St
  Islington
  London EC1V 1NQ
- Behind Angel tube
- 020 7837 4237
- Serving times:
  Mon-Sat 12-9.30pm
  Sun 12-4pm
  Closed bank holidays
  & 2 weeks over Xmas
- Major credit cards
- Smoking throughout
- Licensed
- Children welcome
- 30 seats
- Mains from £5

Candid Café

Tucked away behind Angel tube in the Candid Arts Trust building, you can eat here, enjoy the gallery spaces, see a film, or join a life drawing class. The café has a superb banqueting space for hire and is intimate, candlelit and has wonderful ornate sofas. Popular for film and photo shoots it is, for all that, unpretentious and good value.

The food is European/Mediterranean influenced and there's always something vegan, with a range of organic produce. You will find sandwiches, salads, brie quiche, lasagne and specials such as vegetables with coconut and couscous.

With a great range of cakes, and licensed to serve alcohol with food, there are also freshly squeezed juices and good tea and coffee.

Vegetarian Indian Restaurant

- 422 St John St
  London EC1V 4NJ
- 020 7833 5849
- Serving times:
  Mon-Fri 12-2.30pm
  & 6-10.30pm
  Sat 6-10.30pm
  Sun 12-2.30pm
  & 6-10.30pm
- Major credit cards
- Non-smoking at
  lunchtimes
- Not licensed, BYO
  with no corkage
- Children welcome
- 60 seats
- Lunch buffet £4.50

Ravi Shankar

Ravi's in EC1 is something of an institution with the Islington and City crowd. The outside of the restaurant could probably do with a lick of paint, but don't let that put you off as you'll find the food well above average.

Expect an extensive range of starters, curries, dosas and desserts at the all-you-can-eat lunchtime buffet priced at just £4.50, and a large à la carte menu during the evenings. Ravi's certainly has a café feel to it, and it does get crowded but, if you fancy the place to yourself you could always book a private party there for up to 40 people. Not licensed, but you can bring your own with no corkage charges.

West End & City

Carnevale

Handy for the Barbican, this is one of the few restaurants in the City that's open Saturday evenings. The food is good and original, and you can eat à la carte or take advantage of the three course set menu.

Even the apparently ordinary is taken to new levels – ratatouille comes with Jerusalem artichoke and sorrel potato cakes, and you could also find a celeriac brioche pie with puy lentils, red wine sauce and mustard leaves, or saffron ravioli with ricotta and basil.

Take-out sandwiches have ambition – manchego cheese with quince jelly, or smoked mozzarella, aubergine and grilled peppers on a hot ciabatta. Choose from eight salads in various sizes, and soups such as celeriac and horseradish – a cut above the average. Definitely worth a visit.

- 135 Whitecross St London EC1Y 8JL
- 020 7250 3452
- Serving times:
  Mon-Fri
  10am-10.30pm
  Sat 5.30pm-10.30pm
- Booking recommended
- Major credit cards
- Non-smoking area
- Licensed
- Children welcome
- 24 seats
- Mains from £11.50

The Place Below

This beautiful café is unusually sited in the crypt of Wren's St Mary le Bow. Open for breakfast from 7.30am, have a sweet start to the day with freshly baked muffins, french pastries, porridge with maple syrup and delicious Illy coffee. The exceptional lunch menu changes daily. Soup (the cauliflower and almond comes highly recommended), quiche – for example, field and button mushrooms with feta and chanterelles served with rosemary potatoes and spinach, or a spinach and ricotta bake with patatas bravas.

Or try a main course salad such as fattoush with Neals Yard feta, or a health bowl of rice and lentil salad. Ruin the good work with apple and blueberry crumble and clotted cream. Even if you don't work in the City, this rates a special visit.

- St Mary Le Bow Church Cheapside London EC2V 6AU
- 020 7329 0789
- Serving times:
  Mon-Fri
  7.30am-3.30pm
  Lunch served
  11.30am-2.30pm
- Closed bank holidays
- Major credit cards
- Non-smoking
- Not licensed, but BYO with no corkage
- Children welcome
- 70 seats
- Soup from £3.10, daily special from £7.50

West End & City

- City Point
  1 Ropemaker St
  London EC2Y 9AW
- 020 7588 8087
- Serving times:
  Mon-Fri 7.30am-4pm
- Closed weekends and
  bank holidays
- No credit cards
- Non-smoking
- Not licensed
- Children welcome
- 25 seats
- Wraps from £2

JJ's Wrap Kitchen

This is 'feel good fast food': healthy, tasty fare in the centre of the City. Grab a breakfast waffle and smoothie, cookies, pastries, coffee or juice. Return for a lunch wrap. They've invented the JJ – a falafel-like croquette of fried chickpeas and herbs and spices, which comes in Bengali or Mexican blends. Wraps include Mexican (JJs, guacamole, salsa, sour cream and lettuce), while the Greek is halloumi, rocket, tzatziki, salsa and olives.

There are soup and wrap combos to be had, and many drinks are 25p if you are ordering food. There's also free local delivery, so you don't have to leave your lair to get an omelette, salsa and spinach wrap brought to the desk. Marvellous.

- 53 Marsham St
  London SW1P 3DP
- 020 7233 3402
- Serving times:
  Mon-Fri 7.30am-3pm
  Closed bank holidays
- No credit cards
- Non-smoking
- Not licensed
- Children welcome
- 20 seats
- Lunch deals from £5

Wilkins Restaurant

Wilkins is a deliciously old-fashioned counter-service vegetarian café that's been serving the local community for 30 years. Closed weekends and bank holidays, their customers are mainly office and shop workers who visit for the lunchtime deal of one of the day's main courses with a roll and butter for a less-than-princely £5.

Expect such treats as rice and veg, pasta, spicy chickpeas, spinach and rice, vegetable bakes or, that old favourite – macaroni cheese.

Country-pine chairs and tables give this well-known vegetarian café a homely feel, with three tables outside in clement weather. And they open early, so you can pop in for a spot of breakfast if you're an early-riser (or have had a really good night on the tiles...).

West End & City

Woodlands

Ideal for pre- or post-theatre visits, Woodlands' Piccadilly Circus branch is a smart, busy restaurant with an extensive menu of all-vegetarian curries and glorious desserts.

Drop in on weekday lunchtimes to sample their comprehensive lunch buffet priced at just £6.99, or take advantage of the excellent pre-theatre menu served from 5-8pm for little more than a tenner.

If you're visiting outside these times choose from the extensive à la carte choice – prepared with Woodlands' customary delicate flavouring rather than oodles of fire and spice.

If it's the middle of the day and you've not got time to stop, drop in and pick up one of their lunch boxes – masala dosa, vegetable korma and rice for £4.25.

- 37 Panton St
  London SW1Y 4EA
- 020 7839 7258
- Serving times:
  7 days 12-11pm
- Booking advisable weekends
- Major credit cards
- Smoking throughout
- Licensed
- Children welcome
- 65 seats
- Lunch buffet £6.99

Govinda's

Expect a bit of a queue at lunch and dinner times for counter service at this Hare Krishna-owned restaurant just a few yards off Oxford Street.

Choose your own selection from a mainly organic menu of salads, soup, pizza, baked potatoes and an exceptional lasagne, or go with the flow (and most of the other customers) and opt for the set meal – thali style – of the two daily curries, bean pot, soup, rice, breads and salad. Already extremely good value, this meal actually goes down in price if you order after 7pm. There's also a good vegan selection, including a vegan fruit cake amongst the dozen or so desserts.

Below the Hare Krishna bookshop and Temple if you fancy learning a bit more about the movement.

- 10 Soho St
  London W1V 5DA
- 020 7437 4928
- Serving times:
  Mon-Sat 12-8pm
  Closed bank holidays and Krishna festivals
- Major credit cards
- Non-smoking
- Not licensed
- Children welcome
- 60 seats
- Mains from £2.50

- 3-4 Warwick St
London W1B 5LS
- 020 7434 2922
- Serving times:
  Mon-Thurs
  11.30am-4pm
  & 6-9.30pm
  Fri 11.30-2.30pm
  Sun 11.30-4pm
  Closed Sat
- Major credit cards
- Non-smoking
- Not licensed
- Children welcome
- Evening buffet £7

Country Life

Tucked away round the back of Piccadilly Circus is this unexpected vegan heaven – indeed, dairy products are forbidden at Country Life's restaurant.

Downstairs from the wholefood shop of the same name, it's quite a find. The restaurant is self-service, and at lunchtimes your plate is weighed at the till to work out the price. Choose from 16 salads and two main courses, and sample as many dishes as you like.

They do a busy lunchtime trade with local workers coming for takeaways, while regular diners pick up the week's menu to see what's on offer on a particular day. Favourite dishes feature regularly: spinach and carrot lasagne (with creamy vegan cheese sauce), chickpea a la king, and shepherds pie. There's a choice of soups served with homemade bread, if you want a quick snack. Desserts are a bit of a must and can include the deliciously sinful-tasting (but cholesterol-free) banana carobella. Mon-Thurs evenings feature an all-you-can-eat buffet of main courses at a very reasonable £7.

No alcohol is served – but there's a selection of fresh juices and organic fizzy drinks, plus alcohol-free beer. Children are welcome, with a high chair available and half price portions.

As well as the basement restaurant, there are a few seats at the back of the shop, and on fine days they put a couple of tables out on the pavement.

Country Life is run by a Christian charity whose mission is to teach a healthy lifestyle. Occasionally, they run cookery classes and they sell their own cookbook, so you can relive the experience at home if you're not near enough to visit regularly.

Red Veg

Three cheers for Red Veg. Only two branches exist at the moment, but there are plans for more. Everything is Vegetarian Society certified, and most items can be made vegan. Let's hope they do for veggieburgers what Prêt à Manger has done for sandwiches.

This is fast food with branding – communist stars and manipulated Soviet posters of Lenin with a veggieburger wave two ketchup-smeared fingers at the Golden Arches world domination.

It's cheap as chips, or fries as we call them, and as well as tasty burgers there's falafel, wraps, breaded mushrooms and nuggets. If ease of access and price can introduce more people to eating vegetarian without shaking their fast food habit, this is the way to do it.

- 95 Dean St
  London W1D 3TB
- 020 7437 3109
- Serving times:
  Mon-Sat 12-10pm
  Sun 12-7pm
- No credit cards
- Non-smoking
- Not licensed
- Children welcome
- 12 seats
- From £2.85

Maoz Falafel Café

Does what it says on the tin (of chickpeas). They do falafel sandwiches on pitta bread. Big or small, wholemeal or white. With hummus, with fried aubergine or with salad and sauces, and not forgetting good quality Belgian-style chips. There's fresh carrot or orange juice and they're open until very late, so you can get something to eat while you're waiting for the night bus.

The franchise is growing throughout Europe and if you're interested in starting your own outlet they claim you'll only need three staff. However, given our own attempts to make falafel, one of those people needs to have eight arms and octopus-like suckers to make the stuff stick together.

- 43 Old Compton St
  London W1D 4PD
- 020 7851 1586
- Serving times:
  Mon-Thurs 11am-1am
  Fri-Sat 11am-2am
  Sun 11am-midnight
- No credit cards
- Non-smoking
- Not licensed
- Children welcome
- 25 seats
- From £2.50

West End & City

- 92 Berwick St
  London W1F 0QD
- 020 7437 8591
- Serving times:
  Mon-Fri 11.45am-9pm
  Sat 12.30-9pm
- No credit cards
- Non-smoking
- Not licensed
- Children welcome
- 30 seats

Beatroot

Right in the thick of Soho's Berwick Street market is this gem of a café offering great value all-vegetarian food in a friendly atmosphere. Beatroot has a loyal following made up of local workers seeking a healthy lunch, tourists who happen past, and vegetarians and vegans who travel quite some distance for the exceptional food. Let's be honest – it's not everywhere vegans can indulge in sticky chocolate cake with dairy-free custard!

Beatroot operates a simple serving system – everything is sold by the box (small, medium or large) and you can have any combination of whatever takes your fancy. There are 10 hot dishes – ranging from curry to hot pot, with lentil and mushroom shepherds pie or tofu stir fry for vegans – plus a good selection of salads. They also make the most delicious sausage rolls. Having concocted your selection, you can eat in or take away – the café has a small number of tables inside plus two out on the pavement, which are the only places that smoking's allowed. Sitting outside is quite entertaining as you are opposite a large fruit and veg stall with traders competing loudly for the attention of passers by!

Freshly squeezed vegetable juices are good value and you can have a healthy lunch of a juice and a small box of food for around a fiver. For a quick refresher while trawling the Oxford Street shops, try a mango smoothie and a slice of tofu cheesecake.

Some wheat-free cakes are generally available, and soya milk is no problem in this very vegan-friendly establishment.

Masala Zone

Occupying Cranks' former premises in Soho, this omnivorous Indian is owned by the same group who run Veeraswamy and Chutney Mary. Expect around ten street-food-style vegetarian starters and smaller dishes, noodle bowls, curries and sides.

Masala Zone cooking is zingingly fresh tasting, with really perky spicing, leaving you feeling sated without any oil slick of ghee coating your chops.

The chana dabalroti, a starter, is an unusual rich, chickpea curry which with hunks of bread could be a meal in itself. The thalis may look modest, but are extremely filling, and there's an ayurvedic version suitable for diabetics. Licensed, there's also a couple of freshly pressed juices each day.

- 9 Marshall St
  London W1F 7ER
- 020 7287 9966
- Serving times:
  Mon-Fri 12-2.45pm
  & 5.30-11pm

  Sat 12.30-11pm

  Sun 12.30-3.30pm
  & 6-10.30pm
- Major credit cards
- Non-smoking area
- Licensed
- Children welcome
- 170 seats
- Starters from £3

West End & City

Plant

Plant is a modern, hip and trendy café and restaurant serving fresh healthy gourmet food to eat in or to go. There's a busy counter serving mouth-watering vegetarian and vegan breakfasts and lunches including a selection of salads, wheat-free sandwiches, hot trays, heavenly organic cakes, smoothies and pure fruit juices at the front of the store, whilst at the rear the restaurant offers a choice of tasty à la carte items in very chic surroundings. The seitan stroganoff with seitan strips, mushrooms, caramelised onions, red peppers in a herb cashew cream sauce served with wild rice for £10.50 is a real favourite.

The lunchtime buffets are popular all-you-can-eat events priced at just £7.50, and Sunday brunches are promised soon.

- 47 Poland Street
  London W1F 7NB
- 020 7734 5984
- Serving times:
  Mon-Thurs 8am-11pm
  (Restaurant 12.30-
  3.30pm & 5.30-11pm)

  Fri 8am-3.30pm
  (Restaurant
  12.30-3.30pm)

  Sat 6-11pm

  Sun 12-9pm

  Closed bank holidays
- Major credit cards
- Non-smoking
- Not licensed
- Children welcome
- 50 seats

West End & City

- 45 Lexington St
  London W1F 9AN
- 020 7494 1634
- Serving times:
  Mon-Sat 12-11pm
  Closed bank holidays
- No credit cards,
  debit cards OK
- Non-smoking except
  bar area
- Licensed
- Children welcome
- 60 seats
- Mains from £7

Mildred's

The influences at this bustling centrally located restaurant are global, but not messily so; Japanese dumplings with mirin and soy dipping sauce are listed alongside roasted aubergines with chargrilled flatbread, yoghurt and caramelised butter, plus there's a daily special in all segments of the menu.

If you want to settle down to pie and chips you can – but here it is a stunning mixed mushroom, porcini and ale pie, with mushy peas and decent fries. Burger of the day comes with fruit relish, basil mayonnaise, chips and mozzarella.

Mexican? Burrito with refried beans, salsa, smoked cheddar with sour cream and a leafy salad. There's stir fried vegetables with brown rice or wheat noodles and you can add in tofu or cashew nuts. Their splendid energising detox salad – just reading about it can make you feel exuberant – comes with carrots, sprouting beans, coriander, toasted pumpkin, sunflower seeds, sultanas and a lemongrass and ginger dressing.

Desserts are crumbles, yoghurt, sticky toffee pud, ice cream, or a vegan tofu cheesecake.

The wines are organic, there are great fresh juices – select your own blend which can include a dash of parsley if you're so minded – as well as smoothies and a decent range of soft drinks. Coffee is fair trade, and the tea, milk and soya are organic. The menu is marked up for vegans and wheat-free types.

Be aware: if you're planning to pay with plastic, take a debit card. Credit cards aren't accepted.

Rasa

Expect a predominately vegetarian menu at this branch of Rasa (which does, however, have a small selection of chicken and lamb dishes) tucked just off Oxford Street. The exterior is in Rasa's shocking pink, but there's a classy interior with linen tablecloths and fine glassware.

Specialising in Keralan cuisine, there's a range of freshly prepared tasty dosas (we'd recommend the Chilli Onion Rava version), curries – including rarely found combinations such as beetroot and spinach spiced with mustard seeds and curry leaves, or sweet mango and green banana with yoghurt, chilli and ginger.

Choose from good breads and rice, with a small selection of side dishes including stir-fried savoy cabbage and lentils. Booking essential most evenings.

- 6 Dering St
  London W1S 1AD
- 020 7629 1346
- Serving times:
  Mon-Sat 12-3pm
  & 6-11pm
- Booking recommended
- Major credit cards
- Non-smoking
  ground floor
- Licensed
- Children welcome
- 72 seats
- Starters from £4.25

Rasa Samudra

The extensive wine list at Rasa Samudra complements the flavours in a host of unusual dishes – aubergines cooked in a ground paste of roasted onions, coriander seeds, chillies and tamarind mixed with a yoghurt and cashew nut sauce, or fresh spinach and toor dhal cooked in a thick sauce of garlic, tomatoes and green peppers.

Reputedly one of Jamie Oliver's favourite Indian restaurants, this branch of Rasa also features some Keralan fish specialities, but don't let that put you off – the menu is predominately vegetarian and the cooking is quite exceptional.

An ideal venue for a proper night out. Just round the corner in Rathbone St is Rasa Express – pop in there for inexpensive lunchtime deals.

- 5 Charlotte St
  London W1T 1RE
- 020 7637 0222
- Serving times:
  Mon-Sat 12-2.30pm
  & 6-10.30pm
  Sun 6-10.30pm
- Booking recommended
- Major credit cards
- Non-smoking area
- Licensed
- Children welcome
- 100 seats

West End & City

Vegetarian Indian Restaurant

- 77 Marylebone Lane London W1U 2PS
- 020 7486 3862
- Serving times:
  7 days 12-2.45pm & 6-10.45pm
- Booking recommended weekend evenings
- Major credit cards
- Non-smoking area
- Licensed
- Children welcome
- 75 seats

Woodlands

Woodlands opened its first restaurant in Madras in the 1930s, and now claims to be one of the largest Indian vegetarian restaurant groups in the world.

This smart branch a few hundred yards north of Bond St tube offers the usual (but far from ordinary) Woodlands' range of freshly prepared starters, curries, speciality rice and breads, together with a selection of mouth-watering desserts including the heavenly Badam Halwa: milk, sugar, crushed almonds and saffron.

Open seven days a week, it's a good bet if you've been trawling the shops on Oxford St and, if you work locally, you can take away a low priced lunch deal of curry, masala dosa and rice for well under a fiver.

Vegetarian Diner

- 50 Marylebone High St London W1U 5HN
- 020 7258 8595
- Serving times:
  Mon-Fri 8am-11pm
  Sat 9am-11pm
  Sun 10am-10pm
- Major credit cards
- Non-smoking area
- Licensed
- Children welcome
- 96 seats
- Starters from £4

Eat and Two Veg

An airy American-style diner, serving breakfast until 11am (2pm at the weekend), and a range of dishes from east and west throughout the day.

Starters include meze, satay skewers, grilled halloumi, and a vegetarian alternative to crispy duck with pancakes and plum sauce. You can also enjoy a soya loaf with onion, celery, carrot, egg, breadcrumbs, mustard and garlic served with mashed potato and peas, Lancashire hot-pot, sausage and mash, sweet and sour crispy Chinese balls or Thai green curry. Vegan dishes are clearly marked (with additional vegan options available), and any eggs used are free range and organic.

Choose desserts from the simple crumble to chocolate mousse cake. Eat and Two Veg is licensed, with a good wine list and a great cocktail selection.

Vegetarian's Paradise

Opposite the Alara Organic Health Food Store just north of the Holiday Inn Russell Square, this Indian restaurant is completely vegetarian, with many vegan dishes on its extensive menu.

Expect a wide selection of puris, chaat, vegetable kebabs, thalis, dosas, curries and traditional Indian desserts. If you prefer to go with a thali, the Paradise Deluxe is a substantial three course meal of dhal soup, poppadom, bhajias, four curries, pilau rice, raita, pickles/chutneys, chapatis or puris and a dessert for just £6.95.

Visit at lunchtime for the seven days a week buffet with its varied selection of a dozen dishes including desserts – where you can eat as much as you like for under a fiver.

- 59 Marchmont St
  London WC1N 1AP
- 020 7278 6881
- Serving times:
  7 days 12-3pm
  & 5-11pm
- Major credit cards
- Smoking throughout
- Not licensed, BYO
  with no corkage
- Children welcome
- 46 seats
- Lunch buffet £4.50

West End & City

Mary Ward Café

This is a very popular community café inside a central London college, which means there can be lengthy queues at lunchtime. The menu changes twice daily and there are always interesting vegan choices and a good selection of wheat-free options in the starters, main courses and desserts.

Mainly Mediterranean influenced, the cooking is imaginative – expect to find dishes such as a lentil stew with sautéed rocket and endive served with roast potatoes, or polenta, sweetcorn and carrot cakes accompanied by a variety of veg. There are generally half a dozen good choices along these lines – and they'll definitely be worth the wait.

Good Illy coffee for filter, cappuccino or soyaccino.

- 42 Queens Square
  London WC1N 3AQ
- Inside the
  Mary Ward Centre
- 020 7269 6095
- Serving times:
  Mon-Fri
  9.30am-8.30pm
  Sat 9.30am-4pm
- No credit cards
- Non-smoking
- Not licensed
- Children welcome
- 50 seats

West End & City

West End & City

- 30 Charing Cross Rd London WC2H 0DB
- 020 7836 4233
- Serving times:
  Mon-Sat
  11.30am-11pm
  Sun 12-10.30pm
- Booking recommended weekends
- No credit cards
- Non-smoking area
- Licensed
- Children welcome
- 50 seats
- Starters from £2.50

Gaby's

We love Gaby's; it's an institution and long may its doors be flung open. Right in the heart of theatreland, it's convenient for pre- and post-theatre suppers, and good for lunch, coffee, or just hanging out.

Mediterranean food, cooked salads, hummus, the freshest falafel and latkes – piping hot potato and onion cakes – are comforting, healthy and quick. The giant trays of salad in the window are extremely enticing, and the interior is decorated with autographed photos and theatre posters. This is the real thing; you do see actors, comedians and writers in here, grabbing a quick bite. Gloriously unpretentious, very busy and fine on your own or with a couple of mates.

West End & City

- 52 St Giles High St London WC2H 8LH
- 020 7240 8042
- Serving times:
  Mon-Sat 11am-11pm
  Sun 11am-10.30pm
- Major credit cards
- Non-smoking ground floor
- Licensed
- Children welcome
- 50 seats
- Mains from £5

First Out

London's first lesbian and gay café, close to Centrepoint, offers curries from around the world – for example pumpkin, aubergine and cashew nut or potato and spinach – lasagnes, risotto, veggieburgers, quiche and salad as staples, with plenty of vegan choices in the pastas, soups, bakes and jackets.

You can also enjoy gateaux and tea cakes, and order your tea and coffee with soya milk.

They'll do you a vegetarian Sunday brunch if you're up early (or very late), and Friday night is women's night, where men may come as guests.

The entire ground floor is non-smoking, and there are frequent food and drinks promotions. All in all, a friendly venue featuring good value good food.

Neals Yard Bakery

This old-style café and tearoom offers more than just baked goods and sandwiches. The cooking is international, substantial and delicious: sweet potato and peanut casserole, mushroom and spinach biriani, extraordinary vegetable pasties, beanburgers and soups such as split pea, mint and lemon.

The breads are legendary – the cheese and herb variety is among the best we've tasted – and, if you get the chance, try the brandy fruit bread – rich with fruit, it beats the pants off commercial Christmas cake.

Non-smoking throughout, it fills up quickly during the lunchtime rush, so keep your eyes peeled for a bench, perch or chair outside.

- 6 Neals Yard
  London WC2H 9DP
- 020 7836 5199
- Serving times:
  Mon-Sat
  10.30am-4.30pm
  Closed bank holidays
- No credit cards
- Non-smoking
- Not licensed, BYO
  £2 corkage
- Children welcome
- 25 seats

Neals Yard Salad Bar

This is a wonderful and fabulously busy place. Summer lunchtimes in the courtyard are heaving, but it's always worth queuing. Excellent for a carryout if you work locally – take something intensely delicious, nutritious and substantial back to the desk – you can also grab one of their tables and linger outside.

Juices are fantastic, and shakes can be dairy or soya. Potato salad is elevated to ambrosial levels with lashings of herbs, served hot, and vegans can have a ball here as well. Their quiches are deep and richly flavoured and the homemade pizza with wholemeal dough will stave off pangs for absolutely hours. Bring your hungry hordes here, feed them cinnamon cake and then plunge back into Covent Garden.

- 2 Neals Yard
  London WC2H 9DP
- 020 7836 3233
- Serving times:
  7 days 8.30am-9pm
  Occasionally
  closes earlier
- No credit cards
- Non-smoking area
- Licensed
- Children welcome
- 100+ seats
- Mains from £8

West End & City

- 31 Neal St
  Covent Garden
  London WC2H 9PR
- 020 7836 9072
- Serving times:
  Mon-Sat 12-8pm
  Sun 12-4.30pm
- No credit cards
- Non-smoking
- Not licensed, BYO
  with no corkage
- Children welcome
- 48 seats
- Mains from £4

Food For Thought

This restaurant must be nudging towards its 30th birthday and deserves to be celebrated. Crammed into a whitewashed basement with scrubbed pine tables and benches, local workers and visitors to Covent Garden queue on the stairs for lunch and dinner, squeeze onto tables with strangers, are poked in the back by departing customers and still come back for more. You won't get anything more nutritious and delicious.

The choice always has a soup, stir fried vegetables with rice and two or three other hot mains. There's a quiche, and this is one of the very few places we genuinely welcome it. Crammed with vegetables, never wet and wobbly, it's a viable option for a change. The side salads, which can be a main dish if you like, are superb – many's the time we've gone back to work reeking of garlicky potato salad.

Somehow, the standard dishes of other restaurants become a delight here, probably because they treat them with respect, giving real attention to ingredients and freshness. We cannot rave about the food too highly; you wouldn't come here for a posh night out and it's hard to linger in the busy atmosphere, but this is so good that the very thought of it will brighten a visit to the shopping centre of the universe.

Save room for dessert, their scrunches, crumbles and flapjacks are better than mother used to make. Dishes are marked wheat-free or vegan and you can bring your own booze from the off-licence a few minutes away.

World Food Café

The owners of this café have collected recipes from their travels around the world's spice routes, and the standard of food is exceptional. Everything is made on the premises and they are knowledgeable and capable of dealing with special diets.

There's always a vegan choice, such as West African sweet potato cooked with fresh ginger, garlic, cayenne and peanut butter, served with rice and beetroot salad. The menu ranges from Indian thalis through tortilla to French cakes, which gives an idea of the truly international scope of their cooking. The café is light and airy, is full of plants and serves fresh juices, lassi, lime-soda and herbal teas.

The Neals Yard development has been a bastion of good vegetarian cooking and produce for 30 years or more. Here's to it.

- 14 Neals Yard
  London WC2H 9DP
- 020 7379 0298
- Serving times:
  Mon-Fri
  11.30am-4.30pm
  Sat 11.30am-5pm
  Closed most bank
  holidays
- Major credit cards
- Non-smoking
- Not licensed
- Children welcome
- 42 seats

West End & City

north
london

london • north

North London

north london

Winchmore Hill

Southgate

Edmonton

Whetstone

A1000

Palmers Green

A406

North Finchley

A406

A10

11
Finchley

Wood Green

Muswell Hill

Tottenham

A1

Hornsey

6

Golders Green

13

14

25

Highgate

12

Finsbury Park

26

10

7

Stoke Newington

8 **9**

Hampstead

Highbury

29 **28**

2

30

A503

Kilburn

27 **20**

22

Hoxton

21

19

1

St Johns Wood

4

3

5

Islington

15 **16**

Camden

17 **18**

0   0.5   1
Miles

- **Thai Veg**
- 13 Islington High St
  London N1 9LQ
- 020 7837 7767
- Mon-Thurs 12-12pm
  Fri-Sat 12-1am
  Sun 12-12pm
- Not licensed

- **CTJ**
- 339 Euston Rd
  London NW1 5AD
- 020 7387 5450
- 7 days 12-10.30pm
- Licensed

- **Veg**
- 6 Kentish Town Rd
  London NW1 9NX
- 020 7284 4004
- 7 days 12-10pm
- Not licensed

- **CTV**
- 22 Golders Green Rd
  London NW11 8LL
- 020 8201 8001
- Mon-Fri 12-10pm
  Sat 12-11pm
  Sun 12.30-10pm
- Not licensed

London's Chinese & Thai vegetarian buffets

These wholly vegetarian Chinese and Thai all-you-can-eat buffets have opened all over north and central London in the last couple of years and, if you've not yet eaten at one, you're in for a bit of a treat. The format's fairly similar at all of them: find an empty table, grab a plate and help yourself from a huge range of Chinese and Thai dishes including many featuring soya protein prepared in a way to mimic the textures and flavours of traditional oriental meat dishes. So, when you see options such as sweet and sour 'chicken', 'beef' in blackbean sauce, Beijing 'duck' or 'prawn' crackers, don't worry, it's safe to tuck in.

If you prefer your soya and veg in a more natural state, you won't go hungry either; expect almost unlimited quantities of spring rolls, vegetable chow meins, Thai curries and more simply prepared veg and, for those with a sweet tooth, often a dessert selection as well. If you fancy a takeout, fill one of their lunchtime boxes with your choice from the buffet for just £3 (although we're told it's not polite if the only way you can close the lid is by sitting on it...).

A few aren't licensed (although you can BYO at a couple) – preferring to serve soft drinks, juices and teas – and all are non-smoking. None accepts credit cards – but as these all-you-can-eat feasts are usually priced between £5-6, you can see their point.

Masala Zone

A modern décor café-style restaurant, serving the best of Indian home cooking. Owned by the same group that runs two top London restaurants (Veeraswamy and Chutney Mary) Masala Zone is the racier younger brother. Noodle bowls are huge and satisfying, and there are around ten street-food-style vegetarian starters and smaller dishes.

Masala Zone cooking is zingingly fresh tasting, with really perky spicing, leaving you feeling sated without any oil slick of ghee coating your chops.

The chana dabalroti, a starter, is an unusual, rich, chickpea curry with hunks of bread and could be a meal in itself. The thalis may look modest, but are extremely filling, and they have a children's menu as well as a couple of freshly pressed juices each day.

- 80 Upper St Islington London N1 0NU
- Next to Screen on the Green
- 020 7359 3399
- Serving times:
  Mon-Fri 12.30-3pm & 5.30-11pm
  Sat 12.30-11pm
  Sun 12.30-10.30pm
- Major credit cards
- Non-smoking
- Licensed
- Children welcome
- 125 seats
- Starters from £3

Two Figs

This is a mini-café within a wholefood vegetarian deli; there are only 8 seats, and you buy your selection from the deli counter. Goodies include pasta bakes, sausage rolls, potato pies and quiches, and salads (which are sold by weight). Drinks can be chosen from the shop fridge, but the café is unlicensed.

Tuesday is vegan day – when there's a greater range of hot dishes which can include a dairy- and egg-free puff pastry pie – and there are usually vegan cakes and scones. Visit on a Saturday to sample their Scotch pancakes.

A highly-valued local store, where you can do your shopping before sipping a soya latte.

- 101 Newington Green Rd London N1 4QY
- On corner of Beresford Rd
- 020 7690 6811
- Serving times:
  Mon-Thurs 9am-6pm
  Fri-Sat 9am-4.30pm
  Closed bank holidays
- Major credit cards (over £10)
- Non-smoking
- Not licensed
- Children welcome
- 8 seats
- Snacks from £1.50

North London

North London

- 42 Caledonian Rd
  London N1 9DT
- 020 7278 0679
- Serving times:
  Mon-Fri 12-11pm
  Sat-Sun 1-11pm
- Major credit cards
- Non-smoking area
- Licensed
- Children welcome
- 70 seats
- Starters from £2.50

Addis

Long opening hours are an advantage at this Ethiopian bar and restaurant. The menu demands concentration, as there's the odd bit of fish sneaking into the vegetarian section, but do experiment with some of the other dishes in this unfamiliar and not-yet-trendy style of cooking.

Dishes are served with soft pancake-style home-baked bread. Start with salads or deep fried aubergines with tahini and yoghurt sauce, then move on to main courses which involve a lot of mixed vegetables in various guises. There's spiced spinach cooked with cottage cheese, or green chillies stuffed with onion and tomatoes if you're not scheduled on a hot date later in the day. Try the fuul masalah: crushed spiced fava beans with feta and falafel sautéed in sesame oil.

North London

- 92-93 Chapel Market
  London N1 9EX
- 020 7837 4607
- Serving times:
  7 days 12-11.30pm
- No credit cards
- Non-smoking area
- Licensed
- Children welcome
- 75 seats
- Buffet £2.95

Indian Veg Bhelpoori House

The Indian Veg Bhelpoori House has been at the Western End of Chapel Market since the mid eighties. And if we gave an award for London's best value meal, this is where we'd pin it. For around £3, help yourself to a buffet of freshly prepared south and east Indian cuisine that's almost entirely vegan. In decent surroundings, surrounded by posters and quotes extolling the virtues of a meat-free diet, this is the place to eat well, healthily and for virtually no money.

From noon till late seven days a week, you can expect a good range of curries, dhal, rice, bread, bhajias and salad, or forego the delights of all-you-can-eat dining and order from the menu if the fancy takes you.

Licensed, you can also enjoy a wide range of organic soft drinks or a soya lassi.

Oshobasho Café

Once a cricket pavilion in the middle of the wood, it's now an art gallery and café and very popular with the artsy, media locals and their spawn. The menu changes frequently and is updated on a board. There are special events in the summer, including jazz in the garden.

Many ingredients are organic, and cakes are homemade. The dishes are generic: lasagne, curry, soup, Spanish omelette, you'll just have to find the daily special twist. They are also licensed for wine, beer and spirits. Children (once you've located them in the park) can refuel on pasta in tomato sauce.

The café closes half an hour before dusk and doesn't serve food on a Monday, unless it's a bank holiday.

- Highgate Wood
  Muswell Hill Rd
  London N10 3JN
- 020 8444 1505
- Serving times:
  7 days 8.30am-half
  hour before dusk
  No food on Mondays
- No credit cards
- Non-smoking inside
- Licensed
- Children welcome
- 100 seats

North London

Rasa

Decorated in Rasa's trademark shocking pink, there's no problem locating this one if you're wandering down Stoke Newington Church St.

The first of Das Sreedharan's restaurants (there are five others, but this is the only one that's totally vegetarian), the menu is drawn from his extensive experience and knowledge of Keralan cuisine.

Alongside more familiar dishes, you can enjoy rare delights such as a mango and green banana curry, or beetroot and spinach with coconut and mustard seed.

As you might expect, there's a good vegan choice, and everything is cooked with an attention to flavours and textures that has brought many awards. Definitely not your average High Street Indian restaurant.

- 55 Stoke Newington
  Church St
  London N16 0AR
- 020 7249 0344
- Serving times:
  Mon-Thurs 6-10.45pm
  Fri 6-11.45pm
  Sat 12-2.45pm
  & 6-11.45pm
  Sun 12-2.45pm
  & 6-10.45pm
- Booking recommended
  weekends
- Major credit cards
- Non-smoking
- Licensed
- Children welcome
- 50 seats
- Starters from £2.75

North London

- 32-40 Stoke
  Newington Church St
  London N16 0LU
- 020 7254 2332
- Serving times:
  Mon-Sat 9am-5.30pm
  Sun 10am-5pm
  Store and juice bar
  open later
- Major credit cards
- Non-smoking
- Not licensed
- Children welcome
- 20 seats
- Lunch deals
  from £3.75

Fresh & Wild

A small and bustling café and juice bar that's part of the award-winning Fresh & Wild store in the heart of Stoke Newington's Church St. So when you've finished that fair trade and organic shopping blitz, order a strawberry, banana, yoghurt and apple smoothie and – while you're waiting – go and grab some lunch from the counter-service deli. No longer completely vegetarian, there is, however, still a good range of vegetarian and vegan food such as baked tofu (from a speciality supplier in east London), Thai veg curry, tomato and coconut dhal, winter mash, sweet potato and leek rolls and a handful of more-interesting-than-usual quiches.

There's only a small seating area, and you risk being run over by assorted pushchairs, but it's still a great place for a quick and healthy pick-me-up.

- 101 Stoke Newington
  Church St
  London N16 0UD
- 020 7923 1303
- Serving times:
  7 days
  9.30am-5.30pm
- No credit cards
- Non-smoking area
- Licensed
- Children welcome
- 65 seats

Blue Legume

Find this French-style café and bistro by heading for the building with the 3-foot-long blue aubergine dangling above the awning, and be rewarded with a distinctly un-French selection of vegetarian and vegan food.

Open seven days a week, you can enjoy a full cooked veggie breakfast from 9.30am (as can your children, there's a smaller half price version as well) or more lunchy mains such as nut loaf, stuffed aubergine, vegetarian cottage pie or a chickpea and tahini burger.

Order from the counter and park at one of the hand-made mosaic tables in the cosier section at the front of the restaurant or, on sunnier days, decamp to the small conservatory at the rear.

Peking Palace

Medals at the ready: this is 98% vegan and MSG-free. There's a daily lunchtime buffet, or you can take away or have food delivered if you live locally. The restaurant is discreetly lit, romantic and peaceful with plenty of flowers, plants and unique paintings.

The menu is extraordinary – vegetarian prawns, duck, fish-steaks or smoked veggie chicken, asparagus tempura with sweet and sour sauce, Singapore noodles, spicy veggie beef and organic brown rice and, if you hanker for Mongolian-style veggie lamb, you're in the right place. Three different set dinners for a minimum of two people are marvellous feasts, and a great way of navigating the comprehensive choice. Take a non-vegetarian pal and you may just have another convert on your hands.

- 669 Holloway Rd London N19 5SE
- Close to Archway tube
- 020 7281 5363
- Serving times:
  Mon-Fri 12-3pm & 6-10.50pm
  Sat-Sun 6-10.50pm
  Closed bank holidays
- Booking recommended weekends
- Major credit cards
- Non-smoking
- Not licensed, BYO with £1 corkage pp
- Children welcome
- 40 seats
- Mains from £4.50

Rani

Rani has a 20-year reputation for high quality Gujarati cuisine in elegant and stylish surroundings, and has recently introduced a quite exceptional buffet. Occupying a large area to the side of the main dining area, the buffet includes lots of Rani favourites, but with the bonus of many extra, rarely-found, traditional Gujarati dishes.

It's a great way of dining: discover food with new flavours and textures that you mightn't automatically opt for from an à la carte selection. If you've ever wondered what a fenugreek bhajia or Indian steamed vegetable sausage tasted like, now's your chance.

The selection varies daily – each visit will present you with something new to try – and everything's marked up for vegan or wheat-free credentials.

- 7 Long Lane Finchley London N3 2PR
- 020 8349 4386
- Serving times:
  Mon-Sat 6-10pm
  Sun 1-3pm & 6-10pm
  Buffet served 7 days 7-9pm & Sun lunch
- Booking recommended weekend evenings
- Major credit cards
- Non-smoking
- Licensed
- Children welcome
- 70 seats
- Evening buffet from £9.90

- 161 Stroud Green Rd
London N4 3PZ
- 020 7272 1680
- Serving times:
Mon-Sat 12-1.30pm
& 5.30-10.30pm
- No credit cards
- Non-smoking area
- Not licensed, BYO
with minimal corkage
- Children welcome
- 56 seats
- Starters from £1.50

Jai Krishna

Jai Krishna is a cosy and bustling vegetarian Indian restaurant not far from Finsbury Park. Study the menu (all the usual suspects are there, plus a couple of more unusual dishes such as a red cabbage and apple curry, and pumpkin paneer), fill in your order slip and take it to the counter.

The prices are low, and their friendly staff and welcoming owners ensure it's not at all a canteen-style experience – Jai Krishna is justly popular with couples as well as larger group outings.

Great lassis, including mango and pistachio as well as the regular sweet or salty varieties, and you can BYO wine and beer with very low corkage charges.

London N6

- Jackson Lane Centre
269a Archway Rd
London N6 5AA
- Opposite
Highgate tube
- 020 8348 7666
- Serving times:
Mon-Sun 10-8.45pm
- No credit cards
- Non-smoking
until 6pm
- Licensed
- Children welcome
- 60 seats

Veggie House

Veggie House is in the very busy Jackson's Lane community centre, where plays are staged, courses run and musicians rehearse; it's a very buzzy place. Opposite the tube, so you could nip in here for an inexpensive quick supper on the way home.

There are lunchtime specials and always some vegan choices such as sweet potato and coconut stew or button mushroom curry. From the regular menu you can choose dishes such as stuffed mushrooms, roast aubergine moussaka, broccoli and peanut pie or a lentil and cumin soup with focaccia. If you're not in a rush, dive into the dessert menu for choices including chocolate and banana crumble and various tarts.

Children are looked after with pizzas or baked potatoes, which come with complimentary juices.

Fiction

Visit this attractive former bookshop at wisteria time, as it climbs through the building. The restaurant also has a courtyard garden, which is covered and heated during spring and autumn, making maximum use of a pretty space.

Popular even with meat-eaters, the menu displays a good grasp of balancing flavours, textures and herbs – and you can be sure that eating here will be a sensuous delight. The starters range from simple avocado on black olive tapenade, to homely cumin-spiced roasted pumpkin soup with walnut bread. For a dish where you feel you've made the cook work a bit, there are savoury profiteroles with leek, cream cheese and dill filling.

Main courses and side orders are robust. The more unusual items include the good gamekeeper's pie – puff pastry with mock duck, chestnuts, leek, shitake and button mushrooms and carrots in a red wine and wild herb marinade.

There's also pasta, gnocchi and a wood-roasted butternut squash, filled with lemony mushrooms and served with new potatoes and a chestnut and bay gravy. Sides include a creamy horseradish mash, stir fried mangetout with pak choi and a salad of sprouted seeds and lentils.

Desserts are unbeatable: lemon and sultana cheesecake, apple, pine nut and Bailey's strudel or strawberry, peach and apple crumble with brandy custard. There's plenty of vegan choice throughout the menu, including the wine list. Fiction is also sensitive to wheat-free needs and dishes are marked accordingly.

With cooking of this standard, it's always advisable to book.

- 60 Crouch End Hill London N8 8AG
- Opposite M&S
- 020 8340 3403
- Serving times:
  Wed-Thurs 6.30-10pm
  Fri-Sat 6.30-10.30pm
  Sun 6.30-10pm
- Booking advisable
- Major credit cards
- Non-smoking area
- Licensed
- Children welcome
- 55 seats
- Starters from £4

North London

- 121 Drummond St London NW1 2HL
- 020 7387 5556
- Serving times: 7 days 12-11.30pm
- Major credit cards
- Non-smoking area
- Not licensed, BYO with no corkage
- Children welcome
- 120 seats
- Lunch buffet £5.95

Diwana

Tellingly busy seven days a week, Diwana claims to have been the first UK bhel poori house and has been a favourite lunch and dinner location for vegetarians (as well as their less well-informed brethren) since it first opened in the 1960s.

The lunchtime buffet (12-2.30pm Mon-Sun) is especially popular. Beautifully presented, it's not at all a canteen-style experience, and you'll find a great selection of traditional starters, four curries, decent salads and a range of sweet desserts to pack your plate with. It's very popular with families at weekends.

The evening menu includes four Gujarati thalis with a choice of chapatti or poori. Not licensed, but you can BYO with no corkage or enjoy good fresh orange, lassis and falooda.

North London

- 133-135 Drummond St London NW1 2HL
- 020 7388 6458
- Serving times: 7 days 12-10.45pm
- Major credit cards
- Non-smoking area
- Licensed
- Children welcome
- 75 seats
- Starters from £2.50

Ravi Shankar

Much more of a modern restaurant than the café-style Ravi in the City, but without the lunchtime buffet that seems compulsory in other Indian vegetarian eateries in this part of town.

What you do get is a simple, elegantly decorated restaurant with an enviable tradition and reputation for exceptional Indian vegetarian cuisine.

The menu is simple, but does include some tremendous south Indian specialities like their exceptional dosas, as well as standards such as bhajia, chaat, poori and the usual bhindi, brinjal and saag sides together with a daily-changing curry.

Many would argue that this is the way it should be and, given the loyalty this restaurant engenders amongst its regulars, they may well be right.

Chutneys

Towards the Western end of Drummond St (which may well have London's best range of Indian vegetarian restaurants), we challenge you to peer through their large plate glass windows at the daily lunch buffet, and not feel the urge to go and eat.

Given their name, it's probably not too surprising that you'll find a range of eight fascinating chutneys and pickles (far removed from your standard High Street Indian's usual poppadom-accompaniments) to go with your lunchtime all-you-can-eat feast of breads, samosa, bhajia, salads and half a dozen curries. The buffet is also served all day on Sundays – other evenings see a menu featuring a good range of traditional Keralan cuisine. Licensed, it's a no-smoking restaurant when the buffet's on.

- 124 Drummond St London NW1 2PA
- 020 7388 0604
- Serving times:
  Mon-Sat 12-2.45pm & 6-11pm
  Sun 12-10.30pm
- Major credit cards
- Non-smoking at buffet times
- Licensed
- Children welcome
- 100 seats
- Lunch buffet £5.95

Heartstone

Predominately vegetarian, with impeccable organic credentials and a juice bar where you can have delicious smoothies or fresh juices mixed to order.

There's some good vegan choices – seared tofu, baked borlotti beans, the raw plate or falafel. They'll do you a plate of steamed vegetables with brown rice – which is sometimes all you fancy but damned hard to find – grilled sweet potatoes with stir fried bok choy, spring onions and roasted peanut chilli sauce, good (if slightly expensive) sandwiches on sourdough or gluten-free bread and some interesting salads – how about a roast beetroot, feta, chard and pumpkin seed version with tahini dressing?

Desserts are elegant, including a Californian walnut cake with coffee mascarpone.

- 106 Parkway Camden London NW1 7AN
- 020 7485 7744
- Serving times:
  Tues 10am-9pm
  Wed-Sat 8am-9pm
  Sun 10am-4pm
- Major credit cards
- Non-smoking
- Licensed
- Children welcome
- 30 seats
- Starters from £4.50

North London

- 21-22 Stables Market
  Camden
  London NW1 8AH
- 020 7267 8528
- Serving times:
  7 days 10.30am-7pm
- Credit cards over £15
  taken in downstairs
  bookstore
- Non-smoking
- Not licensed
- Children welcome
- 20 seats

Psychedelic Dream Temple

Upstairs at the Psychedelic Dream Temple record shop and bookstore, next door to the Mingling Bar & Restaurant, this Arabic and Indian influenced tearoom offers a chilled out, relaxed atmosphere – perfect for a reviving tea away from Camden's hectic market.

There's a large range of Arabic teas (served in traditional silver teapots and glasses), organic herbal teas and coffee, freshly-pressed fruit juices, smoothie 'dreams' - with added natural supplements if you want – and Carpe Diem health drinks. The divine cakes (all vegetarian and many vegan) are baked on the premises, and soya cream is available. Choose from chocolate brownies, cheese and blackcurrant cake, baklava, or vegan ginger and carrot varieties, together with dairy-free banana flapjacks.

North London

- 79 Regents Park Rd
  London NW1 8UY
- 020 7586 8012
- Serving times:
  Mon- Sat
  8.30am-6pm
  Sun 9am-6pm
- Major credit cards
- Non-smoking
- Not licensed, BYO
  with no corkage
- Children welcome
- 38 seats

Café 79

Café 79 is a friendly family-owned café, extremely popular for its superb all-day veggie breakfasts with organic free range eggs, vegetarian cheddar, homemade veggie sausages and large flat mushrooms.

The café also offers a tempting range of homemade organic soups (with rolls from Neals Yard Bakery), veggieburgers, pastas, baked potatoes, fresh salads, sandwiches and baguettes. It's a great place to chill out with the papers and a delicious coffee (soya cappuccinos available) with a mouth-watering selection of homemade cakes and scones after a walk in nearby Primrose Hill. Dogs and children are welcome (with half portions and high chairs available for the latter!).

The pavement tables are an ideal place to people-watch in this celebrity-filled part of London.

Saravanas

Heavily vegan and known locally for its dosas, there's also a tremendously good value lunch buffet on Fridays and Sundays.

The main menu features some excellent thalis with starters, vegetable curry, rice and dessert included. The paneer is homemade and cooked in a spicy chilli sauce, simply fried in butter, or with the more usual accompaniment of spinach or peas.

There are lassis and seasonal juices – unusually pomegranate juice, wonderfully refreshing and bitter. They bend over backwards to save you money: there's a 10% discount for midweek takeaway orders over £20, but you'd have to be having a dozen people round to spend that. There's a bar, but alcohol isn't served in the restaurant itself. Book at weekends.

- 77 Dudden Hill Lane London NW10 1BD
- 020 8459 2400
- Serving times: Tues-Sun 12-10.30pm
- Booking recommended weekends
- Major credit cards
- Non-smoking except bar
- Licensed bar, not restaurant
- Children welcome
- 130 seats
- Starters from £1.50

North London

Sabras

This longstanding restaurant has been deservedly garlanded with awards for its breathtakingly good, aromatic, and mainly vegan dishes. Licensed, they also serve fruit juices and delicately flavoured lassi.

The menu is clear and descriptive – reading a little like a recipe book with its detailed information about methods, ingredients and spicing – and you'll find interesting and unusual dishes such as a methi gota with bananas and fenugreek alongside more familiar favourites like masala dosa and mutter paneer.

Breads are made to order, and even the rice selections are far from ordinary: the kashmiri pilau coming adorned with almonds, pomegranate seeds, cashews, raisins and spiced vegetables.

- 263 High Rd Willesden London NW10 2RX
- 020 8459 0340
- Serving times: Tues-Sun 6.30-10.30pm
- Booking recommended
- Major credit cards
- Non-smoking area
- Licensed
- Children welcome
- 32 seats
- Starters from £3.25

North London

- 124 Golders Green Rd London NW11 8HB
- 020 8455 0664
- Serving times:
  Mon-Thurs
  10.30am-10.30pm
  Fri 10.30am-2pm
  Sat 7.30pm-11.30pm
  Sun 10.30am-10.30pm
- Major credit cards
- Non-smoking
- Not licensed
- Children welcome
- 56 seats
- Mains from £7

Milk 'n' Honey

We'd go to this Kosher restaurant in the heart of Golders Green just for the selection of ice creams, where you can enjoy combinations such as vanilla and strawberry with crushed meringue and freshly whipped cream, or mango, lemon and blackcurrant sorbets covered in strawberry sauce, hundreds and thousands and a dusting of icing sugar.

If you prefer something savoury, try starters such as spinach filo parcels, samosas, spring rolls and stuffed mushrooms, or more substantial dishes which include veggieburgers, half a dozen vegetarian pastas, freshly-baked pizzas with your own choice of toppings, and an impressive selection of main course salads.

Probably not the cheapest café-restaurant in the area, but definitely worth the extra.

- 225 Kentish Town Rd London NW5 2JU
- 020 7267 7761
- Serving times:
  Mon-Sat 8am-8pm
  Sun 9am-7pm
- Major credit cards
- Non-smoking area
- Licensed
- Children welcome
- 50 seats

Café Euro Med

Café Euro Med is a bistro-style café, where the Turkish, Greek and Italian-influenced vegetarian dishes haven't just been added as an afterthought.

Although it's waitress service, many of the day's specials are displayed in the counter area (for the thriving takeaway trade), and you can build your own selection from dozens of meat-free choices including stuffed vine leaves, mucver (deep-fried patties of grated courgette, egg, feta, flour, dill, parsley and mint), baked aubergine, spinach, falafel, moussaka, and numerous pastas and salads.

Recently taken over by the cousin of the previous owner, we're promised an even more comprehensive vegetarian selection in the future. We just hope they don't change the lime green and purple décor.

Manna

A long-established restaurant, close to one of London's finest views from Primrose Hill, Manna serves gourmet vegetarian food from around the world. Just a few minutes walk from Chalk Farm tube, you'll feel you've arrived in a gentler, more civilised world. It's always advisable to book (though you wonder if they say that to the celebrity regulars).

You'll be delighted with starters like organic ravioli, portobello mushroom and blue brie stack or stuffed baby squash, and can sample main courses that should have a 'don't try this at home' sticker attached such as cashew and kumquat teriyaki tempeh, or fennel schnitzel with pink peppercorn sauce. Simpler tastes might go for the chef's salad or chimichangas, with side orders of brown rice or fresh bread.

Organic ice cream desserts come with liqueur shots, or there are temptations like star anise brulée with glazed peppered pineapple, organic doughnuts (what kind of mixed message is that!) with cinnamon sugar and chocolate sauce, petits fours or fruit crumble. Dishes are clearly marked for their vegan or gluten-free credentials, and there's a commitment to organic produce.

You can dine outside in the summer, or cosy up in the restaurant's candlelit surroundings the other 51 weeks of the year. Children are made welcome with smaller portions of whatever they fancy (and crayons and paper if they need more diversions), but there's an unwritten rule that any scampering around will have finished by 7.30pm.

The comprehensive wine list is all-vegetarian, with vegan options, and may well have been a factor in the Vegetarian Society's recent award to Manna as the UK's best vegetarian restaurant. Not cheap, but you could always visit between 6.30 and 7.30pm Sunday to Thursday and have two courses for just £13.25.

- 4 Erskine Rd
  London NW3 3AJ
- 020 7722 8028
- Serving times:
  Mon-Sat 6.30-10.45pm
  Sun 12.30-2.45pm
  & 6.30-10.15pm
  Closed between Xmas
  and New Year
- Booking recommended
- Major credit cards
- Non-smoking
- Licensed
- Children welcome
- 50 seats
- Starters from £4.50

North London

- 72 Belsize Lane
  London NW3 5BJ
- 020 7435 7733
- Serving times:
  Mon-Fri 6-10.30pm
  Sat 12-3pm
  & 6-11pm
  Sun 12-3pm
  & 6-9.30pm
- Major credit cards
- Non-smoking
- Licensed
- Children welcome
- 60 seats
- Mains from £8

The Gate

Younger sister of the Hammersmith Gate, this restaurant has a similarly varied and exciting menu. Homemade saffron pasta filled with butternut, dolcelatte, basil and cinnamon with a mascarpone sauce, rocket and parmesan-style shavings would tempt the most jaded palate. For a more vibrant start, the noodle and vegetable salad is finished with a ginger, lemongrass, chilli and lime dressing with deep fried aubergine – this really wakes up the tastebuds and gets the juices flowing.

Main courses are inventive and delicious: Cajun aubergine – deep fried aubergine shells filled with roasted okra, on a bed of chargrilled sweet potato with an avocado and pineapple salsa and roasted pepper and chipotle compote – certainly a riot of flavours and textures. More conservatively, there can be mushroom strudel with leek and stilton, served with artichoke mash and braised baby fennel and kale, or baby aubergine stuffed with a variety of fillings and served with polenta. Red Thai curry features a tangy green papaya salsa and comes with basmati rice, which many prefer to the sticky Thai stuff.

Desserts are impressive: raspberry and lemon crème brulée, chocolate fondant with prunes and armagnac, apple charlotte, cheese. Some require an extra 15 minutes, but we're sure you'll be happy swirling a glass of wine while you wait.

There are some stunning fresh juice cocktails – spinach, apple, carrot and beetroot for example, which would stand in for a starter. Dishes are marked if suitable for vegans, as is the wine list.

Vitaorganic

OK, so you may have heard of the raw food movement, and its celebrity advocates such as Demi Moore and Donna Karan, but now you get a chance to try it at this friendly and welcoming restaurant just north of the Finchley Road tube. If you're a first-timer, go with their recommendations – to get the best from the experience you need to combine foods in certain ways, and as you may find the menu a little confusing at first sight (dishes aren't listed in the traditional starter – mains – puddings way...) their advice is going to help you navigate what's available.

Do, however, try the canapé-style raw pizza: sprouted buckwheat flour is pressed (not baked) into a biscuit-like base which is topped with a cayenne flavoured sun-dried tomato paste, tahini (from raw, not toasted sesame seeds), and finished with thinly-sliced olives and very small chunks of tomato.

Not everything on the menu is, however, uncooked. Soups – like gazpacho, miso and tom yum – can be ordered cooked or raw, and there's a whole speciality section of dishes such as golden dream stroganoff, red pepper sauce moussaka and rainbow mixed veg which are lightly steamed or stewed to maintain flavours and nutrients and, they claim, to retain the benefits of natural enzymes and essential fatty acids.

Drinks (some of which they recommend you enjoy before or after eating, not during the meal) range from a couple of dozen teas, freshly-pressed soya milk – available flavoured with raw almond – and a great range of non-dairy smoothies.

Even if you don't plan to change your eating habits completely, Vitaorganic should be on your well-worth-a-visit list.

- 279c Finchley Rd
  London NW3 6ND
- 020 7435 2188
- Serving times:
  7 days 12-10.45pm
- No credit cards
- Non-smoking
- Licensed
- Children welcome
- 38 seats
- Mains from £7

North London

North London

- 195-197
  The Broadway
  London NW9 7DE
- 020 8203 8522
- Serving times:
  Tues-Fri 12-3pm
  & 6-10pm
  Sat-Sun 12-10pm
- Major credit cards
- Non-smoking
- Not licensed, BYO
  with no corkage
- Children welcome
- 70 seats
- Buffet from £5

Rajens Restaurant

There's an all-you-can-eat buffet lunchtimes and evenings at this popular Gujarati restaurant and, if that wasn't enough, they'll also ply you with a complimentary lassi or soft drink during the week.

If your tastes run to more exotic dishes, you can also choose to order another dozen or so Indian favourites from the menu, including the range of dosas which are available in the evening.

Open all day from midday on the weekend, they aren't licensed, but there's no corkage if you want to bring a bottle or two.

Free local parking has to be another draw, and Rajen's is a completely smoke-free zone.

North London

- 547 Kingsbury Rd
  London NW9 9EL
- 020 8204 1555
- Serving times:
  Mon-Fri 12-10pm
  Sat-Sun 12.30-10pm
- Major credit cards
- Non-smoking
- Not licensed
- Children welcome
- 120 seats
- Snacks from £3

Jays

Busy, fast food-style café/restaurant offering a huge range of Indian, Thai, Chinese and Mexican dishes. The décor is simple and bright and, if you like to order your food with the help of a picture in addition to a description, you're in the right place.

Choose from Indian snacks, breads and curries, Szechaun and blackbean-sauced veg, tortillas, tacos, fajitas and enchiladas or one of a couple of Thai curries – and wash it all down with passion fruit or pomegranate juice, milkshakes or their special faluda.

A welcoming, friendly, no-smoking, no-alcohol restaurant. Very popular in the evenings, it's ideal to take the kids to, and they're unlikely to be in trouble for making a bit of noise.

Rose

A bright, fastfood-style café that's as popular with families as it is as a meeting place for the local youngsters.

The all-day menu features almost 200 vegetarian choices ranging from standard Indian snack food like bhajias and samosas, to toasted sandwiches, soups, curries, tandooris and Chinese-style selections.

You can enjoy a very fine chilli paneer (we fear this dish may be addictive – you have been warned) accompanied by one of a couple of dozen juices, lassis or milkshakes, or enjoy the lunchtime buffet (12-3pm) for under a fiver.

Rose also opens for an all-you-can-eat breakfast deal between 10-11.30am at the weekends.

- 534 Kingsbury Rd London NW9 9HH
- 020 8905 0025
- Serving times:
  Mon-Fri
  11am-10.30pm
  Sat-Sun
  10am-10.30pm
- Major credit cards
- Non-smoking
- Not licensed
- Children welcome
- 32 seats
- Starters from £1.50

Udupi Palace

Tiny 12-seat café in the Kingsbury Market Arcade, right opposite Kingsbury tube, serving pure vegetarian South Indian food at extremely reasonable prices. Udupi Palace offers a huge range of idli, dosas and vegetable curries, mainly under £4 (most snacks £2.50 or less) with freshly made breads starting at 40p. Or select from their special offers – a mini lunch of two parathas and veg curry plus a drink, or the unmissable Bangalore Special Thali of dhal, rasam, sambar, dry veg, kootu, steamed rice, puris, raitha, papad, pickle, sweet and coffee (phew!), currently at £6.99 for two people.

Everything is egg-free, and most snacks and mains are dairy-free, so vegans will have no problem – apart from coping with the unaccustomed choice.

- 12-13 Kingsbury Arcade
  Kingsbury Rd
  London NW9 9HL
- 020 8204 1404
- Serving times:
  7 days 11am-3pm
  & 6-10pm
- Major credit cards
- Non-smoking
- Not licensed
- Children welcome
- 12 seats
- Mains from £2.50

North London

North London

- 658 Kingsbury Rd
  London NW9 9HN
- 020 8204 6208
- Serving times:
  7 days 10am-10pm
- Booking recommended
  weekend evenings
- Major credit cards
- Non-smoking
- Not licensed
- Children welcome
- 50 seats
- Snacks from £2.75

Yogi Ji's

Don't worry too much about in-depth directions to this vegetarian café and restaurant in NW9. Head for Kingsbury Circus and look for the bright orange and black building covered in its proud 'Vegetarian for Vitality' motto. Owner Yogi Morjaria has created a warm, friendly and very reasonably priced café that's popular with family groups as well as the young, and is open until 10pm seven days a week.

The menu ranges from chips and dips to pizza and falafel, chilli paneer to savoury pancakes and enchiladas, and most points in between. There are also some truly delicious desserts, created by the same team that produces speciality wedding and birthday celebration cakes. You won't believe what they can do with (egg-free) cake-mix and a bit of icing.

east
london

london • east

East London

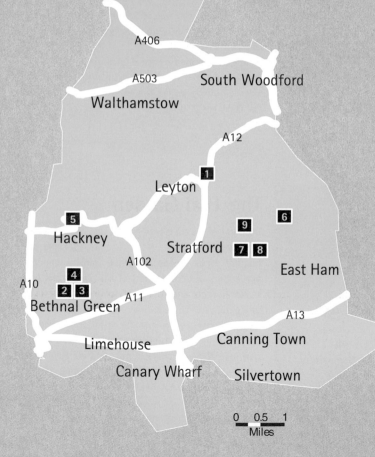

east london

A406

A503

South Woodford

Walthamstow

A12

1 Leyton

5

Hackney

9

6

Stratford

7 8

East Ham

A102

4

A10

2 3

A11

Bethnal Green

A13

Canning Town

Limehouse

Canary Wharf

Silvertown

0   0.5   1
Miles

- 715 High Rd
  Leytonstone
  London E11 4RD
- 020 8539 1700
- Serving times:
  Tues-Sun 5-11.45pm
  Mon opening
  planned soon
- Major credit cards
- Non-smoking area
- Licensed
- Children welcome
- 115 seats
- Mains from £2.50

Chandni

This homely Indian restaurant, with its proper linen, stripped wooden floors and the warm colours employed in the Indian-themed murals, has an almost Mediterranean feel. They did experiment last year with a non-vegetarian (prepared in a separate kitchen) section upstairs, but they've now gone back to what they know best – good, freshly prepared Indian and Indo-Chinese food in a completely meat-free environment.

Completely egg-free, there are plenty of vegan options but, as they're not specifically marked on the menu, just ask the staff.

The upstairs area is opened on busy evenings, has its own bar, and can also be booked for private parties – when a buffet-style celebration can be arranged from just £6.50 per head.

- 249 Globe Rd
  London E2 0JD
- 020 8981 5748
- Serving times:
  Mon-Fri 12-2.45pm
  & 6-10.30pm
  Sat-Sun 6-10.30pm
  Closed bank holidays
- Major credit cards
- Non-smoking area
- Licensed
- Children welcome
- 32 seats
- Mains from £4.50

The Thai Garden

This local restaurant is always busy, and it's no surprise. They use no MSG or GM foods and only serve Thai fragrant rice. Appetisers include larb – chopped mushrooms with fried grains of rice, spices and basil leaves in a hot and sour salad, plus the more usual spring rolls, tempura and satay.

There's plenty of choice in the main courses, rice and noodle dishes including the deservedly popular pad Thai. Look out for the fabulous mix of Thai aubergines, vegetarian mock duck, pineapple, tomato, grapes, bamboo shoots, sweet basil, coconut cream and red curry sauce which will wow the most jaded palate. It's also very easy to eat vegan here, though the menu doesn't specifically list the egg- and dairy-free choices.

Wild Cherry

Close to the London Buddhist Centre, and run on Buddhist principles, there's a relaxed and friendly atmosphere at this vegetarian café and restaurant.

They know to the last raisin what's in every dish, so eating vegan, dairy- sugar- or wheat-free isn't a lottery, and there's a good proportion of organic ingredients. The food draws on influences from around the world, and the brief menu features a couple of starters, a handful of mains, and a good dessert and cake selection. Enjoy dishes such as celery and stilton soup with organic bread, roast vegetables with cream cheese, polenta and salad and a vegan apple crumble with the option of soya cream.

Visit Wild Cherry on a Saturday if you want to try the all-day breakfast.

- 241 Globe Rd
  London E2 0JD
- 020 8980 6678
- Serving times:
  Mon 11am-4pm
  Tues-Fri 11am-7pm
  Sat 10am-4pm
- Major credit cards
- Non-smoking except garden
- Not licensed, BYO with £1 corkage
- Children welcome
- 55 seats
- Starters from £2.50

East London

The Gallery Café

A peaceful, ethical café, run by members of the local Buddhist centre, that's recently started opening a little earlier to serve (continental-style, not the full monty) breakfasts.

Queue at the counter for a lunch selection that includes a couple of soups – for example pea and coconut or a lightly spiced Indian broth – good pastas and salads, sandwiches – such as vegetarian sausage with free range egg mayo or mozzarella, tomato and pesto – and daily specials. There's always something for vegans, as well as a good selection of cakes, sticky flans, fair trade coffees and freshly pressed juices.

A light and airy space, with a conservatory overlooking the garden. A real haven.

- 21 Old Ford Rd
  London E2 9PL
- 020 8983 3624
- Serving times:
  Mon 8am-3pm
  Tues 8am-2.30pm
  Wed-Fri 8am-3pm
  Sat 10.30am-5pm
- No credit cards
- Non-smoking
- Not licensed
- Children welcome
- 40 seats
- Soup from £2.40

East London

East London

- 76a Clarence Rd
  Hackney
  London E5 8HB
- 020 8533 1214
- Serving times:
  Mon–Sun 12-9pm
- Booking
  recommended
- No credit cards
- Smoking throughout
- Not licensed, BYO
  with minimal corkage
- Children welcome
- 33 seats
- Starters from £2

Pumpkins

In the heart of Hackney, close to the station, this long-established restaurant is open daily for lunch, snacks and dinner, and stocks some very good coffees and teas. Most food is vegan, and those dishes that do contain egg or dairy are clearly marked.

Choose from light snacks and starters like toasties, sandwiches, bubble and squeak, vegan bacon sandwiches and falafel, and enjoy main courses (served with a choice of salad or steamed vegetables, chips or roasties) such as a blue-cheese pie with broccoli, leeks and sweetcorn, cashew nut roast or a spicy bean bake. You want gravy with that, or extras like parsnip chips? You got it.

Finish with dairy or vegan ice cream, cakes and deluxe milk shakes.

East London

- 510–512 Romford Rd
  Forest Gate
  London E7 8AF
- 020 8472 5459
- Serving times:
  Mon & Wed-Sun
  10am-7pm
  Closed Tuesdays
- Major credit cards
- Non-smoking
- Not licensed
- Children welcome
- 24 seats

City Sweet Centre

The City Sweet Centre sells not only sweets but also Indian snack food. You can eat in, or it's an ideal place to go on a spree if you want to throw together a quick buffet.

Vegetable or cheese samosas, spring rolls, bhajias and the whole family of moreish sev, chaat and poori goods – we'd be quite happy with a bucket of bhel poori for dinner if you're offering.

You can then move on to the syrupy, sticky Indian desserts and sweets – jewel-like colours, but feel your teeth melting with each bite – including carrot halva, ras malai, gulub jamun and barfis.

Sakonis

With its tiled floors and walls, a large stainless steel buffet, and the counter selling a variety of takeout sweets and savouries, Sakonis in Forest Gate is a distinctly fast food-style experience, but one that's popular with families and larger groups – particularly at weekends.

Open all day, visit between 12-3pm or 7-9.30pm for the all-you-can-eat buffet. Expect a range of curries, rice, dhals and breads, together with some daily-changing buffet specials, and keep going back for more until you're full. Closed on Mondays (unless it's a bank holiday, when they close on the following Tuesday instead). And, should your record collection need bolstering, they also sell a small selection of Indian CDs and tapes.

- 149 -153 Green St
  Forest Gate
  London E7 8LE
- 020 8472 8887
- Serving times:
  Tues-Sun 12-9.30pm
- Major credit cards
- Non-smoking
- Not licensed
- Children welcome
- 100 seats
- Lunch buffet £5.99

Vijay's Chawalla

This popular venue is regularly nominated for various 'Best Café' awards.

The menu is a mixture of street-food snacks, south Indian rice pancakes, dhal or vegetable curry and rice. Look out for the bhel with cashew nuts, peanuts, chickpeas and potato served with garlic chutney. As there's also a different special every day, you could avoid having to make a decision by having one of the two thalis that let you try a bit of everything. You can take your own wine or order fresh juices or a refreshing lassi – beware though, some of the drinks cost the same as a plate of pakoras. Great value food when you're looking for a spicy snack of some kind.

- 268 Green St
  London E7 8LF
- 020 8470 3535
- Serving times:
  7 days 11am-9pm
- Major credit cards
- Non-smoking
- Not licensed but BYO
  with no corkage
- Children welcome
- 50 seats
- From £2.75

East London

East London

- 317 Romford Rd
  London E7 9HA
- 020 8519 2110
- Serving times:
  Tues-Sun 12-9pm
  Closed during January
- No credit cards
- Non-smoking area
- Licensed
- Children welcome
- 40 seats
- Starters from £1.75

Ronak

Expect to be greeted with the heady aroma of Indian spices as you walk through the door of this long-established Indian vegetarian restaurant, which also caters a number of central London hotels and the occasional event at Alexandra Palace.

Bucking the trend, there aren't huge numbers of individual mains – which at least saves time rummaging around a multi-page menu – the form here is to enjoy your favourite starter from dishes such as kachoori, patra and bhel poori whilst you wait for the house thali of the day's curries, dhals, pickles and bread. Ronak is licensed, with a small selection of wines and beer.

Open all day, they do however close in January for their annual hols.

south
london

South London

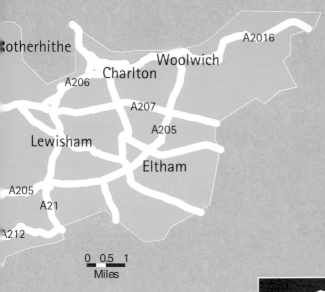

Rotherhithe

Woolwich

Charlton

A2016

A206

A207

A205

Lewisham

Eltham

A205

A21

A212

0 0.5 1
Miles

south london

South London

- 76 Borough High St London SE1 1LL
- 020 7403 8557
- Serving times: Mon-Fri 7am-7pm Sat-Sun 8am-5pm
- No credit cards
- Non-smoking
- Not licensed, BYO with no corkage
- Children welcome
- 30 seats
- Soup from £1.75

Tas Café

Brought to you by the same people who run the restaurants under the same banner, the Tas café is the ideal breakfast stop for a croissant and coffee or a tomato and halloumi sandwich to go with your freshly squeezed orange juice. At lunch, eat in or take away a mixed meze of half a dozen Mediterranean and Middle-eastern dishes such as hummus, tabouleh, kisir or Imam Bayildi. Alternatively, opt for one of the vegetarian soups or salads, or try a chickpea or green lentil casserole. There's also pasta, a range of breads as well as pastries and cakes.

Just a couple of hundred yards from London Bridge Station, you've now got somewhere to go when the 4.15 to Dartford has been cancelled yet again.

South London

- The Museum of Garden History Lambeth Palace Rd London SE1 7LB
- Next to Lambeth Palace
- 020 7401 8865
- Serving times: Mon-Sun 10.30am-4.45pm
- No credit cards
- Non-smoking
- Not licensed
- Children welcome
- 60 seats
- From £3

Courtyard Café
The Museum of Garden History

Between the Houses of Parliament and Tate Britain, but on the opposite side of the river, this café manages to be both out of the way and in central London, right by Lambeth Palace. The museum is worth a visit, and St Mary's church is perfect for rummaging around interesting tombs; Captain Bligh's is of particular note.

The menu changes daily, and there's plenty of vegan choice in the curries and stews. Half the options are wheat-free. They cover the range of bakes, curries, stuffed vegetables and tagines and also have sticky toffee pudding and cakes. Organic juices, bottled drinks and smaller portions for children available. The garden is wonderful. Instant peace and quiet.

Tas Restaurant

Not just one restaurant serving a blindingly good range of vegetarian food in SE1, but a pair. If you add in their café just up the road, and the two Tas Pide restaurants (near The Globe and in the City), you get some idea of the success the Tas group has had with its imaginative and highly regarded cooking. Flavours are well balanced, service attentive without being fussy and there's a welcoming atmosphere in these modern, cleanly decorated restaurants.

Equally popular for larger party groups as well as a more cosy dinner a deux, they're open from midday til late seven days a week, with booking in the evening essential.

The Tas name derives from the traditional Anatolian cooking pots that the Middle-eastern casseroles are prepared and served in, and you won't go far wrong with any of the vegetarian choices. Ingredients are simply listed next to the menu item; there are no flowery adjectives in an attempt to spice things up, and you won't believe just how good even the most basic sounding dish can taste. They're obviously quite happy to let the food do the talking here.

Plan to share, tapas style. Virtually all the cold starters are vegetarian-friendly, and there are also smaller portions of the more substantial vegetarian mains. If you think hummus is just too boring to order in a restaurant, try the Tas version with an oak-smoked flavour and creamy texture the like of which you're just not going to find in the chilled section of your local supermarket. There's fried aubergine with peppers, tomato sauce and yoghurt, deeply satisfying falafel, and almost a dozen casserole-style mains all prepared in the open plan kitchen. And if the choice leaves you bewildered, just opt for the staggeringly good vegetarian meze.

- 72 Borough High St London SE1 1XF
- 020 7403 7200
- Serving times: Mon-Sat 12-11.30pm Sun 12-10.30pm
- Booking essential evenings
- Major credit cards
- Non-smoking area
- Licensed
- Children welcome
- 200 seats
- Full meze from £10

- Another branch at:
- 33 The Cut Waterloo London SE1 8LF
- 020 7928 1444
- Serving times: Mon-Sat 12-11.30pm Sun 12-10.30pm
- Booking essential evenings
- Major credit cards
- Non-smoking area
- Licensed
- Children welcome
- 140 seats
- Full meze from £10

South London

South London

- 20-22 Globe Walk
  London SE1 9DR
- 020 7928 3300
- Serving times:
  Mon-Sat 12-11.30pm
  Sun 12-10.30pm
- Booking recommended evenings
- Major credit cards
- Non-smoking area
- Licensed
- Children welcome
- 100 seats
- Pide from £5.45

Tas Pide

If you liked Tas at Borough High St or The Cut, you're going to love Tas Pide by the Globe Theatre. With a menu equally high in good vegetarian choice, there's the addition of Pide, a traditional Anatolian dish of freshly made dough baked in a wood-fired oven and then stuffed with beautifully cooked fillings like artichoke, peas, carrots, tomato and spring onion, or leek, green lentils, potatoes and raisins. The crisp crust and boat shape of the cooked dough also makes it ideal to eat sans cutlery.

Open seven days a week till late, there's the usual comprehensive and well-priced Tas wine list and, even though it's a 100-seat restaurant, we recommend you book for evenings.

South London

- The Old Courthouse
  43 Renfrew Rd
  London SE11 4NA
- 020 7735 9821
- Serving times:
  Mon-Tues
  9am-3.30pm
  Wed 9am-7.30pm
  Thurs-Fri 9am-3.30pm
  Sat 9am-5pm
  Closed bank holidays
- No credit cards
- Non-smoking
  except garden
- Not licensed
- Children welcome
- 40 seats and garden
- From £3

The Courtyard Café

Literally a courtyard – this café is in a Victorian courthouse that is now a Buddhist centre. This non-profit making café supports the charity 'Compassion in Action' and gives training opportunities for young people with behavioural problems and learning difficulties. The menu changes daily, but is half vegan or wheat-free, with a choice of vegan curries, stews and soups. The food can also be inspired by religious and historical festivals. Main courses can include a lentil and leek bake, artichoke, bean and thyme pie or a roast vegetable tagine.

All the drinks and dry goods are organic. Open until mid afternoon, this is a haven just a couple of minutes away from the Imperial War Museum.

South London

Domali Café

Worth the trek at weekends for the eggs Benedict or eggs Florentine if you're a fan of the posh free range start to the day, Domali Café offers an all-day full veggie breakfast as well.

Good toasties and sandwiches are among the lighter lunch options – mozzarella, sundried tomato and roasted pepper, or a vegetarian salami with salad. For a more lingering meal, there's pasta of the day, vegetable tagine, gourmet sausages and mash, or you can construct your own grazing from olives, chargrilled bread with olive oil, mushrooms and crème fraiche with Dijon mustard or grilled tomatoes with herbs.

A reasonable wine list and some potent cocktails are an added attraction, particularly with the long happy hour from 6pm–8pm.

- 38 Westow St
  London SE19 3AH
- 020 8768 0096
- Serving times:
  Mon-Tues
  9.30am-5.45pm
  Wed-Sun
  9.30am-10.30pm
- Booking recommended evenings
- Major credit cards
- Non-smoking area
- Licensed
- Children welcome
- 35 seats
- Lunch mains from £3.90

South London

Mantanah Thai

There are quirkily named vegetarian dishes here like golden bag, Tony's delight, and Cinderella's best friend. The golden bag starter is a crispy rice paper bag, with sweet potato, mixed vegetables and pickled cucumber sauce. Tony's delight is rice paper rolled with steamed mixed vegetables, ground peanuts, roasted coconut and a slightly hot sweet plum sauce, and Tony may have a point here. Cinderella's best friend is (apparently) deep-fried shredded pumpkin in coconut batter. We wonder if she knows?

The mains include stir fried aubergine with mock chicken, blackbean sauce and chillies, and the 'Easy Dinner' of deep-fried bean curd, bean sprouts and spring onions.

- 2 Orton Buildings
  Portland Rd
  South Norwood
  London SE25 4UD
- 020 8771 1148
- Serving times:
  Tues-Sun 12-3pm
  & 6-11pm
- Major credit cards
- Smoking throughout
- Licensed
- Children welcome
- 32 seats
- Starters from £3.50

Vegetarian Restaurant

- 25 Selhurst Rd
  London SE25 5PP
- 020 8683 4462
- Serving times:
  Tues-Sat 10am-10pm
  Sun 12-8pm
- No credit cards
- Non-smoking
- Licensed
- Children welcome
- 30 seats

Pepperton UK

A recently opened and welcome addition in south-east London, Pepperton UK is a completely vegetarian and vegan restaurant which features a contemporary art gallery on the first floor.

Pop in to exhibitions which have featured work by Tracey Emin and Gavin Turk, and then decamp to the ground floor to recover with coffee and a bun.

If you can stay for longer you could also make lunch or dinner here, with choices such as their popular 'red' soup (kidney beans, peppers and tomato), or try a main course moussaka, spaghetti bolognaise (with soya mince) or the house salad.

Licensed, Pepperton serves a range of fruit wines (including gooseberry, strawberry and elderflower) alongside more traditional beers and wine.

Vegetarian Chinese Café

- 87 Battersea Rise
  Battersea
  London SW11 1HW
- 020 7350 0900
- Serving times:
  7 days 6-11pm
- Major credit cards
- Non-smoking
- Not licensed, BYO
- Children welcome
- 25 seats
- Starters from £3

Battersea Rice

Bring your own wine to this brightly-lit evening café and takeaway. It's very spruce, and you can see right through to the kitchens where some giant woks are in use. There's a filling mixed combo starter for two of spring rolls, satay, wonton and sesame toast, and also a savoury mushroom and seaweed soup among the many choices.

Good creative use is made of tofu and black or yellow bean protein to make dishes such as a tasty mango or lemon 'chicken' and a moreish fillet with black pepper (the flavour reminiscent of bread and dripping, our non-veggie friends advise us). Pad Thai noodles and steamed rice may more or less immobilise you, but you might want to work on through the ice cream desserts.

Fresh & Wild

Small but perfectly formed, a café in a high-end, organic-'til-it-hurts store and juice bar. One of the main attractions here are those stupendous fresh juices, blitzed before your very eyes. And, if you've chosen one of the wheatgrass options, there are little trays on the counter with a baby lawn of the stuff ready to be harvested for your shot.

You can also take away a mixed salad, soup, hot specials, tarts, cakes and flapjacks – name all the things that make a good desk lunch – or eat in at one of the bistro tables or bar stools right in the window.

Emerge feeling powerfully healthy, and then browse the shop's shelves for some fantastic bread and produce.

- 305-311 Lavender Hill London SW11 1LN
- 020 7585 1488
- Serving times: Mon-Sat 12-5.30pm Sun 12.30-4pm Store and juice bar open much longer hours
- Major credit cards
- Non-smoking
- Not licensed
- Children welcome
- 30 seats

South London

Wholemeal Vegetarian Café

This place is a bit of an oasis in an area crammed with fast food nonsense. Start with hummus, garlic mushrooms or marinated olives, and move on to the main course bake or casserole of the day, or a curry, jacket or big mixed salad – including what can only be described as the full monty version with cheddar and cottage cheeses, garlic mushrooms and hummus. Vegans are made very welcome, and gluten-free requests are taken on board. Desserts include trifle, homemade crumbles, cakes and banoffee pie.

Licensed, with a range of organic wines, beers and ciders, you can also enjoy a decent selection of regular and herbal teas. Open till 10pm seven days a week.

- 1 Shrubbery Rd London SW16 2AS
- 020 8769 2423
- Serving times: 7 days 12-10pm
- Booking recommended weekends
- Major credit cards
- Non-smoking
- Licensed
- Children welcome
- 36 seats
- Mains from £5

South London

South London

- 1547 London Rd
  Norbury
  London SW16 4AD
- 020 8679 6275
- Serving times:
  7 days 12-2.30pm
  & 6-11pm
- Major credit cards
- Non-smoking area
- Licensed
- Children welcome
- 70 seats
- Starters from £2

Shahee Bhelpoori

A good suburban Indian restaurant, handy for Norbury station. There are separate lunch and dinner sittings, and possibly the bargain of the century in their all-you-can-eat Sunday buffet at a ludicrous £3.95. Children under six even get this half price!

There's probably nothing on the menu you've not tried before, but this busy local Indian has been running for years and is quite obviously getting it right.

Enjoy the mixed starter of samosa, vegetable cutlet, pakora and potato cake as a snack, as a prelude to dosas, chilli paneer or a selection of vegetable sides, or choose one of half a dozen thalis. Whichever way you go, you're not going to break the bank.

South London

- 192-194
  Tooting High St
  London SW17 0SF
- 020 8672 4250
- Serving times:
  Mon-Thurs 12-2.45pm
  & 6-10.45pm
  Fri-Sat 12-2.45pm
  & 6-11.45pm
  Sun 12-2.45pm
  & 6-10.45pm
- Booking recommended
  evenings
- Major credit cards
- Non-smoking area
- Licensed
- Children welcome
- 100 seats
- Starters from £2.50

Sree Krishna

Tooting is one of London's best areas for Asian cooking, and this restaurant started the trend 30 years ago. The food originates from Kerala, spice capital of the world, and the menu is helpfully laid out in vegetarian and non-vegetarian sections with dishes marked up with one to three chillies to indicate the level of spiciness.

Among the more unusual dishes you will find a beetroot thoran, lightly spiced and with mustard seed and coconut – absolutely delicious – green beans with coconut, and chettinadu vegetable curry with 16 carefully balanced spices. Starters include cashew pakodas (deep fried cashew nuts) which are so moreish they should be a compulsory pub snack in every bar. Popular, with booking recommended for most evenings.

Vegetarian Restaurant

London SW17

Kastoori

Kastoori is the place to go for distinguished Gujarati vegetarian and Indo-African cooking. Smartly decorated, and with serious, knowledgeable staff, it would be famous if it were in the West End.

This is exceptionally high standard family cooking, with some dishes appearing on a set day of the week. There are the expected starters – paneers, kofta dishes and thalis – but also green banana curry, banana stuffed with mild chillies, sweet corn in coconut milk with peanut sauce and more fascinating choices drawing from the owners' years in Africa.

You'll want to return on a different day of the week each time to try something new. Booking essential at the weekends.

- 188 Upper Tooting Rd London SW17 7EJ
- 020 8767 7027
- Serving times: Mon-Tues 6-10.30pm Wed-Sun 12.30-2.30pm & 6-10.30pm
- Booking essential Fri & Sat evenings
- Major credit cards
- Smoking throughout
- Licensed
- Children welcome
- 82 seats
- Starters from £2

Vegetarian Indian Restaurant

London SW17

Sakonis

On a large corner site, this spacious restaurant has something of the canteen about it, but is none the worse for that. They can seat up to 150 people, but on weekday lunchtimes things tick over a little more quietly. Unpretentious, with scrubbed tables, ketchup bottles and menus featuring photos of the food, you're most likely to visit for the bargain daily buffet (£5.99 at lunch, £7.99 evenings) featuring a huge selection of Indian and Indo-Chinese food.

If you're feeling classy and want to order from the menu, there's a good selection of filled dosas, a few more Chinese-style dishes, and plenty of hot and cold starters. A welcoming, alcohol-free venue that's very popular with local families.

- 180-186 Upper Tooting Rd London SW17 7EW
- 020 8772 4774
- Serving times: Tues-Sun 12-9.30pm Closed Mon except bank holidays Buffet served 12-3.30pm & 6.30-9.30pm
- Major credit cards
- Non-smoking
- Not licensed
- Children welcome
- 150 seats
- Lunch buffet 5.99

329

Chutneys

- 31 Hartfield Rd
  Wimbledon
  London SW19 3SG
- 020 8540 9788
- Serving times:
  Mon-Sat 12-2.30pm
  & 6-12pm
  Sun 12-2.30pm
  & 6-11.30pm
- Booking recommended
  weekend evenings
- Major credit cards
- Smoking throughout
- Licensed
- Children welcome
- 50 seats

Near the station and shopping centre, this is an excellent local Indian, smart enough for a Saturday night. Although not totally vegetarian (the menu changed a little while ago), the selection is still very worthy. Skip the starters of vegetable samosas or onion bhajis and try their south Indian pancake specialities of mushroom and garlic or ghee-roasted dosas, or tangy spiced okra flavoured with mango powder.

Other vegetarian dishes include a mild pasanda, choley with chickpeas and a hotly-spiced jalfrezi. Side dishes like jeera paneer – cumin flavoured Indian cheese – are distinguished and they serve excellent breads and rice. Alternatively, enjoy a vegetarian thali to ease the pain of decision making.

Service-Heart-Joy

- 191 Hartfield Rd
  Wimbledon
  London SW19 3TH
- 020 8542 9912
- Serving times:
  Mon-Fri 8am-5pm
  Sat 9am-5pm
- No credit cards
- Non-smoking
- Not licensed
- Children welcome
- 17 seats
- Snacks from £2.50

This daytime café advertises a (very fine) Saturday brunch – conveniently available every day if you can't wait for the weekend – of egg, veggie bacon and sausages, beans, tomato, toast and tea or coffee, for a bargain £3.95. You can also choose cereals or a pancake stack with proper maple syrup if you need to bulk up for a day's shopping in Wimbledon.

There are substantial lunch sandwiches – pre-designed or arrange your own – main salads, omelettes, curries, burgers, baked potatoes and a daily special.

Cakes are homemade with some vegan choices, and their imagination runs riot when it comes to the ice cream sundaes. There's also good, fancy coffee, hot chocolate, herbal tea and fruit smoothies.

Bug

Cream walls, glossy wood tables and gorgeous ecclesiastical pieces here and there, Bug may be one of the most glamorous crypts in London.

Simple starters like rocket, caramelised pear and blue cheese salad, bruschetta and soup, or a platter of onion bhajis with aubergine masala are well presented. Main courses are substantial: nut Wellington en croûte, with braised red cabbage and onion gravy, or mock duck pancakes with sauce, and sides of Cajun potatoes, mash and salads are all featured. Great desserts include passion fruit tart with port and redcurrant sorbet, and there's a good wine list by the glass.

Sunday lunch is a very good deal with a nut roast, Yorkshire puddings, rosemary-roast pumpkin and carrots, mustardy onions and fondant potato.

- The Crypt
  St Matthews Church
  Brixton Hill
  London SW2 1JF
- 020 7738 3366
- Serving times:
  Tues-Fri 5-10pm
  Sat 5-11pm
  Sun 1-9pm
- Booking recommended weekends
- Major credit cards
- Smoking throughout
- Licensed
- 80 seats
- Starters from £3.75

Cicero's

Cicero's is a pleasant local café on Clapham Common, not far from the tube. And in an area which presents either grotty kebabs or expensive fine dining, it's a godsend. Open daytimes, you can have all-day veggie breakfast, wholesome sandwiches, hot ciabattas or just beans on toast – handy if you're on an enforced day with the children. There's also soup, hummus and pitta bread, dishes of olives, salad plates and lunchtime specials like Singapore noodles with Cicero's sauce.

There's always a vegan option, together with vegan cakes and good tea, coffee and juices. You can also book Cicero's for a private dinner party with a more sophisticated menu. £20 per head, BYOB with corkage included in the service charge. Can't be bad.

- 2 Rookery Rd
  London SW4
- Next to the long pond
- 020 7498 0770
- Serving times:
  7 days 11am-5pm
  During winter closes one hour earlier
  Closed for three weeks over Xmas
- No credit cards
- Non-smoking
- Not licensed
- Children welcome
- 20 seats & large outside area
- Snacks from £2.50

South London

South London

- 11 Vauxhall Grove
  London SW8 1TF
- 020 7820 7466
- Serving times:
  Mon-Sun 7pm-11pm
- Booking essential
  (see text)
- No credit cards
- Smoking throughout
- Not licensed, BYO
  with no corkage
- 30 seats
- Mains from £5

Bonnington Centre Café

To eat at this bohemian communally-run South London restaurant, you need to book directly with the chef (check www.bonningtoncafe.co.uk to find out who's cooking on the night you want to visit and get their email address).

Thursday is vegan night, but there's generally a vegan choice anyway, and you can always ask when you book. The range of food on offer crosses continents, and regulars get to know the style of dishes to expect from each chef.

The pace is leisurely, and you can BYO with no corkage charge. Kick back with a glass of your own wine, order from the blackboard and chill. A very special place – you'll feel as though you've stumbled across a secret gig.

South London

- 386 Coldharbour Lane
  London SW9 8LF
- 020 7737 4144
- Serving times:
  Mon-Sun
  5.30-midnight
- Major credit cards
- Smoking throughout
- Licensed
- Children welcome
- 60 seats
- From £4

Asmara

Well established, and round the corner from one of the best indie cinemas in London, this one's a bit different. There's a vegetarian and vegan set dinner for two which includes mixed fried veg, garlic and chilli spinach, two sorts of lentil, chickpeas and a salad, together with other dishes prepared to complement them.

Choose rice, or do it properly and select the fluffy pancake-style bread to act as a wrapper for your veg, stuffed pitta bread style.

Coffee here is a grand and ceremonious production. The beans are warmed in front of you, mildly flavoured with cloves and presented in a jug, with incense wafting and complimentary popcorn. Like we said, different.

Café Pushkar

There's a changing display of artwork for sale, and the staff are probably better painters than they are waiters at this charmingly wonky local café. The menu here is 80% vegan, often gluten-free and organic.

Café Pushkar offers daily specials, regular snacks and light meals, and the falafel can be a bit of a lifesaver if you're in need of instant sustenance.

Specials can include Caribbean bean stew, golden temple curry or moussaka, plus there's a daily soup and freshly squeezed juices. The vegan cakes are exceptional and quite possibly addictive.

Everything is home-cooked with the freshest ingredients and they are licensed with a short, but completely vegetarian, wine list. It can get very busy at the weekends, but weekdays are more laid back.

- 424 Coldharbour Lane London SW9 8LF
- 020 7738 6161
- Serving times:
  Mon-Tues 11am-5pm
  Wed-Sat
  11am-10.45pm
  Closed bank holidays
- Major credit cards
- Non-smoking
- Licensed
- Children welcome
- 36 seats
- Starters from £3

South London

west
london

london • west

West London

A406

Ealing

3

A4020

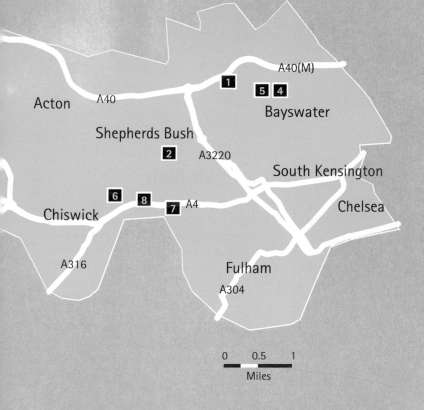

west london

Acton

A40

1

A40(M)

5 **4**

Bayswater

Shepherds Bush

2

A3220

South Kensington

6 **8** **7** A4

Chiswick

Chelsea

A316

Fulham

A304

0   0.5   1

Miles

- 269a Portobello Rd
  London W11 1LR
- 020 7229 5571
- Serving times:
  Mon-Sat 9am-6pm
- Major credit cards

The Grain Shop

The Grain Shop is a vegetarian takeaway and bread shop, easily found by its distinctive Sourdough bread sign and green awning. They're just opposite the Square on Portobello Road, almost underneath the Westway.

Expect a mouthwatering array of pizzas, salads, bakes and cakes all made on the premises – including a good selection of vegan and wheat-free items – around eight daily salads, and a diverse range of hot daily specials such as macaroni or cauliflower cheese, butter beans in tomato sauce or chilli beans with soya mince.

Freshly pressed juices are available in the summer; and they'll be adding a range of teas and coffee very soon. Open from 9am for a morning pastry fix, but closed bank holidays.

- 78 Goldhawk Rd
  London W12 8HA
- 020 8746 1337
- Serving times:
  Mon-Sat
  12.30-2.20pm
  & 7-11pm
- Booking recommended weekends
- No credit cards
- Smoking throughout
- Not licensed, BYO
  £1.25 corkage pp
- 68 seats
- Starters from £5

Blah Blah Blah

Blah Blah Blah offers a truly exceptional gourmet lunch or night out, with a good selection of vegan starters and mains. Drawing influences from all over the world, you'll find yourself choosing a first course from a selection which can include vegetables in a crisp Thai batter with a spiced onion sauce, a Chinese-style noodle salad with a sesame and soy dressing, or a Mediterranean vegetable tart.

Main courses have featured the house pasta (with spinach, shallots and mushrooms topped with pine nuts and basil), a goat's cheese and roast vegetable tarte tatin, and filo pastry-wrapped puy lentils, braised onions and sauté potatoes on winter greens.

It's essential to book at weekends, and you can BYO with a very reasonable corkage charge.

Thai Spice House

In busy west Ealing, this family-run business is open all year except Christmas and Boxing Day. The vegetarian selection is clearly marked on the menu, and you can also enjoy a good value set vegetarian meal for two. There's a loyalty scheme here: collect 12 stamps and get £20 off the bill. What with that and the lunchtime specials around a fiver, we imagine customer loyalty is pretty unshakeable.

If you like a bit of heat, the stir fried mushrooms, chillies and basil should do the trick, or there's a milder pad Thai, stir fried veg with sweet and sour sauce or bean curd with ginger and spring onions. Decent choice, reasonably priced, booking recommended at the weekends.

- 125 Uxbridge Rd London W13 9AU
- 020 8840 2475
- Serving times:
  Mon-Fri 12-2pm
  & 6-10.30pm
  Sat-Sun 6-10.30pm
- Booking recommended Fri–Sat evenings
- Major credit cards
- Smoking throughout
- Licensed
- Children welcome
- 28 seats
- Starters from £3.50

West London

Café Fresco

Handy for Whiteley's Shopping centre, this predominately vegetarian café also serves a stupendous selection of freshly-squeezed fruit and vegetable juices. Open early, start the morning like a superhero with a carrot, beet and ginger energiser.

Pitta sandwiches can be stuffed with halloumi and mint, smoked aubergine and tabouleh, or grilled veg with hummus, or enjoy a special dish of moussaka, baked aubergines with chickpeas, tomato, onion and garlic, vine leaves, or fresh green beans in tomato and olive oil. There's a two-person meze for under a tenner each, or grab a bargain (and extremely healthy) set lunch with a juice for under a fiver.

Absurdly long opening hours means this is a great après shopping, skating, swimming or cinema venue.

- 25 Westbourne Grove London W2 4UA
- 020 7221 2355
- Serving times:
  7 days 8am-11pm
- Major credit cards
- Smoking throughout
- Not licensed
- Children welcome
- 24 seats
- Starters from £3

West London

West London

- 42 Westbourne Grove
  London W2 5SH
- 020 7727 2227
- Serving times:

  Mon-Sat
  Shop 9.30am-8.30pm
  Café 12-8pm

  Sunday
  Shop 12-6.30pm
  Café 12-6pm
- Major credit cards
- Non-smoking
- Children welcome
- 32 seats

Planet Organic

At the front of a huge organic (but not totally vegetarian) supermarket, is this vegetarian café and takeaway, offering loads of vegan choices. You can mix and match hot foods and salads, with prices starting from £2.25 for a small portion, up to £7.00 for a more substantial plateful.

Menus change regularly, but a sample selection might include Malaysian tofu stir fry or butternut squash stew (both vegan), cheesy pasta, or a rather good puy lentil shepherds pie. A choice of fresh organic juice is always available, or you can just drop in for a yummy cake and a coffee – with rice milk or soya milk (sweetened, unsweetened or vanilla) if you prefer.

The organic supermarket is well worth a browse for hard-to-get items and a great selection of veggie treats.

London W4

West London

- 12-14
  Chiswick High Rd
  London W4 1TH
- 020 8994 9333
- Serving times:

  7 days 12-2.45pm
  & 6-10.45pm
- Major credit cards
- Non-smoking area
- Licensed
- Children welcome
- 90 seats
- Starters from £3.25

Woodlands

Woodlands Chiswick is a smart, upmarket, Indian restaurant – and one of four Woodlands venues in London. The cuisine is south Indian, and they claim that their London chefs have at least fifteen years previous experience at their branches in India and Singapore.

Not a place to go for fiercely hot vindaloos and several pints of lager, Woodlands food is more subtly spiced and includes traditional south Indian starters such as idli and pakoda, snacky street food like bhel poori and aloo tikki, and mains of dosas, uthappams and a range of delicately flavoured curries.

A fine venue for a posh(ish) night out, or visit at lunchtime for a takeout lunch box of masala dosa, korma and rice for just £4.25.

The Gate

This haven is just a few hundred yards from the stagnant traffic of the Fulham Palace Road and over-arching roar of the Hammersmith flyover. Discreetly tucked away in an artist's studio, it would be easy to miss this restaurant. And, trust us, you shouldn't.

The menu has all the words that push our buttons – smoked, caramelised, toasted and crusted. It is the judgement of Paris to choose between a three onion tart – leeks and shallots baked with crème fraiche topped with caramelised red onions and basil oil, or the fig and goat's cheese galette – goat's cheese, walnut and fig on puff pastry. For a lighter start try dishes like nori rolls, a dish of olives or soup. Main courses include a pasta of the day and monthly changing specials: couscous crusted aubergine, richly spiced curries, lasagne with smoked mozzarella and deep fried leeks. Side dishes are piquant – rocket salad, sautéed kale, Jerusalem artichoke mash among others.

Rich and flavoursome desserts can include plum and pecan crumble with crème anglaise, Indian chai brulée with date, cardamom and pistachio salsa as well as ice creams and sorbets which are made on the premises.

Open for lunch and dinner, this is a destination restaurant with a modern European slant. There are also three course set meals for groups of 10 or more, and the menu is clearly marked for vegan options or variations.

Not a cheap lunch or night out – expect to spend about £60 for two with a decent bottle – but for some of London's best food, it is extremely good value.

- 51 Queen Caroline St London W6 9QL
- 020 8748 6932
- Serving times:
  Mon-Fri 12-2.45pm & 6-10.45pm
  Sat-Sun 6-10.45pm
- Booking essential
- Major credit cards
- Non-smoking
- Licensed
- 50 seats
- Mains from £8

West London

West London

- 157 King St
  London W6 9JT
- Next to Town Hall
- 020 8741 8563
- Serving times:
  Mon-Fri 12-2.45pm
  & 5.30-10.45pm
  Sat-Sun 12-10.45pm
- Booking recommended
  Fri-Sat evenings
- Major credit cards
- Non-smoking area
- Licensed
- Children welcome
- 60 seats
- Starters from £2.50

Sagar

Next to the Town Hall, this south Indian restaurant has a wide range of delicious options, with starters like Rasa Vada – lentil doughnuts soaked in a hot tangy sauce – and familiar Bombay specialities such as bhel poori. Choose from mains of dosas and uthappams, or go for one of the curries and order some interesting rices and home-baked breads to go with it.

Sagar is licensed, so you can get a beer to go with it, but there's also homemade lemonade if you fancy something slightly different.

There are three course lunchtime specials for under a fiver, and you can also grab a takeout box of a couple of curries with rice, salad and bread for even less.

scotland

scotland

Scotland

See over for Edinburgh and Glasgow

6 Durness

Steornabhagh (Stornoway)

7 Helmsdale

14 Ullapool

4 Garve

Ardersier **3**

Elgin

Fraserburgh

13 Strichen

9 Skye

Inverness

5 Dufftown

1 **2** Aberdeen

Fort William

Montrose

Arbroath

Perth

St Andrews

10 Kilmartin

Glenrothes

11 Lochgilphead

Stirling

Glasgow

Edinburgh

Arran **8**

Kilmarnock

Galashiels

Ayr

12 Moniaive

Dumfries

scotland

Edinburgh

Glasgow

0   0.25   0.5
Miles

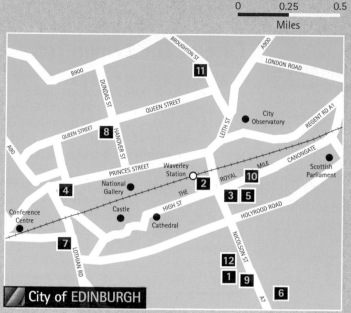

BROUGHTON ST
A900
B900
LONDON ROAD
DUNDAS ST
QUEEN STREET
11
LEITH ST
City Observatory
QUEEN STREET
8
HANOVER ST
REGENT RD A1
A90
PRINCES STREET
Waverley Station
ROYAL
MILE
CANONGATE
Scottish Parliament
4
National Gallery
2
10
THE
3   5
Conference Centre
Castle
HIGH ST
Cathedral
HOLYROOD ROAD
7
LOTHIAN RD
NICOLSON ST
12
1   9
6
A7

City of EDINBURGH

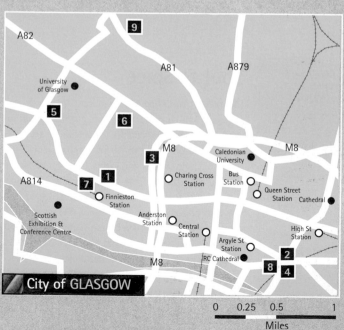

A82
9
A81
A879
University of Glasgow
5
6
3   M8
Caledonian University
M8
A814
7   1
Charing Cross Station
Bus Station
Queen Street Station
Cathedral
Finnieston Station
Anderston Station
High St Station
Scottish Exhibition & Conference Centre
Central Station
Argyle St Station
M8
RC Cathedral
2
8   4

City of GLASGOW

0   0.25   0.5   1
Miles

Omnivorous Café & Bar

- 5 West North St
  Aberdeen AB24 5AT
- 01224 642230
- Serving times:
  Thurs-Sun 12-3pm
- Booking essential Sun
- Major credit cards
- Non-smoking area
- Licensed
- Children welcome
- 150 seats
- Snacks from £2.50

Café at The Lemon Tree

Part of a thriving and busy art centre, where there's a lively programme of music, comedy and theatre, the café is open lunchtimes for the latter part of the week with booking essential for Sunday lunch. Children's activities are programmed every Saturday, there are free lunchtime music concerts and there's a fine selection of single malts at the bar.

Featuring good home cooking, all freshly prepared, the menu offers curried banana and coconut soup, followed by a goat's cheese and red onion tart and key lime pie. You could also enjoy bean casseroles, nut roasts and vegan curries – and, by way of further recommendation, the local vegan group meets here each month. Pre-booked parties can also arrange an evening meal here.

Omnivorous Café-Bar

- 15-17 Belmont St
  Aberdeen AB10 1JR
- 01224 645200
- Serving times:
  Tues 5.30-10pm
  Wed-Fri 6-10pm
  Sat 12-10pm
- Booking advisable
- Major credit cards
- Non-smoking area
- Licensed
- Children welcome
- 70 seats
- Starters from £3.50

Soul & Spice

The only Afro-Caribbean restaurant in north-east Scotland, Soul & Spice offers an excellent range of vegetarian and vegan food. Try the vegetarian set meals for two and go with their recommendation for your choice of three starters and mains. Or, if you're feeling adventurous, dive into the comprehensive vegetarian choice without a safety net. If you've never tasted fried yam balls, spiked with olive and spring onion and mixed pepper, or kose – black-eyed bean fritters, now's your chance, and you can also select from a chickpea curry, groundnut stew or seven-vegetable tagine.

There's often entertainment as well, so give them a call to find out when you can next go and practise your limbo dancing.

Macleod Organics

This café is located in an organic farming centre, close to lovely seaside walks where you can watch the dolphins. This one has to be special!

They juice their own fresh vegetables, and have soya and rice milk available, as well as making sure there are savouries and cakes suitable for vegans.

The menu is short, but is all organic and includes bread and soup, baked potatoes, toasted sandwiches, curries, lasagne and mushroom burgers, with daily specials such as bean casserole and stroganoff.

If you've planned ahead and brought some wine or beer, they're happy for you to have a glass or two with no corkage charge; return the favour by stocking up on their excellent fruit and veg before you go.

- Kylerona Farm
  Ardersier IV2 7QZ
- 01667 462555
- Serving times:
  Thurs-Fri 11am-5pm
  Sat-Sun 10am-5pm
  Closed for two weeks over Xmas
- No credit cards
- Non-smoking
- Not licensed
- Children welcome
- 40 seats
- Snacks from £2

Scotland

Aultguish Inn

Some places have an unfair advantage and this is one of them. Spectacular scenery, a 400-year-old main building and a courtyard. Ghosts too, if you believe.

The inn is popular with outdoor enthusiasts, and there's a separate vegetarian menu of baked spuds, vegetable curry, haggis, lasagne, kiev and spaghetti with a Mediterranean sauce. You can also indulge in the traditional pub side orders of onion rings, chips, garlic bread and mushrooms. Desserts include lemon sponge with lemon sauce and sticky toffee pudding. Scoff one of these down on the basis that you will walk it off in the breathtaking hills outside.

Actually, they could serve you hay and you'd probably be happy to eat it with this view.

- by Garve IV23 2PQ
- 10 miles from Garve on A835
- 01997 455254
- Serving times:
  Mon-Thurs 11am-9pm
  Fri-Sat 11am-9.30pm
  Sun 12.30-9pm
- Major credit cards
- Non-smoking area
- Licensed
- Children welcome
- 80 seats
- Starters from £2.75, mains from £6.75

Scotland

- 20 Balvenie St
  Dufftown AB55 4AB
- 01340 821428
- Serving times:
  Summer 7 days
  10am-5pm
  Winter opening not
  yet finalised
- Major credit cards
- Non-smoking
- Not licensed
- Children welcome
- 24 seats
- Mains from £5

Rainbow

If the distillery tour has worked its magic, and you're
now feeling in need of something to soak up the single
malts, head for Rainbow on Balvenie St.

Maintaining the strong vegetarian reputation built
up over the last few years, the new owners are
promising to maintain the predominately vegetarian
menu, with the emphasis on well balanced, simple home
cooking. You'll find freshly prepared soups, homemade
pâtés, tarts, pies and vegetable hotpots, and a selection
of comfort-food puddings such as fruit crumble and
treacle tart with custard. There are vegan choices, and
tea, coffee and cakes are served all day.

Open seven days a week in summer, but call to
check first if you're planning to visit outside the main
holiday season.

Durness

Omnivorous Restaurant

- 17c Balnakeil
  Craft Village
  Durness IV27 4PT
- 01971 511777
- Serving times:
  Mon-Sun
  10am-5.30pm
  Closed Mon
  October-Easter
  Evening opening
  July-Aug, Cape Wrath
  challenge week and
  themed nights
- Major credit cards
- Non-smoking area
- Licensed
- Children welcome
- 30 seats
- Snacks from £2.50

Loch Croispol Restaurant

Loch Croispol is a relaxed and friendly restaurant in a
bookshop, where you can browse your favourite titles
while you wait for your meal. All-day breakfasts, light
lunches and, during the height of the summer and the
Cape Wrath challenge week in May, you can pop in for
an early dinner.

Breakfasts include a veggie fry-up, and at
lunchtimes you can snack on jackets, quiche, pasta or a
vegetable curry. Evening meals can include homemade
soups, vegetarian haggis and nutty pasta, while on their
monthly themed nights you can choose from cuisine as
diverse as Czech, Cajun or Caribbean.

The Sunday lunch is tempting, with more than just a
token veggie choice and some good puddings.

Ann Purna

An FAQ at the Festival is 'Where can you go for a good curry in Edinburgh?' The answer should be Ann Purna. This restaurant satisfies the cravings for Indian food that sweep over most of us, some more frequently than others. Yes, there are the curries, but with nice extra touches like bhel poori, pakoras and the slightly more uncommon stuffed and steamed patra leaves. Tasty sides include okra made edible – pan-roasted with cumin, herbs and spices. There's a list of lentil and bean dishes, which all come topped with fried onion or garlic – a little thing that lifts the homely dish into poor man's feast level of satisfaction.

Finish with the usual intensely sweet desserts. You won't go broke treating a friend here.

- 45 St Patrick Square Edinburgh EH8 9ET
- 0131 662 1807
- Serving times:
  Mon-Fri
  11.30am-1.45pm
  & 5.30-10.30pm
  Sat-Sun 5.30-10.30pm
- Major credit cards
- Non-smoking
- Licensed
- Children welcome
- 50 seats
- Starters from £2, mains from £4.60

Scotland

Baked Potato Shop

You might think it ridiculous to wax lyrical about a tattie shop, but this place is absolutely fabulous. They use organic and fair trade products where feasible, the cheese is vegetarian, the mayo is vegan and everything is made on the premises.

Have a medium potato (the large are big enough to exert gravitational pull) and enjoy the perfect fluffy interior with a crackling papery skin. There's a choice of hot and really good cold salad fillings, and you can also have salad trays, vegetarian sausage rolls, haggis samosa, homemade soup and vegan cakes.

The staff are consistently charming in the face of a long hungry queue (the only downside). Honestly, if it were bigger and served wine, we'd have our birthday dinners here.

- 56 Cockburn St Edinburgh EH1 1PB
- Off the Royal Mile
- 0131 225 7572
- Serving times:
  7 days 9am-9pm
  Open late during August
- No credit cards
- Non-smoking
- Not licensed
- Children welcome
- 6 seats
- From £2.50

Scotland

- 57-61 Blackfriars St
  Edinburgh EH1 1NB
- 0131 557 6136
- Serving times:
  7 days 6-10.30pm
  Fri & Sat lunch
  12-2pm
- Booking essential
  Fri & Sat evenings
- Major credit cards
- Smoking throughout
- Licensed, and full bar
  next door
- Children welcome
- 35 seats
- Starters from £3.50,
  mains from £10.50

Black Bo's

Just off the High Street, this very popular restaurant deserves the frequent name checking it receives in many 'best veggie restaurant' lists. It sees off the competition with imaginative, luxurious dishes.

An adventurous use of booze (drambuie in the cashew nut and coriander filo pastry, cassis in the cinnamon sauce for the sweet potato and peanut terrine) augurs well. Nor do they shy away from clean, simple tastes like garlic bread topped with tomato and basil or cherry tomato pasta, or a rocket salad with smoked pecans. Comprehensive on-menu vegan selection ensures you're not made to feel like a troublemaker.

Make this a destination for a special evening meal or lunch late in the week.

Edinburgh

Omnivorous Café

- St John's Church
  Princes St
  Edinburgh EH2 4BJ
- 0131 229 0212
- Serving times:
  Mon-Sat 9.30am-4pm
  Closed most bank
  holidays
- No credit cards
- Non-smoking
  except courtyard
- Licensed
- Children welcome
- 80 seats
- Lunch from £3.50

Cornerstone Café

This café is the perfect bolthole if you have been caning the shops and art galleries – it's in a peaceful crypt beneath St John's Church but has a courtyard so you can still see the Castle.

The menu is mainly vegetarian and there are some vegan options. Homemade soup and a roll is a very reasonable £2.50, and you can get proper scones from 9.30 if you need a bit of fortification early on.

Lunch is served 12-2.30pm, and consists of a choice of main salads, baked potatoes, a hot savoury like mushroom goulash, rounded off with home-baked cake or fruit pies. It is licensed, but if you want to book for a private function in the evening you can also BYO.

David Bann Restaurant

This is a smart, slick operation with good looking premises, interesting menu, and should definitely be on your itinerary if you're visiting Edinburgh. People take other people to eat here, as in 'my people should talk to your people over lunch'. The tables are well spaced, dark wood with oversize chairs that look uncomfortable but are in fact very supportive and allow you to spend ages over your meal if you're so inclined. You can get very hot, however, in the window seats in full sun.

The menu has starters, light meals, main dishes and desserts and they do a good brunch at weekends. Dishes are marked for vegans or vegan possibilities. The flavour is international, but not messy. Japanese nori timbale, dim sum, grilled polenta and soup can be in the starters. Crêpes, pasta, dosa and tartlets all feature in light meals and each makes the ordinary exceptional. A homemade burger of aduki beans and courgette, with salad and baby potato wedges makes a childhood taste into something sophisticated.

Our Scottish pals rave about the vegetarian haggis, and we rave about the risotto. Really fresh vegetables and good care make all the difference here. Side dishes like the superb dauphinoise potatoes are very reasonably priced. Homemade desserts including amaretto cheesecake and meringue and lime parfait are exceptional. They also serve hot port, which you won't find in too many places. Have one at the end of your meal, but make sure you're not far from bed – it's a magnificent sleeping draught.

- 56-58 St Mary's St Edinburgh EH1 1SX
- 0131 556 5888
- Serving times: 7 days 11am-11pm Booking recommended, essential Fri & Sat evenings
- Major credit cards
- Non-smoking 12-3pm & 6-10pm
- Licensed
- Children welcome
- 80 seats
- Mains from £10

Scotland

Scotland

- 19 St Leonards Lane Edinburgh EH8 9SD
- Behind St Leonards Police Station
- 0131 662 0040
- Serving times:
  Mon-Thurs
  10.30am-3.30pm
  Fri 10.30am-2.30pm
- No credit cards
- Non-smoking
- Licensed
- Children welcome
- 48 seats
- Soup from £1.50

Engine Shed

This vibrant café in an early 19th century building has been operating for 15 years and attracts interest as a thriving small business and a successful training organisation for people with learning disabilities. They've succeeded in business because they're good at what they do.

Lots of their produce is organic and they are keenly aware of gluten- and sugar-free diets. There's a daily hot vegan dish like roasted vegetables and couscous or nutballs with pasta, and all soups are vegan. If you're OK with dairy, add quiches, lasagne, curries and an even bigger range of desserts. We don't know what a passion pot is, but we're having one next time we're here.

Edinburgh

Arthouse Cinema Café Bar

Scotland

- 88 Lothian Rd Edinburgh EH3 9BZ
- Next to Festival Square
- 0131 229 5932
- Serving times:
  7 days 10am-10pm
  Main menu served from midday
- Major credit cards
- Non-smoking area
- Licensed
- Children welcome
- 150 seats
- Soup from £1.85, lunch from £4.10

Filmhouse Café Bar

We'd make this kind of café compulsory in all cinemas. Eat properly and watch the film without an auditorium picnic. You could spend your weekend here, taking in a couple of independent films or meeting friends for a glass of wine and dinner. The modern cooking has a wholefood bias, three-quarters is vegetarian and there are vegan options.

Handy for the West End shops, the café takes care of your needs, be it a substantial lunch – broccoli, leek and fennel pie in a mature cheddar sauce with mixed salad and a baked potato, chickpea and coconut curry – or a quick refuel with their vegan soup, sun-dried tomato salad or some comforting apple pie and cream. There's also a comprehensive vegetarian choice on the children's menu.

Hendersons

In the heart of Edinburgh's gorgeous New Town, Hendersons has provided delicious healthy food in a relaxed, if busy, atmosphere since the 1960s. You can queue at the Salad Table (where there are also hot dishes, baked potatoes and desserts) – and eat in that part of the restaurant or the adjoining wine bar – or compose a superb takeaway from the shop upstairs. Alternatively you can be waited on in The Bistro around the corner in Thistle St.

Local producers are favoured, food isn't prepared in haste and the wine is carefully chosen. There are lunch and dinner two course deals and always something vegan. Whether you pop in for a cheese scone and a coffee early in the morning or decamp there for dinner in the wine bar, you're in for a vegetarian treat.

So, the food. There's a choice of soups – for example spiced lentil and apricot – or lemon and rosemary hummus with bread or oatcakes for a starter or snack. Main courses like a brie and broccoli crumble, spinach galette, curry or lasagne feature at lunchtime, with more sophisticated dishes for the evening such as pine nut risotto with apricot and coriander sauce, mushroom chasseur with red wine and mushroom rissoles, and nut pâté crostini. Desserts include superb fruit trifle, dried fruit compote (that's been requested and served daily for 40 years) and chocolate mousse. There's also a fully vegetarian children's menu. The salad selections are stars in their own right, providing a balanced and joyously colourful and vibrant main course or accompaniment.

Henderson's is a long-established and justly popular institution providing excellent value, comfortable surroundings and superb cooking.

- 94 Hanover St
  Edinburgh EH2 1DR
- 0131 225 2131
- Serving times:
  Mon-Sat 8am-10pm
  Open Sun during
  the Festival
- Major credit cards
- Non-smoking wine bar
- Licensed
- Children welcome
- 170 seats across three
  restaurants

Scotland

- 2-3 St Patrick Square
  Edinburgh EH8 9EZ
- 0131 667 9890
- Serving times:
  Mon-Thurs 12-2pm
  & 5.30-10.30pm
  Fri-Sat 12-2pm
  & 5.30-11pm
  Sun (June to August
  only) 6-10.30pm
- Book during the
  festival
- Major credit cards
- Non-smoking
- Licensed
- Children welcome
- 70 seats
- Mains from £5

Kalpna

This restaurant is handy for the University, so we imagine there's a great take up for its £5.50 buffet lunch and Wednesday gourmet evenings.

You may think if you've seen one south Indian vegetarian restaurant, you've seen them all, but each one has something that its neighbour doesn't and this has aloo firdoshi – potato barrels stuffed with pistachio, raisins, coriander and spices – and hara kebabs – shallow-fried spinach and green pea cakes stuffed with saffron flavoured yoghurt. Delicious.

There are some great main courses, with lots of nuts, saffron and cream, as well as coconut and other special rices. Plenty of vegan choice and you can get a takeout. Book during the Festival.

- 240 Canongate
  Edinburgh EH8 8AB
- 0131 557 4416
- Serving times:
  Mon-Thurs 12-2pm
  & 6-10pm
  Fri-Sat 12-10.30pm
  Sun 6-9.30pm
- Major credit cards
- Non-smoking area
- Licensed
- Children welcome
- 75 seats
- Lunch mains from £5

Pancho Villas

Addictive starters like nachos frijoles (tortilla chips, refried beans, guacamole, soured cream and jalapeño chillies) or a quesadilla with salsa may well be rich and filling enough to stop you in your tracks. When you do feel ready for your mains, there are some attractive variations like vegetarian fajitas with garlic and chilli, or enchiladas espinacas – tortillas with spinach, potato, red peppers in a mild chilli and cream sauce with rice, melted cheese and refried beans. Sides of sour cream, guacamole, refried beans etc are very reasonably priced.

Just off the Royal Mile, they have soya milk for tea and coffee, or choose tequila or kahlua to find your inner beast.

Rapido

This is a welcome sight during a night on the tiles. It's hot, it's cheap, and you can eat it walking along the road if you're a complete slob. So, if you've an urgent need for sustenance after midnight, Rapido might well be your place.

They have pakoras, spicy mushroom wraps, spicy vegetable burgers and pizzas. They don't serve alcohol, but as you'll probably be eating here as a prelude or aftermath to an evening's drinking and dancing, that's no problem. Flagging sugar levels can be boosted with caramel apple pie or lemon cheesecake.

Highly regarded, they're noted in The Scotsman's top ten Edinburgh takeaways. Bring on the salt'n'sauce.

- 79 Broughton St Edinburgh EH1 3RJ
- 0131 556 2041
- Serving times:
  Mon-Fri 10.30am-2pm & 4.30pm-1am
  Sat 10.30am-2pm & 4.30pm-2am
  Sun 4.30pm-2am
- Major credit cards
- Non-smoking
- Not licensed
- Children welcome
- 14 seats
- From £2

Susie's Diner

Susie's is an informal, counter service diner that also serves Scottish fruit wines and organic wine and beer.

You pay according to the size of the plate (medium £4.75, large just £1 more), and can choose from a selection of dishes including sweet and sour stir fry, quiches, cottage pie, lasagne, wraps, enchiladas and a good range of salads. Vegans aren't neglected with dairy- and egg-free options in the carrot, millet and lentil bake, kofta balls and dhal, which all feature regularly. Children are welcomed with smaller portions and high chairs, and it's a non-smoking space during the busy lunchtime period.

Open Monday to Saturday until mid-evening, opening hours are extended (and include Sundays) during the Festival.

- 51 West Nicolson St Edinburgh EH8 9DB
- 0131 667 8729
- Serving times:
  Mon 12-8pm
  Tues-Sat 12-9pm
  Open later, and Sun, during Festival
- No credit cards
- Non-smoking at lunchtimes
- Licensed
- Children welcome
- 55 seats
- Mains from £4.75

Scotland

- 36 Kelvingrove St
  Glasgow G3 7RZ
- 0141 564 5201
- Serving times:
  7 days 12-10pm
- Booking recommended
  weekends
- Major credit cards
- Non-smoking area
- Licensed
- Children welcome
- 54 seats
- Starters from £4

Air Organic

The aim at Air Organic is to achieve a 95% organic menu, with lots of vegetarian choice, including interesting vegan dishes such as glass noodles with shitake and miso broth or a Thai watermelon curry with sticky rice and cashews.

They recognise you may prefer to graze rather than follow the traditional starter-main-dessert formula, but there is a good value set lunch deal of two courses for under a tenner. Food is a fusion of Asian and European with risotto, crostini, tempura, noodles and some imaginative salads. A cool, stylish place to relax with decent food. There's no need to book during the week, but reserve your place early if you fancy an evening table at the weekends.

Scotland

- 24 Candleriggs
  Glasgow G1 1LD
- 0141 552 4251
- Serving times:
  Mon-Thurs 5-10pm
  Fri-Sat 12-11pm
  Sun 12.30-10pm
- Booking
  recommended
- Major credit cards
- Non-smoking except
  bar area
- Licensed
- 50 seats
- Starters from £2.95

Arisaig Restaurant

This is a venue that's going places. Already nominated for 'Best New Restaurant', by the Scottish Chefs' Association, Arisaig also won the 'Best Vegetarian Food in an Omnivorous Restaurant' category at the Vegetarian Society 2003 awards.

For starters, choose between kale and nettle-leaf dumplings with grilled smokehouse cheddar sauce, or beetroot in beer batter with sour cream. (How ungrateful would you be not to go for the nettle dish?) Mains have featured lavender and lentil loaf on a spinach mash, deep-fried vegetarian haggis dumplings or vegetarian honey-roast sausages. Desserts can include cheesecake, drambuie-poached fruit with shortbread ice cream, and fruit dumplings with butterscotch sauce. Arrive hungry.

Grassroots Café

- 93-97 St Georges Rd
  Glasgow G3 6JA
- 0141 333 0534
- Serving times:
  7 days 10am-10pm
  Closed some bank holidays
- Major credit cards
- Non-smoking area
- Licensed
- Children welcome
- 35 seats
- Mains from £5

Just round the corner from the renowned Grassroots Organic shop, Grassroots Café is a completely vegetarian and largely organic café and restaurant – and one that's open seven days a week.

Drop in for their full veggie breakfast (served until 3pm on weekends), a light lunch of soup, sandwiches or salad, or try one of their freshly made and wholesome mains such as bangers and mash, risotto cakes or Thai green curry. More than half the menu is vegan, with additional vegan options available, and gluten-free choices are clearly marked.

As well as a good place just to pop in for a coffee, Grassroots is a popular venue for Xmas and Burns night celebrations, and also hosts occasional speciality nights with Moroccan or Chinese themed menus.

Mono

- 12 Kings Court
  King St
  Glasgow G1 5RB
- 0141 553 2400
- Serving times:
  7 days 12-10pm
- Booking recommended weekends
- Major credit cards
- Non-smoking area
- Licensed
- 48 seats
- Snacks from £2

You don't get more vegan than this – not just a totally dairy- and egg-free menu, but an associated grocers specialising in vegan, organic and fair trade products – so you won't be surprised to learn that Mono recently won the Vegan Society's 'Best Catering' award.

The menu runs through cooked breakfasts (and yes, you can order a full monty fry-up in the middle of the evening if the mood takes you) to more sophisticated fare such as sweet pepper and courgette potato cakes, wonton with smoked tofu, stuffed butternut squash or a chestnut and vegetable loaf. You can also pop in to snack on a (no)bacon sandwich, and enjoy dairy-free cheesecake, ice creams and chocolate truffles.

A real tribute to the vision of owner Craig Tannock, who also runs the vegan music venue Stereo.

Scotland

- 106 Byres Rd Hillhead Glasgow G12 8TB
- Close to the University
- 0141 334 6200
- Serving times:
  Mon-Fri 9am-5.30pm
  Sat 10am-4.30pm
  Sun 11am-4.30pm
- No credit cards
- Non-smoking
- Not licensed
- Children welcome
- 18 seats

Naked Soup

With everything made each day on the premises for optimum freshness, one visit here should fulfil your daily requirement for five portions of fruit and veg.

Soups and casseroles are served with bread and your choice of fruit, and coconut milk is often substituted for dairy which will keep the vegans among us happy. The divine red lentil, sweet potato and coconut soup occasionally features on the menu, as do spicy Thai, and corn and coriander. You can also enjoy dishes such as oriental pumpkin stew, and roasted pepper risotto. Expect a large selection of smoothies, juices and sorbets as well as herbal tea and decaf.

It's a bar stools kind of place for a quick lunch or snack, and they're open every day except Christmas and New Year's day.

Scotland

- 61 Otago St Glasgow G12 8PQ
- 0141 337 2282
- Serving times:
  7 days 12-4pm & 5-9pm
- Booking recommended weekends
- Major credit cards
- Non-smoking area
- Licensed
- Children welcome
- 40 seats
- Lunch from £5

Otago

There are separate lunch and evening menus here – and lunch runs until late in the afternoon if you're keeping unusual hours. For lunch (when around half the choices are meat-free), Otago offers soup or bruschetta to start, followed by Spanish omelette, a couple of savoury tarts and salad, pasta or a toasted sandwich with chips.

You can dine à la carte in the evenings, but you might prefer the pre-theatre menu – when you can fortify yourself with two courses for little more than a tenner. Worth a visit: partner Mario Pelosi has been in the trade for years, and these aren't just token vegetarian options.

Stereo

A live music pub rather than a restaurant, but one with a totally vegan range of meals and bar snacks. Dishes such as tofu ravioli, veggieburger and chips, soup and bread are the standards, or there's a 'dub and grub' evening on Thursdays with a themed (Asian, Mexican, Japanese, Middle Eastern etc) three course menu to a dub soundtrack.

The live music Sunday–Wednesday means there's a teatime sound-check, which becomes a gig in itself if you stop by for more than a quick one.

It's smoking throughout, and probably not your first-choice venue if you're with children, but if you're looking for meat- and dairy- free food with your music, you're in the right place.

- 10 Kelvinhaugh St Finnieston Glasgow G3 8NU
- 0141 576 5018
- Serving times: Mon-Fri 5-11.45pm Sat-Sun 1-11.45pm
- Major credit cards
- Smoking throughout
- Licensed
- 40 seats

The 13th Note

This lively music venue, handily situated for the Tron Theatre, is open all day, does a five quid Sunday breakfast (including tea or coffee) and is 95% vegan. They can also serve you a soya latte or cappuccino with fair trade coffee.

Choose from a selection of burgers – veggie, curried tofu, spicy, with a variety of toppings including fried onions, garlic mayonnaise and mushrooms, served with salad. There's haggis, neeps and tatties, spinach and ricotta lasagne – properly flavoured with nutmeg – and a Caesar salad among the mains. Great side dishes – choose flavoured mash, onion rings, side salads and some good starters that double as snacks.

Finish up with vegan banoffee pie for dessert, or delicious ice creams and cheesecakes.

- 50-60 King St Glasgow G1 5QT
- 0141 553 1638
- Serving times: 7 days 12-10pm
- Booking recommended Fri & Sat evenings
- Major credit cards
- Smoking throughout
- Licensed
- Children welcome until 6.30pm
- 40 seats
- Mains from £3.60

Scotland

- 920 Maryhill Rd
  Glasgow G20 7TA
- 0141 945 4164
- Serving times:
  Mon-Thurs 4.30-11pm
  Fri-Sat 4.30-midnight
  Sun 4.30-11pm
- Booking advisable
  at weekends
- Major credit cards
- Smoking throughout
- Licensed & BYO
  £3.50 corkage
- Children welcome
- 60 seats
- Starters from £3.20,
  mains from £5.50

Wong's

Fantastic! A Cantonese restaurant with no headache-inducing MSG, and you can bring your own wine if you've a favourite bottle to accompany Chinese food.

This candlelit restaurant is open long hours, seven days a week. Take advantage of the pre-theatre three course vegetarian menu (offered Monday to Thursday) with a choice of four soups, then mixed vegetables or beancurd in various sauces followed by banana fritters and tea or coffee for just £7.80. If you aren't rushing away to a show, try the deep-fried seaweed with sesame seeds, beancurd in a crispy noodle nest and a mouth-tingling orange sorbet.

Best to book at weekends, children under 10 eat for half price.

Scotland

- 214 Dunrobin St
  Helmsdale KW8 6JA
- 01431 821457
- Serving times:
  7 days 12-9pm
- Major credit cards
- Non-smoking area
- Licensed
- Children welcome
- 60 seats
- Starters from £2

Bunillidh Restaurant

Hitch your kilt, head for the Highlands. This family-run restaurant has a large vegetarian menu, and there's a grand choice to be had. As well as the old favourites – spicy tomato pasta, vegetable burgers and vegetarian lasagne – you could also enjoy their famous vegetable haggis or the windy-sounding rumbledethumps. A short word of warning though: their other speciality is seafood – so, be prepared for the possibility that the table next to you is tucking into a mountain of fruits de mer. Maybe, if we asked nicely, they'd introduce a fish-free area in the dining room?

They show a willingness to cater for vegans, and you can also enjoy the great surroundings for longer by staying in their B&B.

Isle of Arran

Scotland

Arran Hotel

There's a vegan and vegetarian bar meals menu at this hotel, next to the Co-op, and they'll also provide soya milk for your coffee, if you request it prior to arrival. (Presumably a day or so – this is an island. A quick coup de mobile 10 minutes before you get there won't necessarily do it.)

The menu runs the gamut from vegetable tikka masala to macaroni cheese, via korma, balti and vegetarian sausage casserole. Vegans can knock themselves out with bean and courgette Provençal, Thai red curry or country vegetable casserole with herby dumplings.

If you're on the island, you'll be glad to know this place is here.

- Shore Rd Brodick
  Isle of Arran KA27 8AJ
- Look for the pink building next to the Co-op!
- 01770 302265
- Serving times:
  7 days 6pm-8pm
  Food not served September-March
- Major credit cards
- Non-smoking
- Licensed
- Children welcome
- 30 seats
- Mains from £5.25

Isle Of Skye

Scotland

Tables Restaurant

Members of the Vegetarian Society's Food and Drink Guild, this traditional Highland guesthouse uses as much fresh, local and organic produce as possible and also hosts a 'mushroom lunch' at the island's annual food festival in September.

Around half the choices are vegetarian, and the menu changes on a regular basis. Beansprout, dulse and walnut salad, deep-fried highland brie with homemade Japonica jelly, or smoked tofu and aubergine pâté can appear as starters, main dishes can include aduki bean and brazil nut roast with onion and sherry sauce, or green lentil, mushrooms and calabrese hotpot with black olive bread. Desserts include cranachan (raspberries, whisky cream and toasted oatmeal), or tofu chocolate cheesecake.

- Dunvegan
  Isle Of Skye IV55 8WA
- 01470 521404
- Serving times:
  Mar-Oct 6-8pm
  July-Aug 8am-5pm & 6-8pm
  Closed Nov-Feb
- Booking preferable
- Major credit cards
- Non-smoking except conservatory
- Licensed
- Children welcome
- 24 seats
- Evening mains from £6

363

- Kilmartin House
  Kilmartin PA31 8RQ
- 01546 510278
- Serving times:
  7 days 10am-5pm
  Open Thurs evenings
  Easter-Sept
- Major credit cards
- Non-smoking
- Licensed
- Children welcome
- 40 seats
- Mains from £5

Kilmartin House Café

This museum café is open seven days a week, and offers a substantially vegetarian lunch menu between 12.30-3pm, with home-baked goodies available at other times. They also open one evening each week during the main holiday season.

There are Scottish influences in the food choices, and the café is committed to cooking with local, natural produce. In summer they'll make use of native wild plants like sorrel for soup or salad, and Scottish drinks dominate the alcohol choice. Sample menus include hummus or hazelnut and sage pâté as starters, with pearl barley risotto or nut and courgette bake to follow.

If you're a large group visiting the museum and planning to eat, they appreciate pre-booking.

- The Old Bank Chapel St
  Moniaive DG3 4EJ
- 01848 200131
- Serving times:
  Tues-Thurs 11am-5pm
  Fri-Sat
  11am-5pm & 7-9pm
  Sun 11am-6pm
  Open bank holiday Mon
  Nov-Apr open Thurs-Sun
- Booking recommended
  for lunchtimes
- No credit cards
- Non-smoking
- Not licensed, BYO
- Children welcome
- 26 seats
- Mains from £4

The Green Tea House

From her tearooms in a converted bank in Moniaive, Catherine Braid produces high quality vegetarian food, and also runs a thriving outside catering business. The emphasis is on organic local produce cooked with care, and particular attention is given to wheat-free and vegan diets.

The specials board can feature stuffed vine leaves, spicy bean risotto or a lentil and mixed vegetable casserole. The soups are always vegan, as are the chocolate brownies and date and apple slice.

There's also a wide range of teas, and Catherine runs gourmet theme nights once a month. Booking essential for these, and for the busy lunch period 12-2pm. Opening times vary with the season, The Green Tea House closes Mon-Wed in the winter.

Pinto's

It's no surprise that people travel to and stay in Lochgilphead specially to eat at Pinto's – a pleasant, relaxed bistro café by day, turning into a candlelight-and-linen restaurant by night. There's a good soup and sandwich deal at lunchtime, or a more substantial casserole of the day, Yorkshire pudding with vegetarian sausage, salads, pastas and a really savoury proper Welsh rarebit.

The evening menu is a bargain, with three courses for £15.50. The yum factor is provided by dishes like chestnut Wellington (mushrooms, chestnuts, onions, puff pastry and red wine gravy) while the vegetable cobbler follows hard on its heels – mixed vegetables, white wine sauce and a savoury scone topping. My internal mum asks how they can do a fancy Wellington for the same price as a stir fry or chilli beans. It's probably that they're just too good to us. All dishes come with potatoes and vegetables of the day or salad, often sourced from local organic suppliers.

Desserts run the gamut from homely apple and pecan crumble to the floozier white chocolate profiteroles with a raspberry coulis. Lunch or dinner, vegans will find themselves in dairy- and egg-free heaven, and all the beer and wine are suitable for vegetarians.

With regular banquet nights on the last Sunday in the month, together with Sunday brunch during the summer, this is the sort of restaurant that has you building holiday plans around mealtimes.

Pinto's was Scotland's only finalist for the Vegetarian Society's UK vegetarian restaurant of the year 2003, and with cooking like this, booking is always advisable.

Scotland

- 1 Argyll St
  Lochgilphead PA31 8LZ
- 01546 602547
- Serving times:
  Mon-Tues 11am-2pm
  Wed-Sat 11am-2pm
  & 7-9pm
  Summer opening:
  From 10.30am and
  open Tues evenings
  and Sunday brunch
- Booking recommended
- Major credit cards
- Non-smoking
- Licensed
- Children welcome
- 20 seats
- Lunch mains from
  £4.95, three evening
  courses from £15.50

- 65 High St
  Strichen AB43 6SQ
- 01771 637218
- Serving times:
  7 days 11am-9pm
- A la carte menu
  from 6pm
- Major credit cards
- Non-smoking
- Licensed
- Children welcome
- 50 seats
- Starters from £1.95,
  mains from £6.95

White Horse Hotel

Woo-hoo! How did Strichen village get so lucky? This local hotel is much nominated, and a finalist in more awards than there's room to mention.

There are always vegan soups and mains, and the regular dishes include baked camembert with a selection of fruit and crusty bread to dip into its molten midst, grilled polenta stacks, Jamaican stuffed pawpaw, vegetable Wellington or quorn in white wine. There's choice and lots of it, and all the main courses come with potatoes and fresh vegetables.

You can also taste a selection of mini desserts if you can't bear to choose between the delights on offer. Booking is recommended, but the bar menu is perfectly acceptable if you've turned up on spec.

- 14 West Argyle St
  Ullapool IV26 2TY
- 01854 612103
- Serving times:
  Mon-Sat 8am-9pm
  Sun 8.30am-9pm
- Booking advisable
  evenings
- Major credit cards
- Non-smoking
  evenings
- Licensed
- Children welcome
- 40 seats
- Snacks from £3.50

The Ceilidh Place

Open from breakfast through to dinner, you can start the day with a vegetarian cooked breakfast, including potato scones, and end it sipping a single malt after a good dinner. Vegans can be catered for by arrangement and children are allowed small portions of all dishes.

There are some great lunch ideas – soda farls (hot soda scones) stuffed with local blue cheese, rosemary and red onion, some really good salads with focaccia, including roast pear, rocket and parmesan, or the traditional veggieburger.

In the evening an artichoke and gruyere tart could well hit the spot and you can follow it with more local cheese, chocolate amaretti and raspberry trifle or a poppyseed and apricot parfait.

wales

Wales

12 Holyhead
11 Conwy
Prestatyn
3 4 Bangor
Wrexham
Machynlleth
13
14 Montgomery
1 2 Aberystwyth
16 Rosebush
5 Brecon
17 St David's
10 Carmarthen
Abergavenny
Milford Haven
Merthyr Tydfil
Usk 22
Llanelli
18 19
Swansea
15 Newport
20 21
Bridgend
6 7 Cardiff
8 9

wales

- 13 Cambrian Place
  Aberystwyth
  SY23 1NT
- 01970 612363
- Serving times:
  Mon 10am-3.30pm
  Tues 10am-2pm
  Wed-Sat
  10am-3.30pm
- No credit cards
- Non-smoking
- Not licensed, BYO
  with no corkage
- Children welcome
- 26 seats
- Light lunch
  from £2.95

Ancient Rain

Half vegetarian, half vegan and offering vegan crêpes, this is a superb place to chill out.

They serve French bread sandwiches and baked potatoes, but the range of fillings is more inspired than your average café; curried lentil or aubergine and tomato are just two of the vegan options – or why not try black olive tapenade or good old peanut butter? The soup – usually vegan – is served with garlic bread, and there are also tofu burgers with sauté potatoes, a dhal, or good bread with a slab of brie and mixed olives.

The sweet pancakes come with lime and sugar, apple and syrup or kiwi and banana in addition to the old favourites. Good choice of Indian and herbal tea, cold drinks and pressés.

- 14 Baker St
  Aberystwyth SY23 2BJ
- 01970 615791
- Serving times:
  Mon-Sat 12-4pm
  Closed bank holidays
- Major credit cards
- Non-smoking floor
- Licensed
- Children welcome
- 50 seats
- Mains from £4.95

The Tree House

This virtually vegetarian café and restaurant, with organic principles and a commitment to local produce for environmental reasons, also has an excellent organic store on the ground floor.

Special diets are not a problem, and normally half the specials are vegan. Wine and beers are all organic. Choose from soups like tomato and basil or Mediterranean green lentil and vegetable, or a mushroom and lentil cottage pie with salad, caramelised red onion and goat's cheese tart. The quiche of the day can be served as a snack or as a more substantial main course with deep-fried potato wedges and salad. There are also veggieburgers, baked potatoes with various fillings and plenty of herbal and regular tea, coffees and hot fruit punch.

Herbs

Herbs' regular daytime menu is vegetarian-friendly, as are the special 'Summer Lunch' deals – two courses from a dedicated menu for around £7.00.

During the daytime, help yourself from the salad bar, and add a toasted goat's cheese bruschetta or mushroom pâté. Larger plates include tortilla wraps and cheese chilli beans with roasted vegetables. On Fridays and Saturdays the restaurant is open for orders until 9pm, and this evening menu – although with fewer vegetarian choices than available earlier in the day – can include mushrooms in a garlic, cream and white wine sauce, pitta with hummus and guacamole or a roast vegetable and goat's cheese en croûte. Herbs also caters for private parties of 10+ on other evenings if you give them advance notice.

- 162 High St
  Bangor LL57 1NU
- 01248 351249
- Serving times:
  Mon-Thurs
  10am-3pm
  Fri-Sat 10am-9pm
- Major credit cards
- Non-smoking
- Licensed
- Children welcome
- 45 seats
- Evening mains from £7

Wales

Java Restaurant

With its graphical map-format menu of Europe, west of Europe and east of Europe, the dithering is taken out of ordering. It's substantially vegetarian during the day, but there's enough choice on the more omnivorous evening menu, and special diets will be catered for to order. Try the west of Europe breakfast – Canadian pancakes with bananas and maple syrup, a Greek lunch – jacket potato with basil oil, olives, feta, hummus and tzatziki, or an east of Europe chilli-coriander veggieburger with chips.

There are plenty of sides, dips and garlic breads, ice cream sundaes and other desserts. The evening menu offers a savoy cabbage stuffed with risotto among around half a dozen other choices, and a wine and beer list to help it all along.

- High St
  Bangor LL57 1PA
- 01248 361652
- Serving times:
  Mon-Tues 10am-4pm
  Wed-Sat 10am-4pm
  & 6-10pm
  Occasionally Sun
  11am-4pm
  Closed bank holidays
- Booking recommended
  Fri & Sat nights
- Major credit cards
- Non-smoking area
- Licensed
- Children welcome
- 50 seats
- Light meals from £3.95

Wales

- 86 The Struet
  Brecon LD3 7LS
- Follow signs for
  cathedral
- 01874 622044
- Serving times:
  Mon 6.30-9.30pm
  Tues-Sat 12-2.30pm
  & 6.30-9.30pm
  Sun 12-2.30pm
  & 7-9.30pm
- No credit cards
- Smoking throughout
- Licensed
- Children welcome
- 40 seats
- Mains from £6.45

The Bull's Head

Expect a detailed vegan and vegetarian bar meal menu
from the people at this committed real ale inn, who also
know which of their bottled beers are vegan-friendly .

Not content to offer just the one vegetarian chilli,
they prepare one with beans, celery and coriander, or a
slightly hotter green and red pepper variety – both
dairy-free. You could also enjoy a Thai curry, stroganoff,
or mushroom and nut fettucini from the daily choice of
around eight mains on the separate vegetarian menu,
but they also occasionally slip a couple of extra meat-
free choices onto the specials board – presumably to
confuse the dedicated carnivores.

If you're a fan of live music, visit on the first
Saturday or third Sunday of the month; they also hold
regular quiz nights.

- Unit 8c
  Mermaid Quay
  Cardiff CF10 5BZ
- 029 2049 6555
- Serving times:
  Mon-Thurs 12-3pm
  & 6-midnight
  Fri-Sun midday-1am
- Booking recommended
  weekends
- Major credit cards
- Smoking throughout
- Licensed
- Children welcome
- 160 seats

Café Naz

With views across Cardiff Bay, chef Stephen Gomes'
180 seat mughal restaurant caters for Cardiff's discerning
lovers of Indian vegetarian food. Ultra modern and
stylish, with a plate glass partition between restaurant
and kitchen, and a huge (but thankfully silent) video
wall playing classic Hollywood movies, almost half the
menu is vegetarian. Go with friends so you can sample
as many of the 25 vegetarian starters and mains as is
possible in a single sitting in polite society.

There's a large selection of beer, wine and fresh fruit
juices, and, unusually for many Indian restaurants,
most of the desserts are homemade. Booking is
recommended at weekends. In the summer, ask for an
outside table on Mermaid Quay for the best views.

Crumbs

Judi Ashley still runs this vegetarian restaurant which she opened in 1970. Ahead of her time, many then regarded it as a little way-out to open a restaurant which didn't serve any meat, but the world's now caught up, and Judi's still there.

As you would expect, there's a wide range of freshly prepared salads – a country mile away from those uninspired plates of soggy lettuce that occasionally appear when you order at other establishments – or you can choose from a range of hot dishes including curries, chilli and pasta. There's always vegan choices, wheat-free options, and smaller portions for children. You can also take away – convenient if you're looking for a little something for the match at the nearby Millennium stadium.

- 33 Morgan Arcade Cardiff CF10 1AF
- 029 2039 5007
- Serving times: Mon-Fri 10am-3pm Sat 10am-4pm
- No credit cards
- Non-smoking
- Not licensed
- Children welcome
- 80 seats

Wales

Greenhouse Café

A good local restaurant, handy for the Sherman Theatre, with an interesting menu that aims to use mostly local ingredients, organic where possible. The chef is a former wine merchant, so expect some interesting bottles on offer, and they also have delicious Austrian fruit syrups. It would be graceless to bring your own booze, but you may, with £3 corkage.

There's a price-per-course structure and the menu changes regularly. Expect dishes like beetroot and apple soup with crème fraiche, dill and a slug of Calvados, or Mexican rarebit: grilled polenta with chipotle chilli purée, smoked cheese and salsa. The mains draw from similarly international roots: stir fried vegetables with tofu and miso sauce and Asian greens, or spinach and goat's cheese filo parcels with Greek beans and salad.

- 38 Woodville Rd Cardiff CF24 4EB
- 029 2023 5731
- Serving times: Tues-Sat 6.30-10pm
- Booking advisable
- Major credit cards
- Non-smoking
- Licensed
- Children welcome
- 30 seats
- 2 courses from £13.95

Wales

Wales

- Chapter Arts Centre
  Market Rd
  Cardiff CF5 1QE
- 029 2039 7999
- Serving times:
  7 days 9am-9pm
- Major credit cards
- Non-smoking in
  café area
- Separate bar
- Children welcome
- 110 seats

Market Café

The Chapter Arts Centre is home to two independent cinemas, a theatre and gallery as well as the café. The light, high ceilinged and airy space (the arts centre is housed in a building which was previously a school, and the café is in the old hall) is shared with a bar, and there's also a garden area.

Expect a good selection of vegetarian food available from morning till evening. In addition to baguettes with a variety of meat-free fillings such as smoked cheese and quorn fillets, expect mains of vegetarian chillis, curries, risottos and bakes with daily specials such as stuffed aubergine or grilled mushrooms. Vegan dishes can include the daily soup or an aubergine and lentil bake. Open seven days a week.

Carmarthen

Vegetarian Restaurant

- 23 Lammas St
  Carmarthen SA31 3AL
- 01267 236521
- Serving times:
  Mon-Sat lunch served
  11.30am-2pm
  Tea, coffee and cakes
  at other times
- Major credit cards
- Non-smoking
- Licensed
- Children welcome
- 48 seats
- Lunch from £4.50

Waverley

The Waverley vegetarian restaurant is located in a large health food shop which has been a well known local grocery store for over 100 years. Lunch is served six days a week between 11.30am and 2pm, with morning and afternoon teas and cake – all vegetarian, of course – available at other times.

Organic produce features heavily, and there are also gluten-free options. Choose from a daily range of soups, lasagne, quiches or spinach bread pudding, and load up with greens at the salad bar. Vegan options can include cottage pie or potato cakes. Half price children's portions available. Morning coffee or afternoon tea and cake for under £1 has got to be a bargain.

Bistro Conwy

If you're touring North Wales, take the time to sample the vegetarian food at Bistro Conwy, set within the walls of Conwy Castle – Edward I's massive fortress. Specialising in local Welsh produce, the vegetarian section of the evening menu can include Wyau Ynys Mon (baked Anglesey eggs on leek and potato mash), the vegan salad haf or a field mushroom tart.

Mains have included vegetarian versions of traditional Welsh supper dishes as well as less local recipes like vegan spring rolls stuffed with vegetables, cashew nuts and mixed beans, or a red Thai curry.

There's a small courtyard area for outdoor dining, and booking is advisable, especially on Friday and Saturday evenings in summer.

- Bishops Yard
  26 Chapel St
  Conwy LL32 8BP
- Behind Police Station
- 01492 596326
- Serving times:
  Tues-Thurs
  11.30am-2pm & 7-9pm
  Fri-Sat 11.30am-2pm
  & 7-9.30pm
  Sun 11.30-2.30pm
  Open Sun evening on
  bank holiday weekends
- Booking advisable
- Major credit cards
- Non-smoking
- Licensed
- Children welcome
- 30 seats

Harvest Moon Café

This colourful, funky vegan café shares a building with Judy Williams's healing centre and lending library, and is close to Anglesey's ferry terminal. Regular travellers to and from Ireland pop in to fill up on the homemade snacks, cakes and teas which are mainly organic, and made with ingredients sourced locally wherever possible.

Try one of Judy's unique own-recipe burgers, a jacket with a great selection of fillings (we'd try the avocado and mango chutney), or a bap stuffed with vegan sausage and tomato. Great range of teas, including Rooibosch caffeine-free and Turkish, or try the Harvest Moon special of hot apple juice. There's also an excellent range of homemade vegan cakes.

- 4 Newry St
  Holyhead
  Anglesey LL65 1HP
- Opposite the cinema
- 01407 763670
- Serving times:
  Tues-Sat 10am-5pm
- No credit cards
- Non-smoking
- Not licensed, BYO
  with no corkage
- Children welcome
- 24 seats
- Snacks from £2

Wales

- Heol Maengwyn
  Machynlleth
  SY20 8EB
- 01654 702624
- Serving times:
  Mon-Wed
  9am-4.30pm
  Thurs 9am-2pm
  Fri-Sat 9am-4.30pm
- No credit cards
- Non-smoking
- Not licensed, BYO
  with no corkage
- Children welcome
- 40 seats
- Mains from £4

Quarry Café

This café celebrated 25 years of business in 2004 and is associated with the nearby Centre for Alternative Technology. They are unlicensed, but you can buy organic beer and wine from their shop a few doors down, and there's no charge for corkage.

There's always something vegan – including soup and dishes such as spicy bean casserole – and the bread is home-baked. The simple menu features one starter, two or three main courses with a mix of four salads, and a couple of desserts like fresh fruit trifle and an apple and cinnamon crumble.

Very child-friendly, with half portions, high chairs, baby changing and feeding facilities and a toybox. You can also get organic baby food here.

Wales

- 8 Broad St
  Montgomery
  SY15 6PH
- 01686 668795
- Serving times:
  Mon-Thurs
  9.30am-4pm
  Fri-Sat 9.30am-4pm
  & 7-10pm
  Sun 12-4pm
- Booking recommended
  Fri & Sat evenings
- Major credit cards
- Non-smoking area
- Licensed
- Children welcome
- 30 seats & outside
  seating area
- Soups from £2.50

Castle Kitchen

An inn dating from the 15th century, in an historic town square, where you can order breakfast, lunch, teas and, at weekends, dinner from a weekly-changing menu.

The blackboard lunch menu (available between 12 and 3.30pm) has quiches, homemade lasagne and pasta dishes, but there are also baked potatoes, bruschettas and a ploughmans lunch you'd actually want to order.

The dinner menu is always loaded with good vegetarian choices: tapas, toasted goat's cheese with Muscat-soaked sultanas – to lend distinction, wild mushroom pancakes with Madeira and cream sauce, or potato gnocchi with pine nuts, cherry tomatoes, cream and rocket. Desserts can include lemon torte, sticky toffee pudding and two cheese plates.

Hunky Dory

A traditional-style café, family-run, and one that's exclusively served vegetarian food since it opened in the 1980s. Enjoy vegan options including their dairy-free garlic bread, salads, some main courses and homemade flapjacks (with soya ice cream, anybody?) or, if you're OK with eggs and milk, choose from dishes like cheese and spinach pie, quiches, cauliflower cheese and a range of veggieburgers. There's a lot of choice, and they'll make you feel very welcome.

Just a few hundred yards away from Newport's main shopping area, it's handy to know about if you fancy a spot of lunch but prefer not to frequent a global horror with a token veggie option.

- 17 Charles St
  Newport NP20 1JU
- 01633 257850
- Serving times:
  Mon-Sat 10am-3.30pm
  Closed bank holidays
- No credit cards
- Non-smoking
- Not licensed
- Children welcome
- 26 seats

Wales

The Old Post Office

This friendly and homely bistro-style restaurant-pub-café-tearoom has a great range of home-cooked food, with a good vegan and vegetarian choice.

Pop in for tea and cakes, sample their extensive range of real ales, or do it properly and stay for lunch or dinner. The soups are vegetarian (often vegan), or try the deep-fried veg or garlic mushrooms. The vegetarian mains aren't just a token selection, and can include Moroccan-style stuffed peppers, red onion and thyme tart or a goat's cheese and pepper flan. Desserts are always vegetarian, and owner Ruth Jones is renowned for her vegan pancakes. Children are made extremely welcome and can have smaller portions from the main menu, or veggie nuggets and chips if they're feeling the need for something they can slap the ketchup on.

- Rosebush SA66 7QU
- 01437 532205
- Serving times:
  Tues-Sat 12-10pm
  Sun 12-2.30pm
  Closed Tues Jan-Easter
- No credit cards
- Smoking in bar only
- Licensed
- Children welcome
- 24 seats

Wales

St Davids

Wales

- Cross Square
  St Davids SA62 6SL
- 01437 720422
- Serving times:
  7 days 12-2.30pm
  & 6-8.30pm
  Open later during
  summer. Opening
  hours may be
  restricted in winter
- Major credit cards
- Non-smoking
  except bar
- Licensed
- Children welcome
- 100 seats
- Light meals from £3

Omnivorous Restaurant

Cartref Restaurant

This café is in a lovely old building with traditional beamed ceilings and exposed stone walls, with space to sit outside in fine weather.

The daytime menu offers sandwiches, veggieburgers, toasties and jacket potatoes, filled Yorkshire puddings, and daily specials like stilton and vegetable bake. Children have their own menu with a good vegetarian selection and the price of their meal includes ice cream and a wafer. After six o'clock the vegan menu comes into play, with a cashew and chestnut roast or aubergine rolls among other goodies.

The café stays opens later in the summer and you can have a drink with your meal and soya milk in your coffee. Good to know this place is there.

Swansea

Wales

- 55 Walter Rd
  Uplands
  Swansea SA1 5PY
- 01792 473379
- Serving times:
  Mon-Fri 12-3pm
  & 6.30-10pm
  Sat 6.30-10.30pm
  Closed bank holidays
- Booking recommended
  Thurs-Sat
- Major credit cards
- Non-smoking area
- Licensed
- Children welcome
  before 8pm
- 40 seats
- Starters from £2.95,
  mains from £8.25

Omnivorous Bistro

Bizzie Lizzies Bistro

It's recommended that you book for dinner on Thursday to Saturday nights at this very vegetarian-friendly Swansea bistro, while the restaurant's beer garden won a prize from Britain in Bloom in 2003, so you may want to lunch outside.

Unusually, they actively encourage people to send in menu suggestions and favourite recipes. We fancied the oven-baked tomatoes stuffed with rice and dressed with a balsamic reduction followed by a filo parcel of mushrooms broccoli and cauliflower. Free range eggs also make frittata a reasonable option.

Keep your eyes peeled for their special all vegetarian nights – you wouldn't want to miss out on dishes like a Normandy bake of vegetables in a white wine sauce with charred spring onions and chestnuts.

Garuda

The only Indonesian restaurant in Wales, Swansea's Garuda offers a separate vegetarian section to their menu, with most dishes suitable for vegans (check ingredients with the knowledgeable staff). From the more familiar (gado-gado – mixed vegetables with spicy peanut sauce) to the rare (tempeh with spinach cooked in coconut sauce, or soya bean and potato fritters), there are new tastes to experience. If you have space left for dessert, try the exotic bubur (black rice pudding with cream of coconut) or banana and coconut pancake. Garuda serves soft drinks and coffee, but you can bring your own wine or beer.

Owner/chef Ani and Millie the dog (who apparently prefers Indonesian food to normal dog food) promise a warm welcome.

- 18 St Helens Rd
  Swansea SA1 4AP
- 01792 653388
- Serving times:
  Tues-Fri 12-2pm
  & 7-9.30pm
  Sat 7-9.30pm
- Booking recommended weekends
- Major credit cards
- Non-smoking
- Not licensed, BYO with no corkage
- Children welcome
- 38 seats
- Starters from £5

Govinda's

One of a couple of completely vegetarian restaurants in Swansea – and one where vegans are looked after as friends – their menu is an interesting combination of east and west: lasagne, pizza, moussaka (all with salad or chips), jacket potatoes, dhal and rice, spring rolls and samosas.

You can enjoy freshly squeezed carrot and apple juices as well as homemade lassis and milkshakes, and great desserts including vegan alternatives for cheesecake and ice cream.

They'll cater for private parties and make cakes and bread to order. Open until mid-afternoon most days (6pm on Fridays) it's advisable to book on Saturdays. Worth a visit, not least for the woodland décor.

- 8 Cradock St
  Swansea SA1 3EN
- 01792 468469
- Serving times:
  Mon-Thurs 12-3pm
  Fri-Sat 12-6pm
  Sun 12-3pm
- Booking advisable Saturdays
- No credit cards
- Non-smoking
- Not licensed
- Children welcome
- 45 seats
- Mains from £3.50

- 36 St Helens Rd
  Swansea SA1 4AY
- 01792 411076
- Serving times:
  Mon-Sat 10am-5pm
  Sun 11am-5pm
- Major credit cards
- Non-smoking
- Not licensed
- Children welcome
- 20 seats
- Mains from £3.25

Khushi Khana

This recently opened café is the place to be if your sweet tooth insists on venues with a choice of thirty-five desserts and sweets from around the world.

Before you get to the sweet stuff, choose a starter or main from a predominately Gujarati menu featuring authentic Indian dhals, curries and biryanis, as well as snacks like Kenyan style Chevdo – a sort of African Bombay mix. This small, simply decorated café offers a lot of organic and vegan choice, as well as a good range of non-alcoholic drinks including juice, various lassis and coconut juice. Currently a daytime-only café, it does open Sundays, however, from 11am and there's a small retail area for you to stock up on specialist herbs and spices.

- Llanfihangle-
  Tor-y-Mynydd
  Llansoy
  Usk NP15 1DT
- 01291 650256
- Serving times:
  Mon-Thurs 11.30am-
  2.30pm & 6-9pm
  Fri-Sat 11.30am-
  2.30pm & 6-9.30pm
  Sun 12-8pm
- Booking advisable
- Major credit cards
- Non-smoking
  except bar
- Licensed
- Children welcome
- 50 seats
- Mains from £5.50

Star Inn

All you need to know: 17th century pub, views of the Usk valley, beer garden, open log fires and a veteran of the Good Beer Guide.

Where possible local produce is used to make the vegetarian choices, which include some vegan options. Cider and butter bean casserole, aubergine bake, roast vegetable terrine, stuffed peppers or feta and olive salad can be found in the separate vegetarian section on the menu. There's a mixed tropical fruit fondue to wrap up, and your children can have vegetable nuggets if you can't persuade them of the merits of lightly cooked fresh asparagus.

There's a small registered caravan site alongside, so hitch up that second home and head for the hills.

index

index
by restaurant name

Index by restaurant name

Index by restaurant name

Index by restaurant name

Index by restaurant name

index

Index by location

Index by location